D1610704

WARSHIP 1992

WARSHIP 1992

Edited by Robert Gardiner

CONWAY
MARITIME PRESS

Frontispiece:
The coast defence ship Sverige *protecting Swedish neutrality during the Second World War. The unusual genesis of this class, and in particular the part played by public pressure, is outlined by Daniel G Harris in this issue.*

© Conway Maritime Press Ltd 1992

First published in Great Britain by
Conway Maritime Press Ltd
101 Fleet Street
London EC4Y 1DE

British Library Cataloguing in Publication Data
Warship . .
   1992–
   1. Warships
   623.825

   ISBN 0–85177–603–5

Design, typesetting and page make-up by
The Word Shop, Bury, Lancashire
Printed and bound in Great Britain by
Butler & Tanner Ltd, Frome

CONTENTS

EDITORIAL

Warship has always aimed to satisfy a range of naval interests – chronologically, geographically and thematically. This was the policy as a journal and was carried over into the yearbook. Providing something for everyone, inevitably, results in a *potpourri*, and one of the more analytical reviews of the last annual suggested that the coverage of each edition is a little too diffuse and it would be better adopting a single broad theme. This is an interesting idea and warrants some thought.

The principal merit is that a unifying theme is more intellectually satisfying; the whole book is *about* something, and if put together properly would become essential reading on that topic. In this respect, each volume would resemble the published papers of a conference – individual contributions varying in subject and approach, but addressing aspects of the chosen theme. However attractive the idea, it is open to a couple of serious reservations, namely the difficulty of making it meaningful, and the wisdom of attempting it at all.

To expand on the first objection: such a work would only succeed if the theme were narrow enough to promise largely original material but broad enough to interest the majority of potential readers ('purchasers' would be more accurate, since we operate in a market economy). It is likely that the majority of contributions would have to be invited, and this implies that many writers would have to produce work specially and do the necessary research. Most technical history in the warship field is the product of spare-time work by people who are in the best sense amateurs; in the present issue, for example, no contributor supports himself by his writing alone, though they devote considerable time to their interest and most have also written books. However, they pursue personal enthusiasms as a hobby, so it is unlikely that they could be persuaded to stray too far from their chosen area. It is possible, therefore, that the only themes that could inspire enough contributors might be so broad as to be effectively meaningless.

That an idea is difficult to execute is no reason to dismiss it entirely, but in this case we should ask if it would be in the long-term interest of the subject as a whole. *Warship* has always functioned as a vehicle for pieces of research that might not otherwise see publication – those regarded as too technical for general magazines, while dismissed by the academic journals as historically insignificant (although technical history is becoming steadily more 'respectable'). It is significant how many naval historians were first published by *Warship*, but perhaps even more remarkable is the number who have gone on to produce complete books. It is too pretentious to

see the journal as a nursery for naval writers, but the element of encouragement in the early stages has been important for many now highly respected authors. To close off the pages of *Warship*, even in its once-a-year format, to *ad hoc* research would be to threaten this process. To commission contributions on a particular theme would inevitably mean that only established writers of known interests could be approached, and new talent would have to look elsewhere.

For the moment the discussion is academic, since this year's edition was well advanced before the review appeared, but the 'broad theme' concept is worth further consideration.

This issue is as wide ranging as ever, from the mid-nineteenth century to the present day, touching on most major navies and most principal warship types. All have something original and/or interesting to impart, but a few unusual features deserve special mention. The article on the mutually destructive battle between the raider *Kormoran* and HMAS *Sydney* is somewhat different from usual *Warship* territory because it does not concentrate on the technicalities of the ships, but looks at the assorted theories surrounding the disappearance of the cruiser with all hands. This issue has been somewhat controversial in Australia in recent years and Kim Kirsner's painstaking research attempts to reconcile conflicting surviving evidence.

Ever since the war the Japanese resort to Special Attack Weapons – all loosely referred to by the Allies as *kamikazes* – has roused passionate debate but little understanding. Dr Jiro Itani gives a Japanese perspective on the reasons for their development and is particularly interesting on the ethos of their employment. While admitting that Japanese traditions made its ritualisation possible, he argues that accepting the virtual inevitability of death in battle is a phenomenon understood and tacitly countenanced in most armed forces. Taking on heavy odds even in what may be regarded as conventional warfare was often tantamount to suicide, and unlike Special Attack tactics did not always offer the prospect of seriously damaging the enemy. On the brink of defeat most nations adopt desperate measures and one has to ask, for example, whether the German pilot of a Me 163 rocket fighter or a Neger manned torpedo seriously expected to see out the war. In fact, the high loss rate among all combatants' special forces underlines the nearly suicidal risks involved: 'What really counts is that there are men ready to die . . . to inspire and fortify future generations.' This sentiment was expressed not by a Japanese but by Major Teseo Tesei, who developed the Italian 'maiale' or manned torpedo; he had no illusions about their mode of operation.

The rest of the main features have much to offer: important but unsung areas like naval balloons or magnetic mine countermeasures; thought-provoking pieces like David Brown's well supported contention that cruiser armour was proved unnecessary by the events of the war; more on the little-known activities of the Romanian navy in the Second World War; an unusual collection of photos of captured Allied ships; and detailed analyses of significant warship classes, from the controversial battleship *Maine* to the last prewar French destroyers.

Robert Gardiner

THE SHIPBOARD BALLOON – THE BEGINNINGS OF NAVAL AERONAUTICS

The story of the naval airship has frequently been told, especially the menacing role of the German Zeppelins in the First World War. Less well known is the history of the unpowered naval balloon, a device that had already been in use for decades before the first practical airship thrummed through the skies. R D Layman and Stephen McLaughlin trace the history of these undramatic but valuable craft in naval service.

THE origins of the balloon are obscure. It may have first appeared in pre-Columbian South America, in Portugal in 1709, or in Russia in 1731. It enters fully documented history in France in 1783 with the first man-carrying ascents in the hot-air craft devised by brothers Etienne and Joseph Montgolfier. But the hot-air balloons lost their lifting power as the contents in their envelopes cooled; this limited the time they could remain aloft, given the low heat efficiency of the fuels available to early aeronauts and the necessarily large radiating surface of the balloons. This handicap was overcome within weeks of the first manned flight by the introduction of hydrogen, which remained the favoured lifting gas until after the First World War – although hot-air ballooning survives to this day as a popular recreation. With the basic problem of lift solved, a wonderful proliferation of ideas for propulsion soon followed, but none proved workable. So the familiar tethered balloon long remained the most common type of flying device.

Proposals for the military use of the balloon were legion during its early decades, among them, naturally enough, the idea of tethering it to a ship to provide an observation post with a visual range far beyond that of the loftiest crow's nest.[1] This was first suggested to the Royal Navy in 1803 by Rear-Admiral Charles Henry Knowles, who advocated equipping a frigate with a balloon to reconnoitre Brest harbour.[2]

A more offensive-minded plan came in 1818 from one Charles Rogier of Cheshire. In what may have been the first proposal for a specialized aviation vessel, he outlined a ship fitted to loft free-floating balloons which would drop explosives automatically by means of a clockwork-and-fuze device of his invention. He saw a harbour-bound fleet as an ideal target.

A similar scheme was broached by American balloonist John Wise in 1846 during the Mexican–American War. He called for dropping explosives on the Vera Cruz fortress from a balloon attached to a five-mile cable – long enough to be out of range of Mexican guns – that would be manoeuvred either from a point on land or a ship at sea.

However, this form of aerial attack was not actually carried out until the Austrian siege of Venice in 1849. Lacking long-range artillery, the Austrians bombarded the city with small free-floating hot-air balloons equipped with mechanisms calibrated to drop explosive charges. Most of these were despatched from land, but on 12 July 1849 the sidewheel steamer *Vulcano* floated a few from her deck – the first use of an offensive aerial weapon by a warship. However, contrary winds blew some of them back over the ship, an unsettling development that put an end to the operation.

This venture proved that the free-floating, bomb-dropping balloon was what its critics had maintained – a fickle weapon, always at the mercy of the wind and as

much a danger to its user as to an enemy. Nevertheless, it popped up again as late as the 1880s in a proposal to the Admiralty from an inventor named Frederick Allen Gower for a ship to carry 'aerial batteries'. By this time the science of meteorology had advanced considerably, and Gower believed its application would permit accurate charting of the air currents that would take the balloons over their targets. Consequently, in his view, 'A vessel may be constructed especially for carrying aerial batteries; and, thus dispensing with weight of armament, may be given a rate of speed such as to make her capture practically impossible. . . '.[3]

However, Gower's proposal came to nought, and the bomb-carrying balloon was not seen again until Japan's lighter-than-air campaign against North America in 1944–45.[4] As part of that desperate campaign, submarines *I 34* and *I 35* were fitted out as balloon carriers – but never saw operational service as such.[5]

A spherical balloon on the deck of French torpedo boat carrier Foudre *during Mediterranean manoeuvres.* (Courtesy of William P Avery)

A cable wound around the conning tower of this unidentified German torpedo boat was the primitive mooring attachment for the first experiment in towing a kite balloon by a ship, at Kiel in 1897. (Courtesy of William P Avery)

Early Manned Naval Balloons

For obvious reasons, the manned free balloon could rarely be employed for observation; only a moored craft could perform that function reliably. Inflation, mooring and controlled ascent and descent were fairly simple on land but extremely difficult at sea during the age of sail. A ship's maze of masts, spars, rigging and sails left scant room for carrying or inflating a balloon – not to mention the possibility of ship's rigging and mooring lines fouling one another, hindering the handling of both balloon and ship. Not until steam replaced canvas was the maritime balloon a really feasible proposition. Thus its first relatively extensive use occurred during the American

Civil War, although this employment was limited to rivers and sheltered coastal waters.

Use of balloons by the Union Army began on an *ad hoc* basis, with aeronauts volunteering their services to corps or district commands. Among the first of these was John La Mountain, who on 3 August 1861 made ascents from the deck of the army single-screw gunboat/transport *Fanny*, a former tug. A later flight by La Mountain may have taken place from a steamer named *Adriatic*. These were almost certainly the first manned balloon flights from a ship.

Earlier in 1861 an embryonic Union balloon corps began to form under the general supervision of Thaddeus Sobieski Constantine Lowe, a prominent figure in early American aeronautics. One of his major innovations was the use of a telegraph line to transmit information from air to ground, a method far faster, more accurate and more reliable than previous systems. This form of balloon communication later saw widespread use until superseded by the telephone.

The balloon corps, which never had an official name, was a ramshackle affair from its beginning until it disintegrated in mid-1863, 'a loosely organized, poorly administered, and decentralized mixture of civilian and military personnel, often hindered by the administrative regulations and red tape of the army, and at the same time frequently denied the benefits of military efficiency'.[6]

Nonetheless, it was responsible, under Lowe, for the operation of the first craft in the history of naval war specially and solely configured for aerial service. This tiny and crude ancestor of the aircraft carrier was a barge acquired by the Washington Navy Yard in August 1861 to carry coal and turned over to Lowe after he requested a vessel to serve his balloon posts along the Potomac River. It was apparently he who christened it *George Washington*

Park Custis. Under his supervision, the Navy Yard fitted it with a flat ellipsoid deck, a small deckhouse aft and a portable hydrogen generator, another of Lowe's inventions. A balloon could be inflated and carried amidships on the 122ft deck.

Thus equipped, carrying Lowe, an assistant, a balloon named *Washington*[7] and a group of infantrymen to manhandle the balloon, *Custis* on 10 November 1861 undertook a reconnaissance on the Potomac, towed by the sidewheel steamer *Coeur de Lion*. The *Custis* continued in service on the Potomac, towed by a variety of ships, until March 1862, when it was sent on an unsuccessful search for the whereabouts of the Confederate ironclad *Virginia* (ex-USS *Merrimack*). Later it operated on the York River during the Peninsula campaign.

In August 1862, *Custis* was assigned to provide aerial observation for a bombardment of Confederate Port Powhatan. Towed by the tug *Stepping Stones*, it joined with a screw sloop, two gunboats and an armed transport to form what has been called, with some exaggeration, 'the first carrier task force'.[8] It is unclear how this operation turned out.[9] The rest of the balloon boat's career is obscure; it was returned to the Washington Navy Yard in early 1863 and thereupon vanishes from history.

During mid-April to early June 1863, aeronaut John B Starkweather operated the balloon *Washington* from the 262-ton army gunboat *May Flower*,[10] based at Port Royal, South Carolina. Starkweather and an army engineer officer serving as an observer apparently spotted a Confederate ironclad, probably either *Atlanta* or *Georgia*,

Sweden's Ballondepotfartgy Nr 1 *lofting its German Parseval-Reidinger kite balloon.* (Statens Sjöhistoriska Museum, Stockholm)

A spherical balloon built by Fyodor A Postnikov in free flight over Vladivostok in 1904. (S F Post photo, R D Layman collection)

under construction at Savannah, Georgia, but that would seem to be the only useful information gained before the balloon was irreparably damaged by striking the ship's superstructure during a gale that drove *May Flower* aground.

Far inland from these activities, another Union balloonist, John H Steiner, made aeronaval history in an episode that seems to have been almost immediately forgotten. Assigned in February 1862 to the Army of the Mississippi, headquartered at Cairo, Illinois, he was treated with ridicule and contempt by the army staff – probably because of his feeble command of English (his native language was German). Consequently, he offered his services to US Navy Commodore Andrew H Foote, commanding a flotilla of gunboats and mortar boats battering away at a Confederate stronghold called Island No 10. The island's batteries commanded a hairpin turn in the river and had to be reduced before a further advance could be made. The Union bombardment had been ineffective:

> Since the mortar boats were anchored above the Island beyond the bend of the river, their officers were unable to observe accurately the effect of their high-angle fire which was delivered diagonally across the protruding neck around which the meandering river flowed.[11]

Foote, correctly judging that aerial observation might rectify this, had Steiner, the balloon *Eagle* and a hydrogen generator installed on a large barge – flatboat in Mississip-

pi parlance – at Cairo, towed to the flotilla and moored near his flagship, the ironclad *Benton*. On 25 March Steiner took aloft two officers of the mortar boat division. They observed that

> The direction of fire was satisfactory, but the elevation and propelling charges were too great, thus causing the mortars to overshoot their targets. The defect was ordered corrected at once, with the result that the mortar fire became accurate and effective.[12]

Although other sources disagree on the effectiveness of the bombardment, there can be no doubt that this was the first time in which an aerial device directed gunfire from surface vessels, and it would not be repeated in combat for nearly fifty years.

The Confederacy did not operate a large number of balloons, but one of them did see service afloat in July 1862, albeit briefly. Constructed in Savannah earlier that year, it was employed during the Seven Days Campaign before being embarked on the 64-ton former tug *Teaser*, which had been used previously to lay torpedoes (mines) in the James River. Inflated by coal gas from the Richmond, Virginia, municipal gas works, it ascended from *Teaser* on the first three days of July. The next day *Teaser* was shelled and captured, along with the balloon, by the Union gunboat *Maratanza*. The balloon, which apparently was not aloft at the time, was later cut into souvenir scraps.[13]

The Kite Balloon

Save for some isolated experiments by a few navies, the shipboard balloon languished during the decades im-

A German-manufactured kite balloon at Vladivostok, one of three sent overland to augment Postnikov's spherical craft. (S F Post photo, R D Layman collection)

mediately after the American Civil War. Three factors coalesced to revive interest in it during the 1890s. First, advances in artillery were gradually increasing the range of guns beyond the horizon of a mast-top observer. Experiments aboard the French battleship *Formidable* showed that an observer in a balloon could see up to 25 miles farther than was possible from the vessel itself. The second factor was the ever-increasing threat of submarines and mines. It was found that in certain conditions these underwater perils, invisible from ships, could be detected from the air.

The final factor was the development of the kite balloon, the first basic change in balloon design since the eighteenth century. For more than a century the vast majority of balloons had been spherical (or pear-shaped).

Such balloons ride smoothly when free floating, but when towed they are unstable except in calm winds; they would 'oscillate, bounce and twist in a manner too violent for the strongest of stomachs to stand'.[14]

The kite balloon, developed in Germany in the early 1890s, remedied this by a series of fins and vents that kept it stable in all but the strongest of winds. Its shape led to the nicknames *Drache* (meaning both kite and dragon) or sausage balloon. Here at last was a craft that could be towed comfortably by a warship, as proved by the first German experiment with the combination in 1897, when a kite balloon was towed by a torpedo boat at Kiel. Ironically, the experiment was marred by a problem that Lowe had solved long before – the balloonist was unable to communicate with the ship by any means. But this was only a temporary and easily corrected problem, and examples of this new balloon were soon to be found in the armed forces of other nations, despite early attempts by the Germans to keep the type a military secret. Although the spherical balloon continued in military use – if for no other reason than that the kite balloon required more elaborate ground-handling apparatus and therefore larger ground crews – the kite balloon clearly had far greater potential.

The Royal Swedish Navy was the first to adopt the kite balloon, and consequently the first European nation to

Transport Kolyma *lofting a spherical balloon at Vladivostok. Canvas windscreens to shelter the balloon have been erected on the entire aft portion of the ship.* (S F Post photo, R D Layman collection)

A kite balloon aboard Kolyma, *which now has only a forward windscreen.* (S F Post photo, R D Layman collection)

possess what could be called an aviation vessel. This was *Ballondepotfartyg Nr 1* (balloon depot ship No 1), completed in 1904. This unprepossessing craft was a 220-ton, 154ft unpowered barge, a throwback to the *George Washington Parke Custis*, but unlike that converted vessel was the first surface craft *designed* and *built* for aeronautical purposes. It operated a German-made kite balloon and mounted hydrogen generation and compression gear powered by two petrol motors. Its lack of independent mobility was a handicap, however, and it was transferred from the seagoing fleet to coastal defence service in 1915. It was employed in annual manoeuvres until 1929, when it was stricken from the navy list.

The navies displaying the greatest interest in balloons around the turn of the century were those of France and Russia. Both conducted shipboard trials of balloons and both established naval balloon bases, the French on the Atlantic and Mediterranean coasts, the Russians on the Baltic and Black seas. The French torpedo boat carrier *Foudre* (later to become a seaplane carrier) operated balloons during Mediterranean manoeuvres in 1898 and 1901, and French balloonists were pioneers in detecting submarines from the air.

Although these manoeuvres demonstrated the usefulness of the balloon at sea, the French navy abandoned aeronautical efforts in 1904. The reason was a problem that had plagued the balloon from the start: the danger posed to ships by hydrogen. This gas, the lightest of the elements, has excellent lifting power but is highly inflammable – the slightest spark could touch off a devastating inferno.[15] The French navy judged that the

man-lifting kite offered all the advantages of the balloon without its potential danger, and so turned its attention to that device.[16]

The Russo–Japanese War

Although the Imperial Russian Navy had shown considerable interest in balloons and kites, these devices contributed almost nothing to the conduct of the war with Japan in 1904–05. The war inspired a flurry of aeronautical activity in the Russian navy, but it was the Japanese who drew first blood through the use of a balloon.

This occurred on 9 August 1904 when the commander of the land-based Japanese navy siege artillery ascended to direct the fire of the two 4.7in guns of the 3rd Naval Battery against the vessels in the eastern basin of Port Arthur harbour. The battleship *Peresviet* was hit, but only slightly damaged, by the last of ten shells aimed at her, and then fire was switched to the battleship *Retvisan*. She was hit at least ten times and a lighter alongside preparing to take off some of the ship's secondary guns to bolster the landward defences was sunk. Three crewmen were killed and Captain 1st Rank E N Stchensovich, her commander, was slightly wounded. The only damaging hit, however, was one that tore a large hole two metres (6.5ft) below the waterline; the ship took on 400 tons of water, causing a 6- to 7-degree list. This was corrected by counter-flooding and the hull was successfully repaired, but the flooded double bottom was not pumped out, reducing *Retvisan*'s speed to 14kts the next day when she sortied with the squadron. This damage, however, did not affect her performance during the resulting Battle of the Yellow Sea.

More interesting, and certainly more obscure, was the aeronautical work carried out at Vladivostok under the direction of the energetic and ingenious balloonist Fyodor A Postnikov, an army engineer captain.[17] Having found that he could detect sunken hulks in the Neva River from the air, he believed balloons could be used to spot Japanese mines.

Assembling a makeshift force of sailors and local workers, he succeeded in constructing three spherical balloons, devised a novel way of producing hydrogen and began to train naval officers in aeronautics. Later, three kite balloons and fortress balloon personnel were sent overland to Vladivostok, and by the end of the war Postnikov commanded an 'air force' of more than 100 officers and men from both the army and the navy, many of whom had made tethered and free-floating ascents.

There was considerable experiment in taking both types of balloon to sea, at first from a steam cutter, *Diomed*, and later from the transports *Ussuri, Argun, Kamchadal* and *Kolyma* and the armoured cruiser *Rossia*, flagship of the Vladivostok cruiser division. Some smaller craft were also involved. Canvas screens were erected on some of these ships to shelter the balloons. In 1905 *Kolyma* was modified for kite balloon operation by removing the mainmast and placing a wooden platform between the midships superstructure and the poop deck. Tall poles on each side of the platform supported canvas windscreens. To facilitate shipboard carriage, one of the kite balloons was shortened.

Despite all this ingenuity, there is no indication that the Vladivostok balloonists accomplished anything useful. Attempts to detect mines were unsuccessful, and communication was troublesome because the necessary telegraph equipment was lacking. Attempts to direct gunnery practice by *Rossia* against land targets were inconclusive.

The raiding cruise in the Sea of Japan by *Rossia* and squadron-mate *Gromoboi* on 9–13 May 1905 presented the balloonists with an opportunity to contribute to the war at sea, but it ended in disappointment. A kite balloon was embarked on *Rossia*, where space was created for it on the starboard deck by raising the arm of the mizzen mast and removing the backstays. The balloon made thirteen

Rossia's crewmen manhandling the balloon back aboard ship (S F Post photo, R D Layman collection)

The hydrogen-manufacturing apparatus devised by Postnikov at Vladivostok. A kite balloon appears to be under inflation. (Courtesy of Boris V Drashpil)

Officers and ratings at the hydrogen-generating apparatus aboard transport Kolyma. *Postnikov is at the right, in white uniform.* (Courtesy of Boris V Drashpil)

manned and unmanned flights, controlled by a capstan. On 11 May, however, hemp ropes were used instead of steel cables, which were in the process of being rewound; the hemp parted, and the unmanned balloon rose to an estimated 6000ft and drifted for an hour before falling into

Russian balloon ship Russ, *showing the balloon shelter and handling deck.* (Courtesy of L L von Münching)

the sea. Although it was retrieved by a cutter and manhandled back aboard, it had lost much of its hydrogen and there was none on board to replace it. It was deflated that night when rough weather was encountered.

Aside from the balloon incident, the cruise appears to have been uneventful and certainly unproductive. Postnikov later claimed that a number of Japanese small craft had been sunk, but no evidence, Russian or Japanese, can be found to confirm this assertion. The voyage was, however, a minor landmark in naval history – the first blue-water operational employment of a balloon by a warship during hostilities.

Meanwhile, back in the Baltic, the Russian navy was creating what can without exaggeration be called the

A deflated spherical balloon at Vladivostok. (S F Post photo, R D Layman collection)

world's first aviation vessel, in the sense of an ocean-going, independently-propelled ship intended to operate several aerial devices. What impelled the navy to do so is unclear. Captain Nikolai L Klado, a critic of the navy's policy during the war, stated that after the death of Admiral Stepan O Makarov, the 'newly appointed com-mander' wanted balloons and 'war-kites' to be included in the equipment of the squadron being assembled for the Far East.[18] A later commentator, however, says that this 'seems to have been the result of a Press campaign which regarded balloons as a new war-winning weapon . . .'.[19]

Whatever the motive, the outcome was that the vessel should sail with Rear-Admiral Nikolai Ivanovich Nebo-gatov's Third Pacific Squadron. The ship chosen for conversion was a former North German Lloyd liner, the 9600-ton *Lahn*. This roomy but decrepit vessel, dating from 1887, was purchased by Count Sergei Stroganov for 700,000 roubles for presentation to the navy.

Lahn may have been selected for conversion simply because the navy did not know what else to do with this white elephant. At any rate, she was designated a second-class cruiser, renamed *Russ* and taken in hand for conversion at Libau in November 1904 under the supervision of Lieutenant M N Bolshev, an early navy balloonist who had also flown in man-lifting kites while commanding the aeronautical station at Sevastopol.

Bolshev apparently was responsible for the vessel's thorough redesign. An aft area for carriage and inflation of balloons was created by removing the mainmast and portions of the after superstructure. This was surrounded by a system of windscreens; below it were three deck levels of aeronautical equipment, including three electrolytic hydrogen generators, compressors and gas containers. The generators and balloon winches were powered by auxiliary engines and dynamos. Nine balloons were to be carried – one spherical and four kite balloons for observation and four small kite balloons for signalling. A thousand metres (1100yds) of telephone cable were stowed for air-to-ship communication, and provision was made for aerial photography. Aeronautical personnel amounted to 118 officers and men over and above the ship's regular complement.[20] A contemporary illustration shows that the vessel was armed, but the number and calibre of the guns are unknown.

While *Russ* was well and efficiently equipped as a balloon ship, she was in hopeless disrepair otherwise. Nebogatov, contemplating the long journey to the Far East, found cause for concern over her inclusion in his squadron when an inspection revealed that her boilers were in terrible shape, one with 250 patches. He was

Rossia's *balloon down at sea. A boat from the cruiser is approaching it.* (S F Post photo, R D Layman collection)

further disillusioned when a trial balloon inflation he had ordered could not be performed because a breakdown prevented the electrolytic generators from functioning. When he suggested that the chemical process for producing gas be used, he was told that it was too dangerous, two men having been burned during it previously.

The chagrined admiral asked to be relieved of the vessel, but was told that the pressure of public opinion

The kite balloon aboard Rossia *before the cruise of May 1905.* (S F Post photo, R D Layman collection)

Italian cruiser Elba *with a spherical balloon aboard. This was replaced by a kite balloon.* (Courtesy of L L von Münching)

demanded she sail with his squadron. Nebogatov obeyed, but he was still determined to get rid of her; he found his chance after reaching the Skagerrak, where 'it appeared that the condensers [of *Russ*] were full of wooden plugs. I formed a committee of enquiry and quickly sent her back to Libau . . .'.[21]

Criticism of *Russ*'s decrepitude aside, a question that seems never to have been raised is what she was intended to do. There was no doctrine for her use, and the fleet was unpractised in aerial observation. The only thing that can be said with near certainty is that, had she managed to reach Tsushima, she would have never survived the battle.

The Italian Experience

Italian experiments with the shipboard balloon began with a spherical type lofted from the cruiser *Elba*; it was replaced by a kite balloon when the cruiser took part in manoeuvres off Sicily in 1907. Her sister cruiser *Liguria* was similarly equipped from 1908 to 1911. *Elba* continued as a balloon vessel until 1914, when she became a seaplane tender.

The Italian campaign in Libya during the 1911–12 war

HMS Canning *lofting a Caquot Type M balloon, venue and date unknown.* (Courtesy of John B Hollingworth)

with Turkey witnessed the first employment of an organized air service, with Italian aeroplanes, airships and balloons pioneering nearly all the functions that aircraft would perform in future wars. Because of their telephonic communication, the German-manufactured kite balloons quickly proved themselves useful in directing army artillery fire, and ways were sought to extend this utility to the navy for coastal bombardment. A balloon vessel was therefore created at Tripoli by removing the mainmast and foremast rigging from a brigantine named *Cavalmarino*.

Towed by the naval tug *Ecole*, it lofted a kite balloon during November/December 1911 – conflicting dates are given – to spot for bombardments by the cruiser *Carlo Alberto* and the battleship *Re Umberto*. This service was short-lived, however, for on 12 December the balloon was carried off the vessel's deck during a storm; it was found inland two days later, a total loss. Brief as this service was, it marked the first time since 1862 that an aerial device had guided warship gunfire in combat.

The First World War

Except as a sport, ballooning was in decline by the outbreak of the First World War. The aeroplane had arrived and, more importantly in the minds of many, the airship – originally called the 'dirigible balloon'[22] – had been perfected. The mobility of these craft seemed to offer far more utility to navies than the balloon, forever a captive of its mooring lines. Balloon air-to-surface communication remained for the moment superior, but aerial wireless was under development.

Consequently, except in the case of the Italian navy, the balloon began to vanish at sea. The French navy, as noted earlier, abandoned aeronautics in 1904. The Russian navy turned its aeronautical equipment over to the army after the war with Japan. On the other hand, the British army, which had been well served by balloons during the Boer War (but which apparently did not recognize the fact), gave all its lighter-than-air craft to the Admiralty. These weary spherical balloons and few small airships were no great gift to a navy that had already turned its attention (however briefly) to the man-lifting kite after a disappointing experiment with balloons aboard a destroyer at

Gibraltar in 1903 or 1904.

But although the balloon saw only limited use during the early months of the First World War, 1915 saw a dramatic revival in aeronautics. For navies, the reasons for this were threefold. We shall explore these separately.

Balloons in Coastal Operations

Royal Navy involvement with balloons began in October 1914 when a Naval Balloon Section was formed to aid the Royal Naval Division defending Antwerp, but that city had fallen before it could be dispatched. Later that month Rear-Admiral Sir Horace Hood requested that some be sent to the Franco–Belgian coast. The targets of his ships supporting the left flank of the Allied line were often obscured by dunes, and Hood hoped that balloons would be able to assist in directing their gunfire. The Naval Balloon Section was therefore sent to Dunkirk, where it arrived on 14 October, equipped with some of the old Boer War spherical balloons, one engine-powered and two manually-powered winches. Its work was unrewarding; visibility was frequently bad and communication with the ships was less than timely – 'by telephone to the Belgian Headquarters, thence by messenger to a field wireless station, and thence by wireless to the fleet'.[23] The biggest handicap, however, was the instability of the spherical balloons.

There was a German kite balloon operating in the sector, and also a German-manufactured Belgian kite balloon. The British balloonists were quick to notice the greater stability of these craft and the higher altitudes they could reach. Their plea for similar equipment was heeded, and by early March 1915 development of the kite balloon had been undertaken and the Royal Naval Air Service had established a balloon depot and training centre.

The balloon vessel made its Royal Navy debut soon after. It had its origin in a request for the dispatch of balloons or man-lifting kites to the Allied forces in the Aegean, where preparations were under way for the assault on the Gallipoli Peninsula. The intent apparently was to operate these ashore to supplement the work of the seaplane carrier *Ark Royal*; however, since the peninsula's coast offered few spots large enough for safe balloon operations, the decision was made to base them aboard a ship.

The ship chosen was the fifteen-year-old merchantman *Manica*. In the amazingly short time of seventeen days she was converted at Birkenhead to her novel new usage by 'fitting a long sloping deck from forecastle to waist, fixing a dynamo to drive a hydrogen compressor, installing [a] winch and connecting it to the main engines, building a wireless telegraphy house [and] building quarters for officers and men'[24] – including eighty-nine balloon personnel. Since there was as yet no British kite balloon, a French type, along with its winch, was acquired. It was sheltered at sea by canvas windscreens.

The balloon well of HMS Canning. *Hydrogen was piped through the line protruding from the bulkhead.* (Courtesy of John B Hollingworth)

The British balloon barge Arctic. *The balloon appears to be a Spencer type.* (J M Bruce/G S Leslie collection)

Manica arrived at Mudros on 9 April 1915, having made a trial inflation of the balloon en route. Ten days later she spotted for the bombardment of a Turkish position by the cruiser *Bacchante*. She was active during the 25 April landings on Gallipoli, spotting for gunfire and observing enemy positions. Her balloon was initially more useful in this work than *Ark Royal*'s seaplanes because of its superior communications and longer endurance in the air. The campaign was soon mired in stalemate, during which *Manica* continued artillery spotting. In September she departed for a refit at Birkenhead; her balloon platform was replaced by a well, anti-aircraft armament was added and she was equipped to operate a seaplane. From April 1916 to May 1917 she supported coastal operations in East Africa.

Meanwhile, two merchant vessels dating from the 1890s joined the ranks of the balloon ship. These were near-sisters *Hector* and *Menelaus*; the former joined *Manica* in the Aegean in June 1915 and the latter was assigned to the Dover Patrol the next month, assisting operations off the Belgian coast. In March 1916 she was relieved by still another converted merchantman, *City of*

The balloon well deck of Arctic. (J M Bruce/G S Leslie collection)

Oxford, which had earlier been a member of the Special Service Squadron of merchant vessels rigged to resemble battleships. Her conversion at Belfast amounted to a rebuilding and took nearly a year, and resulted in 'the ship which most nearly approached the ideal for balloon service'. *City of Oxford* served at Dover until August, when she was assigned to the Battle Fleet at Scapa Flow. In October she became the balloon depot ship for the Battle Cruiser Force at Rosyth.

Canning, the largest of the British balloon ships, was converted from merchant service at Birkenhead during June–September 1915 and replaced *Manica* at Mudros in October. She assisted during the evacuation of Gallipoli in December and was then assigned to Salonika. In May 1916 she landed her balloon for service ashore and sailed homeward with the wreckage of the German army airship *LZ 85*, which had been shot down by British warships. Refitted at Birkenhead during June–December, she served as a balloon depot for the Grand Fleet until January 1919.

At the other end of the scale was the 357grt tug *Rescue*, hired by the Admiralty in March 1915 as a salvage vessel and converted in May 1915 to operate one of the old spherical balloons. The purpose apparently was to serve as a decoy to draw enemy fire from the kite balloons operating off Gallipoli, and it is uncertain whether manned ascents were ever made. The whole thing was called off after what was termed 'a few days of unrewarded experiment'. Later, when *Manica* became too tempting a target for Turkish artillery, her hydrogen generator and compressor were transferred to *Rescue* to inflate *Manica*'s balloon at sea. This function ceased in August.

Another even smaller balloon craft was a barge hired in January 1916. This steel craft, named *Arctic*, was converted at Liverpool. It was given a hold 82ft by 22ft to accommodate a kite balloon and equipped with a dynamo to power an electric balloon winch. Intended to supplement the balloon work of the Dover Patrol, it was used in operations off the Belgian coast, usually towed by a monitor, until November 1917.

By early 1917, however, the value of the balloon ships as spotters for gunfire was in rapid decline. In areas such as East Africa, they could accomplish nothing as operations moved inland, and as aeroplanes and their communications gear improved, these far more mobile aircraft began taking over the observation and fire spotting roles. Another factor was the development of airborne armament; balloons were quite literally sitting targets – and large ones at that.

A report by the Grand Fleet Committee on Air Requirements on 5 February 1917 opined that the continued investment in balloon ships was unproductive and recommended that *City of Oxford*, *Menelaus* and *Canning*, which were of 'considerable mercantile value . . . should be paid off as soon as possible'.[25] *Hector* had already ceased balloon service, and *Manica* was soon to revert to mercantile status. *Menelaus* became an ammunition carrier. However, *Canning* continued as a balloon depot ship for the Grand Fleet and *City of Oxford* was converted into a seaplane carrier for service in the Levant.

A kite balloon ascending from HMS Campania, *an observer manning its basket. The balloon appears to be a British Spencer type.* (Courtesy of John B Hollingworth)

Balloons With the Grand Fleet

The success of *Manica* at the Dardanelles and *Menelaus* off Belgium, due mainly to the superiority of their balloons' reliable telephonic communication over the primitive wireless gear of aeroplanes, led Admiral Sir David Beatty, commander of the Battle Cruiser Fleet, to recommend balloons for reconnaissance with the Grand Fleet to the Board of Admiralty in memoranda dated 20 August and 23 September 1915. He was seconded by the Grand Fleet's commander-in-chief, Admiral Sir John Jellicoe. In response, a kite balloon section was sent to Rosyth, where experiments in balloon towing at high speed were conducted by the seaplane carrier *Engadine* under the personal supervision of Admiral Hood, the balloon enthusiast of 1914 who now commanded the 3rd Battle Cruiser Squadron. These showed that a balloon could be towed up to 3000ft at 22kts in a rough sea while maintaining perfect communication with the ship.

In a report to Beatty, Hood stated, 'I think I have proved the value of the kite balloon for reconnaissance purposes; in a suitable vessel the strategic and tactical value will be very great; at 3000ft there will be a radius of vision of 60 miles and the communication will not be of the sketchy kind in use from aeroplanes . . .'.[26] Beatty concurred when he forwarded the report to the Admiralty. Jellicoe advocated a special balloon ship for the fleet; however it was stated that 'the urgent demands for large fast merchant ships for other purposes had first to be met',[27] and instead it was decided to equip the Battle Fleet's aviation vessel, *Campania*, with a balloon when she was taken in hand for modification in November 1915.

This old former Cunard liner had been acquired in 1914 as a seaplane carrier, fitted with a forward platform for launching trolley-borne floatplanes. Operations showed that a longer platform was required for larger aircraft; this was accomplished by dividing the forward boiler uptakes and extending the platform between two athwartship funnels. When the remodelled *Campania* returned to the fleet in April 1916 she carried the Royal Navy's first French M type kite balloon, a tri-lobe craft developed by *Captaine d'Aerostiers* Albert Caquot.[28] It proved superior in stability and altitude to the British Spencer type[29] and to an earlier Caquot design and by the end of the war was the principal type employed by the British, French and American navies.

Campania missed her chance to test the balloon in action when she failed to receive the signal to sally with the fleet on the eve of the Battle of Jutland. Another opportunity was lost when the fleet sailed to counter the August sortie of the High Sea Fleet. This time *Campania* was laid up with machinery defects. By chance, however,

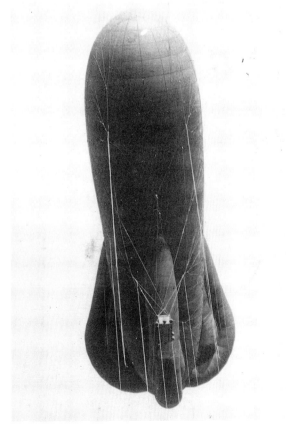

A Caquot M Type as seen from the deck of HMS Campania, *a view showing the type's configuration.* (Courtesy of John B Hollingworth)

Two views of HMS Campania *lofting a Caquot balloon*. (Courtesy of John B Hollingworth)

her balloon had been transferred to the battleship *Hercules* for a sea-going endurance test. This is presumably the reason why the balloon carried no observer during the 28 hours it was aloft during the operation. Even if it had been manned, 'It would have been of little use for reconnaissance . . . since it was so far back that its range of vision could hardly have out-distanced the observation from the forward cruisers'.[30] It was finally hauled down and deflated to prevent it from disclosing the position of the fleet to the Germans.

The possibility that balloons might reveal the presence of the fleet, and even indicate its composition and movement, to enemy eyes, became a matter of controversy. Opponents of balloons argued that they could be seen before the aerial observers could spot the opposing fleet. Indeed, this did happen on two occasions when elements of the Grand Fleet exercised against each other.

The dispute came to a head in early 1917 after Jellicoe became First Sea Lord, Beatty succeeded him as Grand Fleet C-in-C, and the fleet shifted its main base to Rosyth. In a report to the Admiralty, Beatty came out strongly for the balloons. Conceding that they might be seen before they could see, he nevertheless declared the information they could obtain, especially if they were placed in the advance scouting line, would more than compensate for that disadvantage. Implicit in this argument was recognition of the problems plaguing the Grand Fleet's aerial reconnaissance – lack of long-range airships and the

difficulty of operating seaplanes from ships.

Beatty also opined that in the future balloons might be used to spot fire for the battle line, a function they did practise later in the war.

His view prevailed. In May 1917, Vice-Admiral Sir John de Robeck, commanding the 2nd Battle Squadron, was placed in charge of fleet balloon matters. Balloon winches were ordered to be installed on nine battleships, two battlecruisers, the 'large light cruisers' *Glorious* and *Courageous*, four light cruisers and three destroyers (over and above those fitted with balloons for anti-submarine work – see below).

The trend continued, and by November 1918 ships fitted to operate balloons (again exclusive of anti-submarine craft) numbered 17 battleships, 2 battle-cruisers, the 2 'large light cruisers', and 7 light cruisers.

Balloons Versus U-boats

The shipboard balloon made its debut in anti-submarine warfare (ASW) in July 1917. By this time British wireless intelligence had gained considerable knowledge of the routes followed by U-boats traversing the North Sea, and independent 'hunting' sweeps against them had been carried out by destroyers. Several submarines had been sighted, but the few attacks possible against them had been unsuccessful.

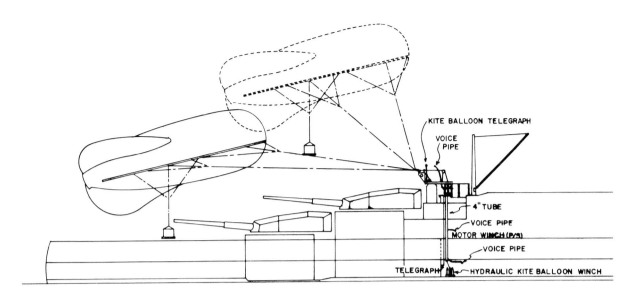

The kite balloon arrangements as installed on HMS Colossus, *1918, typical for capital ships. All balloon winches on British capital ships were of the hydraulic type except for* King George V, *which had an electrically powered winch.* (By Stephen McLaughlin based on a drawing in PRO Air 1/2103)

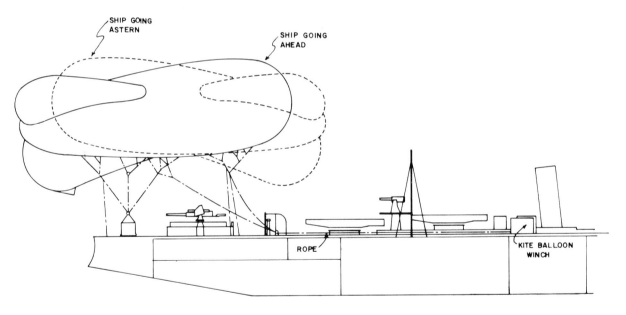

A typical kite balloon installation on British destroyers in 1918. (By Stephen McLaughlin based on a drawing in PRO Air 1/2103)

Beatty, believing aerial observation would give greater chances for success, formed a special Kite Balloon Force of six destroyers, five of them with balloons, 'to spread out across the U-boat tracks and make an experiment in co-operative stalking'.[31]

The first operation, carried out by all six destroyers during 5–8 July, resulted in several sightings, but no attacks could be made. The second sweep, by five destroyers, three of them towing balloons, began on 11 July. Early the next day the balloon observer of the destroyer *Patriot* sighted a surfaced submarine at a distance of 28 miles. It submerged as *Patriot* headed for it, resurfaced and dived again when the destroyer opened fire. The observer guided *Patriot* in a successful depth charge attack on what was later identified as *U 69*.

This first success, however, was also the last. The chances of finding so small a target in so large a sea were slight indeed. As the British official naval history put it, 'even though ten such operations had been proceeding simultaneously, their combined effect would not have been great'.[32]

Moreover, with the introduction of convoy in 1917 such

independent operations became even more unproductive. The balloon soon found a role as a convoy protector, however, over objections that it would simply serve as a marker to guide U-boats to a target. The counter-argument was that the advantages outweighed the draw-backs, and in fact the presence of a balloon seems to have been a considerable deterrent to attack by U-boats. The low underwater speed of the submarines necessitated surface runs to reach an advantageous submerged firing position, and during these runs the U-boats could be spotted by balloon observers. Very few vessels were lost

An unidentified British destroyer (at stern of merchant vessel) towing its balloon as it returns to Devonport after convoy escort duty. (R D Layman collection)

HMS Snapdragon, *an* Arabis *type sloop of the 'Flower' class, showing the modifications, including removal of the mainmast, to fit the vessel for balloon operation.* (R D Layman collection)

An unidentified Anchusa *type sloop of the 'Flower' class lofting a Caquot balloon. Again, the mainmast has been removed.* (R D Layman collection)

from convoys having balloon escort. Therefore, although the balloons posed little danger to the submarines, they could by their mere presence keep the raiders from getting into attack position.

That great faith was placed in the balloon as an ASW weapon is indicated by the large number of Royal Navy escort vessels fitted to operate it – destroyers, sloops, P-boats, trawlers and others.[33] Modifications to permit this usually were minor, but a number of 'Flower' class sloops had mainmast, gallows and sometimes the aft gun removed to allow installation of a balloon-handling platform.

Whether this faith was justified and the expense rewarded must remain moot points. It is impossible to quantify the contribution of the balloon to ASW of the First World War. But it unquestionably was a deterrent – and in protection of shipping, deterrence is a vital factor.

Balloons in Other Navies

The United States Navy, which had steadfastly ignored lighter-than-air craft since 1862, entered the First World War with precisely two balloons. One of them, a kite type manufactured by the Goodyear Tire & Rubber Company,

had been tested for shipboard use aboard the battleships *Nevada* and *Oklahoma* in November 1916; professional opinion on its utility was divided, but these vessels and the battleship *Utah* operated balloons while stationed at Bantry Bay, Ireland, in 1918. So did the battleship *New York* while flagship of the 6th Battle Squadron serving with the Grand Fleet.

The balloon used in the 1916 tests apparently was the one experimentally lofted and towed in June 1917 at Pensacola, Florida, by armoured cruiser *Huntington*[34] (one of three cruisers also briefly equipped with catapults for seaplanes). If so, it was presumably also the balloon blown off *Huntington* on 17 September 1917 during the cruiser's first wartime crossing of the Atlantic. Its observer was rescued from the sea by a shipfitter who thereby won the first Medal of Honor awarded in the war.

Displaying the zeal of the convert, the American navy had by early 1918 become an ardent advocate of balloons for ASW; an advantage pointed out was that a balloon could accompany a convoy beyond the radius of action of an aeroplane or airship – all the way across the Atlantic if necessary.[35]

Lack of experience with kite balloons, however, prevented the US Navy from turning rhetoric into reality. Of the 215 balloons acquired during the war (either manufactured domestically or transferred from allies) only a handful saw service afloat between July and November 1918.[36] By the end of the war six destroyers based at Brest had operated balloons, using two types of steam-powered winches, but the use had been almost entirely experimental. Operational use would have been expanded had the war continued, for a number of the new destroyers were equipped with balloon winches. When some of these were found aboard the four-pipers being recommissioned in 1939 after years in reserve, the balloon had been so thoroughly forgotten that it required 'voluminous correspondence with all the material bureaus and the Chief of Naval Operations'[37] to discover their purpose.

It would seem that the only other American vessel to operate a balloon during the Great War was the converted yacht *Mohican*, which embarked one on 23 August 1918 during her duty as a patrol, escort and guard ship in New York waters.[38] Winches were installed on a few other vessels but never used.

The French navy also used kite balloons for convoy escort, starting in 1917, but little has been published about these operations. There is no official source for the number of naval balloons, but unofficial sources agree it was approximately 200 at the end of the war, with at least 24 vessels equipped to operate balloons. These included the pre-dreadnought battleships *Condorcet*, *Vergniaud*

and *Voltaire*, which had their mainmasts cut down to facilitate balloon towing.[39]

Despite its auspicious start in 1911, the Italian navy lagged in use of balloons at sea. Official statistics list only sixteen captive balloons at the end of the war.[40] There were also two powered lighters, *Luigi Mina* and *Umberto Missana*, built in 1916 and 1917 respectively as balloon vessels.

Operational Problems

Operation of balloons from a conventional ship presented several difficulties. Foremost was the danger inherent in thousands of cubic feet of highly inflammable hydrogen. For this reason, balloons going aboard warships were inflated on shore or on depot ships and were already aloft when transferred to the towing vessel. They were kept in the air, untenanted, and hauled down only for an observer to get in or out of the basket. Balloons were not infrequently struck by lightning, with spectacular results.

US armoured cruiser Huntington *trailing an early Goodyear kite balloon at Pensacola, Florida, 23 June 1917. The devices suspended from the balloon are drogues intended to improve stability; they were later eliminated. The cruiser is fitted with an afterdeck catapult, a Curtiss N.9H floatplane is aboard and another seaplane is in the air at right. (National Archives)*

New York's balloon put on such an unscheduled display for the King and Queen of Belgium while they were visiting the ship in July 1918.[41] Even without the threat posed by the hydrogen, the average vessel had no clear deck space adequate to park a balloon (the Caquot M type was 92ft long) and no means of sheltering it from wind or sea.

Duty in the basket could prove strenuous and dangerous. Even the inherently stable kite balloon could be buffeted badly by strong winds, which could also snap its mooring line. Loss of gas by leakage could reduce buoyancy, in which case the craft's nose could collapse ('dished in', in aeronautical jargon). At best this would make hauling down a harrowing experience; at worst the balloon would fall on its own. Admiral of the Fleet Sir Roger Keyes described his sensations in a wildly gyrating balloon towed by the battleship *Colossus* while watching another balloon being blown away and a third dipping into the sea during haul-down.[42] Fortunately, loss of life from such accidents was rare, the balloon basket usually being unmanned.

Decline and Fall

The shipboard observation balloon saw its greatest use during the First World War, but ironically that same conflict inspired developments that led to the balloon's eclipse in military operations.

Interest in it, however, remained high for a time in the American navy. In early 1919 six battleships of the Atlantic Fleet operated balloons at Guantanamo Bay, Cuba, with the former minelayer *Shawmut* as their depot ship. Additionally, it was intended to convert three incomplete merchantmen to balloon ships along the lines of the earlier British vessels. But disillusionment soon set in. In March 1920, balloons trailed by the battleships *Nevada* and *Florida* 'dished in' and were lost, and two men were killed. Use of balloons by the Atlantic Fleet ended, and the first and only balloon ship, USS *Wright*, was rebuilt as a seaplane tender. The Pacific Fleet continued to employ balloons for a time, but they, too, shortly went into limbo.

More important than the accidents as a cause of the naval balloon's demise was the rapid development of other forms of aviation. The long range flying-boat had been perfected, the introduction of helium made the airship a more viable proposition, the flight-deck aircraft carrier had arrived, and development of catapults for shipboard seaplanes was under way. Advances in aerial wireless made these craft superior to the balloon for scouting and gunnery direction. Although a few kite balloons were retained ashore, the majority of the USN's balloons between the wars were free-floating types for training airship personnel.

The balloon lingered somewhat longer in a few other navies. The Japanese battlecruiser *Kongo* employed a kite balloon during manoeuvres in 1924 and the light cruiser *Tatsuta* was equipped with one as flagship of the First Destroyer Squadron in 1927. Balloons may also have been used by a few other Japanese ships.

Probably the last time a shipboard observation balloon was employed during hostilities was in 1925 when the Spanish seaplane/airship/balloon carrier *Dédalo* supported the Franco–Spanish suppression of the Moroccan rebellion.

The Second World War saw a revival of the kite balloon, but only as an unmanned form of aerial defence. Large numbers of these barrage balloons were flown from vessels in British, German and Italian harbours and from landing craft in Europe and the Pacific. A few manned balloons were employed on land early in the war by Poland and the Soviet Union, and later by Japan.

Today the balloon serves a host of scientific, military, commercial and recreational purposes, in the course of which it often ascends from ships, but Jacques Cousteau's employment of a ship-moored captive balloon on some of his oceanographic expeditions was probably the last gasp of the manned maritime balloon. It is pleasant to reflect that, after its long history as a tool of war, its final service was in the cause of science and peace.

Notes

1 For details of many of these proposals, and for a general history of the early balloon, see F Stansbury Haydon, *Aeronautics in the Union and Confederate Armies With a Survey of Military Aeronautics Prior to 1861* (John Hopkins Press, Baltimore 1941); C F Snowden Gamble, *The Air Weapon, Being Some Account of the Growth of British Military Aeronautics From the Beginnings in the Year 1883 Until the End of the Year 1929* (Oxford University Press, London 1931) and R D Layman, *To Ascend From a Floating Base: Shipboard Aeronautics and Aviation, 1783–1914* (Associated University Presses, Cranbury, NJ, and London 1979).

2 See 'Documents Contributed by Mr D B Smith: Kite Balloon Ships', *The Mariner's Mirror* 13, No 2 (May 1927). 'Kite balloon' in this title is a misnomer; this type did not exist until the 1890s.

3 Quoted in Snowden Gamble, *Air Weapon*, p68.

4 For a complete history of this campaign, see Robert C Mikesh, *Japan's World War II Balloon Bomb Attacks on North America* (Smithsonian Institution Press, Washington 1973).

5 Eugene Kolesnik, 'The Japanese Balloon Bombing Offensive', *Warship* 4 (October 1977).

6 Haydon, *Aeronautics*, p280.

7 The Union balloons were individually named, gaudily painted and decorated with patriotic emblems.

8 W T Adams, 'The Birth of the Aircraft Carrier,' *United States Naval Institute Proceedings* 102, No 4 (April 1976).

9 No account of it appears in the US Naval History Division's massive *Civil War Naval Chronology 1861–1865* (Washington 1971).

10 The Union Army operated a considerable 'navy' of its own – gunboats, mortar boats, transports and tugs. Most were converted riverine merchant vessels.

11 Haydon, *Aeronautics*, p395.

12 *Ibid*, p396.

13 A contemporary illustration of this action, which may or may not be accurate, shows no balloon. Many facts concerning this and other Confederate balloons remain obscure; Haydon's projected second volume, which would have covered the

subject, was never published. A short but useful pamphlet which seems to embody all available information is *The Air Arm of the Confederacy* by Joseph Jenkins Cornish III, published in 1963 by the Richmond Civil War Centennial Committee.

14 John R Cuneo, *Winged Mars*, Vol 1: *The German Air Weapon 1870–1914* (Military Publishing Co, Harrisburg, PA 1942), p13.

15 Research into the possibility and techniques of production of non-inflammable helium did not begin until 1917.

16 Shipboard use of man-lifting kites was also explored by the Russian and British navies, and, briefly, by the American.

17 All information on the Vladivostok balloons is taken from Postnikov's log books, 'Reports on flights and ascents of the kite balloons and spherical balloons for the years 1905–6 of the Naval Aeronautical Park', 2 vols, dated 23 July 1904 – 4 November 1905 (Old Style). The originals are held by the Naval Historical Foundation, Washington. A copy made available to R D Layman was translated by the late Boris V Drashpil. Postnikov retained these when he emigrated to the United States in 1906. Anglicizing his name to Post, he had a varied career as a journalist, farmer, balloon instructor and consultant on airship construction. The change in name and his continued lighter-than-air activity has sometimes caused him to be confused with Augustus Post, a well-known American balloonist of the period. The photos accompanying this article were provided by Postnikov's son, the late S F Post, and other family members.

18 By 'newly appointed commander,' Klado apparently means Admiral Nikolai Ilarionovich Skrydlov, who was appointed to command the Pacific Fleet after Makarov's death. Skrydlov was to assume overall command of the Port Arthur and Vladivostok squadrons, but he was unable to reach Port Arthur before the Japanese siege closed around the port (allegedly because he spent too much time making speeches and accepting icons before departing), and so wound up at Vladivostok with little to do. Klado was on Skrydlov's staff and so would have been in a position to know if the admiral had wanted vessels equipped with balloons and 'war-kites'.

19 J N Westwood, *Witnesses of Tsushima* (Sophia University, Tokyo 1970), p147.

20 Data on *Russ* are from a report by a Russian army balloonist, Staff Captain Michael V Agapov, dated 14 February 1905 (Old Style) held by the former Soviet Central State Military History Archives. A copy was supplied to R D Layman by the late Edgar Meos.

21 Quoted in Westwood, *Witnesses*, p148.

22 The term derived from the French 'dirigeable,' the noun form of the verb 'diriger,' one definition of which is 'to steer'. A 'dirigible balloon' is thus simply a steerable lighter-than-air craft, and from this term stems 'dirigible' as an English synonym for 'airship'. The French noun remains that language's term for airship.

23 Conrad Cato, *The Navy Everywhere* (Constable, London 1919), p141.

24 *Ibid*, pp144–45.

25 Quoted in S W Roskill (ed), *Documents Relating to the Naval Air Service*, Vol 1: *1908–1918* (Navy Records Society, London 1969), p472.

26 H A Jones, *The War in the Air*, Vol 2 (Oxford 1928), p368.

27 *Ibid*, p369.

28 Caquot, often misspelled 'Cacquot,' was not only an authority on aeronautics and electricity but an engineer internationally known for construction of bridges and dams. He was for a time president of the French Academy of Science.

29 Developed by the family firm of C G Spencer & Sons. The family's involvement with aeronautics dated from the early nineteenth century.

30 Jones, *op cit*, p419.

31 Jones, *The War in the Air*, Vol 4, p63.

32 Henry Newbolt, *Naval Operations*, Vol 5 (Longmans, Green, London 1931), p123. This volume describes the first operation in detail but does not mention the second.

33 The exact number cannot be determined. However, Air 1/2103, Public Record Office, states that 180 ships were equipped for balloon operation. Deducting the 28 such vessels in the Grand Fleet leaves a total of 152.

34 *Huntington* is erroneously credited as the first American warship to operate a kite balloon in R D Layman, *Before the Aircraft Carrier: The Development of Aviation Vessels 1849–1922* (Conway Maritime Press, London 1989). The earlier experiments are noted in *Kite Balloons to Airships . . . The Navy's Lighter-than-Air Experience* (Published by the Deputy Chief of Naval Operations and the Commander, Naval Air Systems Command, Washington nd).

35 Air 1/273 and Air 1/649, Public Record Office. Excerpts are in Roskill *op cit*.

36 The official figure of 215 includes both free and kite balloons. Kite types numbered 117, according to Gordon Swanborough and Peter M Bowers, *United States Navy Aircraft Since 1911* (3rd ed, Naval Institute Press, Annapolis 1990), p567. This source also states that 99 of these were manufactured in the United States, of which 48 were sent overseas.

37 John D Alden, *Flush Decks and Four Pipes* (Naval Institute Press, Annapolis 1965), p21. This volume incorrectly states that the purpose of the balloons was 'anti-aircraft defense'.

38 *Dictionary of American Naval Fighting Ships*, Vol 4 (Naval History Division, Washington 1969).

39 Jean Labayle Couhat, *French Warships of World War I* (Ian Allen, London 1974).

40 *The Italian Navy in the World War, 1915–1918: Facts & Figures* (Office of the Chief of Staff of the Royal Italian Navy [Historical Section], Rome 1927).

41 Francis T Hunter, *Beatty, Jellicoe, Sims and Rodman: Yankee Gobs and British Tars, as Seen by an 'Anglomaniac'* (Doubleday, Page, New York 1919), pp62–3.

42 R Keyes, *Scapa Flow to the Dover Straits: The Naval Memoirs of Admiral of the Fleet Sir Roger Keyes*, Vol 2 (Thornton Butterworth, London 1935), pp127–28.

THE SECOND CLASS BATTLESHIP USS MAINE

William C Emerson illustrates the design, construction and brief career of the early American battleship whose loss was an important cause of the Spanish American War.

I n 1883 the US Navy, primarily made up of old Civil War relics, was ranked twentieth among naval powers. Unwilling to engage in the massive building effort needed to reach parity with European navies, Congress concerned itself with possible enemies in Latin America. Recent warship acquisitions had given Brazil, Argentina, and Chile navies more powerful than the USN, and there was fear that in a conflict American interests could not be adequately protected. In 1886 Congress authorized the building of a number of vessels – among them was an armoured cruiser named USS *Maine*. Reclassified a Second Class Battleship before commissioning, she and a near-sister were America's first steel capital ships.

Built by the New York Navy Yard from designs furnished by the Bureau of Construction and Repair of the Navy Department, *Maine* was then the largest vessel built in a US Navy Yard. Displacement was about 6650 tons and like the majority of her rivals, she was driven by two screws. Contract price for the hull and machinery was $2,500,000. The keel was laid on 11 October 1888, and her hull launched on 18 November 1890. Difficulties in obtaining armour and guns stretched out the construction process, and she was some six years building. With sailing contemplated to help save coal during long voyages, the original design called for a three-masted barque-rigged vessel, but as her construction proceeded this design was altered in favour of two military masts.

With her heaviest armament in turrets *en echelon*, offset from the centreline and extended beyond the side for the ship, *Maine* had a distinctive and unusual appearance. This feature reflected the design influence of the earlier British *Inflexible* and the more recent Brazilian *Riachuelo*. The concept of offset turrets was seen as a way to optimize fire-power from the main battery. The idea was that in battle, when approaching an enemy to ram (ramming was still considered an offensive option), both turrets could fire forward, and likewise to the rear.

Early design concepts included three masts and a full set of sails. Eventually eliminated were the torpedo boats (shown here on chocks above the bridge between the midship and aft superstructures), sails, and one of the masts. (US National Archives)

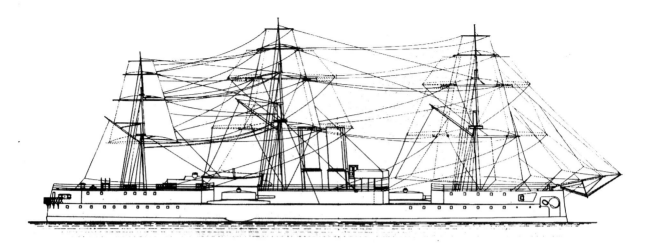

Congress was fearful of Latin American naval acquisitions such as the Brazilian Riachuelo, *shown here. The design of* Maine *was clearly influenced by this ship*. (US National Archives)

Maine *at anchor in this photo taken early in her short career, painted white to superstructure deck level and buff above. Her unusual off-centreline turret arrangement was intended to improve fore and aft firepower but was unsuccessful and not repeated in later US ships*. (Naval Historical Center)

Broadside firepower was theoretically optimized as well since guns in either turret could be turned to fire across the deck through openings between the superstructures. Experience showed, however, that blast damage to decks and superstructure made the arrangement impractical. Tried on *Maine* and a near-sister, *Texas*, the arrangement was never again used on a US ship.

Before HMS *Dreadnought* (1906) demonstrated the virtue of all-big-gun warships and long range gunnery, capital ships were expected to fight at relatively close ranges and thus carried a number of secondary weapons.

Stern view at Bar Harbor in 1895. The segmented gun shields for the port 6in gun are open, revealing the 2in thick moveable shield beneath. (Naval Historical Center)

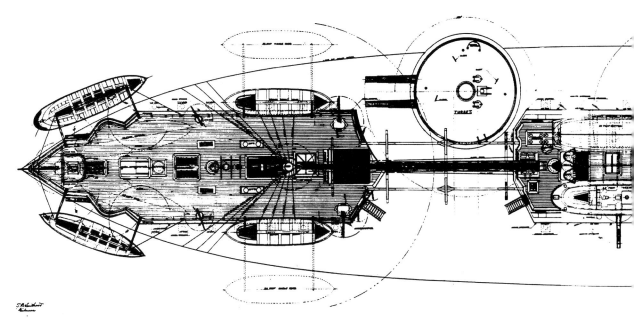

Superstructure deck plan of Maine. *This plan was taken from work and shows the ship as she was finally built.* (US National Archives)

Lines of Maine *taken from original construction plans.* (US National Archives)

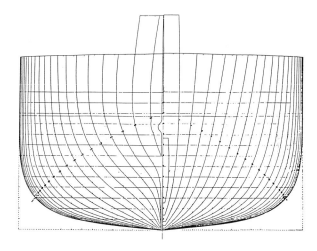

Half-breadth and sheer plans. (US National Archives)

Maine was no exception: besides the twin 10in turrets, her armament included six 6in breech-loading rifles and some twenty secondary rapid-fire weapons. While not expected to be decisive in battle, secondary weapons were intended to rain shells upon a luckless enemy, disrupting operations, starting fires, and damaging unarmoured portions of a vessel.

Maine was initially designated to carry two large torpedo boats on platforms aft. These steel craft were to be 61ft (18.6m) in length and armed with 18in Whitehead torpedo and 1pdr rapid-fire guns. Each was to be powered by a quadruple expansion steam engine with a single screw. Cylinders were from 6 to 15¾in in diameter with a stroke of 8in. With no accommodation or mess facilities, these boats were not intended for independent action but would be lowered over the side in the proximity of an enemy to provide tactical support. Found to be too slow for the role intended, only one was ever built and it was never carried aboard, though the chocks and stowage gear was fitted and remained aboard *Maine* until her loss.

Maine carried ten boats of more conventional design. Two were steam cutters (33ft and 28ft) and were powered by compound engines. These were carried on skids mounted over the superstructure deck, along with a 32ft sailing launch, two cutters (30ft and 28ft), and a 20ft dinghy. Two 28ft whaleboats, one 30ft barge and a 28ft gig were carried on davits aft.

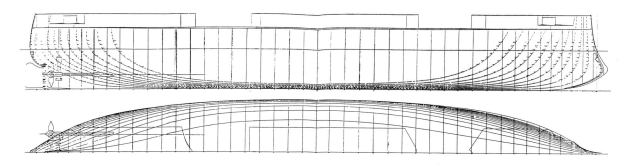

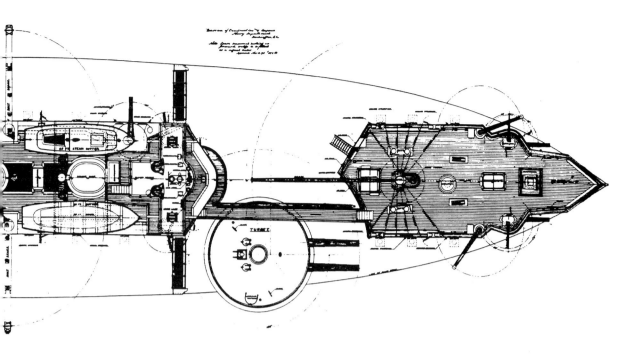

Maine *at anchor. Early design concepts included three masts and a full set of rigging. She was finally built with two military masts. (From* The American Navy)

Signalling class on port side, looking aft. Note the details of the boat crane and stowage of boats. (From The American Navy)

One of Maine's *four torpedo tubes, with the five-strong crew who manned it. Torpedoes were moved into position on an overhead trolley and fired from the tube with compressed air generated by a steam driven compressor.* (*From* The American Navy)

This photo shows the crew of Maine *manning the boats in a practice amphibious assault. In the centre is one of the canopy covered steam cutters.* (*From* The American Navy) ▼

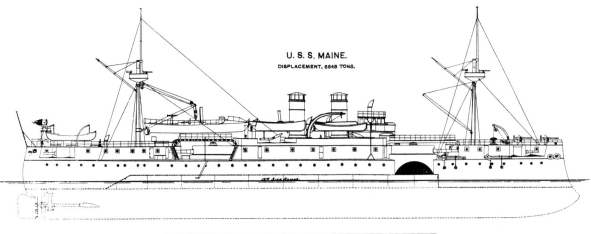

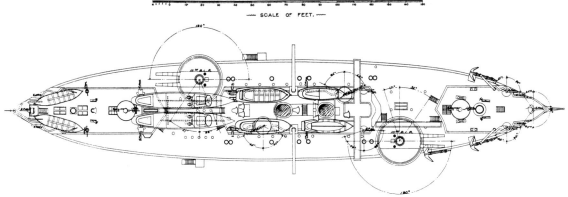

U. S. S. MAINE.

DISPLACEMENT, 6648 TONS.

— SCALE OF FEET. —

▲
Sketch of Maine *which appeared in an 1893 professional
publication. She was built essentially as shown here. The
smokestacks were soon raised and the stovetop covers
eliminated.* (Society of Naval Architects and Marine
Engineers)

Starboard quarter view of Maine *at Bar Harbor, Maine,
in 1895. Here is the colour scheme she carried until sunk
in 1898 – white hull, and buff superstructure.* (Naval
Historical Center) ▼

*The overhanging turrets housed 10in rifles which could
theoretically fire directly ahead or astern. This, however,
was impractical due to blast damage.* (US National
Archives)

Hull

The hull was built of mild steel, and was divided into 198
water-tight compartments. With 310ft between perpendiculars, *Maine* was slightly more than 324ft overall. Her
extreme beam was 57ft, had a mean draft of 21ft 6in and a
displacement of 6650 tons. A double bottom spanned
some 196ft amidships, with frames along this length
spaced every 4ft. The double bottom extended up the side
of the ship, ending in a shelf which was the lower support
for the armour belt. Frames elsewhere were at 3ft
intervals.

There were twenty coal bunker compartments, ten on
each side, located below the protective deck. Coal
bunkers were filled through scuttles in the main deck
which were connected to the bunkers by trunks leading
down. There was some 35,000 cubic feet of bunker space,
with a maximum capacity of 825 tons. Access to the
bunkers was possible through escape trunks to allow
trimming to properly balance the load.

Ashes from the firerooms were discharged through a
single chute, located on the midship superstructure deck.
Ashes were discharged through the side of the ship just
above the side armour belt.

Early concept plan of Maine. *The sloping turret armour
proved too difficult for the infant steel industry, and was
dropped in favour of the cylindrical turrets reminiscent of
Civil War days.* (US National Archives)

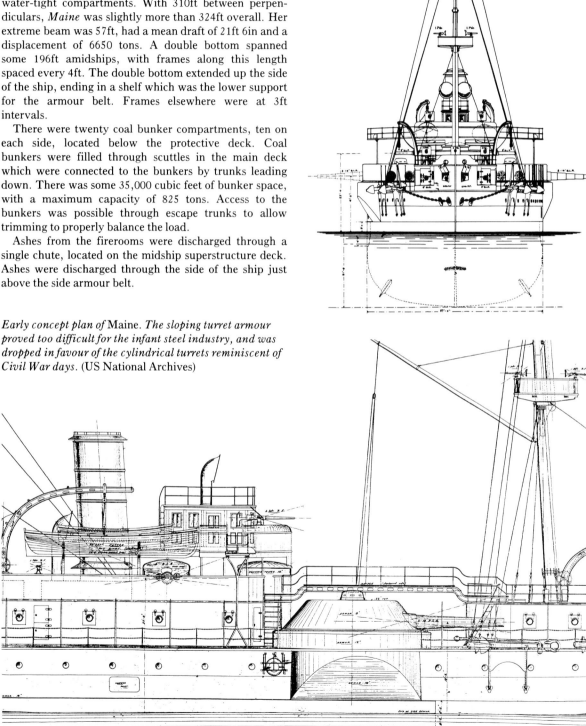

Stern of Maine *in dry-dock. Note the four-bladed propellers, the bilge keel to reduce rolling in bad weather, and the stern searchlight.* (US National Archives)

Armour

As with many armoured cruisers and battleships of her day, *Maine* had elements of protection which grew out of the 'armoured citadel' concept from earlier decades. This protection included waterline armour, a transverse armoured bulkhead at the forward end of this belt, and a protective deck to cover machinery spaces. Added to these were the ever-present armoured conning tower and turrets.

The waterline armour belts covered some 180ft amidships and were flush with the outside surface of the ship. This armour extended 3ft above and 4ft below the waterline, and was 12in thick near the top, tapering to 7in at the bottom. It was backed by 8in of teak and two ½in steel plates. The armour was attached by bolts up to 2.8in

in diameter, with nuts and india rubber cups and washers on the inner ends of the bolts.

A transverse bulkhead at the forward end of the belts was 6in thick and mounted similarly to the belt armour. A protective deck ran the entire length of the armoured belts and attached at the bow to the armoured bulkhead. This deck was flat over the engine spaces but sloped downward toward the sides, meeting at the bottom of the side armour. It also sloped down aft, and no armoured bulkhead was included here. The deck was two layers of 1in plates of steel on the flat portions and increased to three layers on the slopes. The conning tower had sides some 10in thick and an armoured communications tube carrying steering gear, voice tubes and electrical wires. Fixed barbettes with 12in of armour protected the moving parts of the turrets and the spaces for working and loading the guns.

During the extended construction period, improvements in the hardening of armour were made, so while the previously mentioned armour plates were made of mild steel, the 8in of turret armour was Harveyized hardened steel. This early process, named after its inventor,

Maine *TECHNICAL SPECIFICATION*

Construction Data

Builder	New York Navy Yard
Authorized	6 August 1886
Contract price	$2,500,000
Laid down	11 October 1888
Launched	18 November 1890
Commissioned	17 September 1895

Design particulars

Rig	Two military masts
Displacement (tons)	6650 tons
Trial speed	17.45kts
Length overall	324ft (98.75m)
Max breadth	57ft (17.37m)
Draft	21ft 6in (6.55m)
Coal capacity	825tons

Armament

4–10in (254mm) breech-loading rifled guns
6–6in (152mm) rapid-fire guns
7–5pdr Driggs-Schroeder rapid-fire guns
4–1pdr Hotchkiss
4–1pdr Driggs-Schroeder
4 Gatling machine-guns
4–18in (457mm) Whitehead torpedo tubes

Armour

Sides	12in (30.48cm)
10in turrets	8in (20.32cm)
10in barbettes	12in (30.48cm)
6in guns	2in (5.08cm)
Conning tower	10in (25.4cm)
protective deck	
(flats)	2in (5.08cm)
(slopes)	3in (7.62cm)
Bulkhead	6in (15.24cm)

Machinery

Boilers	8 single-ended
Engines	2 vertical triple expansion reciprocating
Max indicated hp	9293
Propellers	2

Complement	31 officers
	343 men

improved the penetration resistance of armour by about 40 per cent, allowing dramatic reductions in armour thickness.

Armament

As with most battleships in the era before *Dreadnought*, *Maine* mounted her largest calibre guns in two turrets. Each offset turret mounted two 10in, 26-ton breech-loading rifles. Both the turrets and the guns were powered by hydraulic gear. Additional armament was six rapid-fire 6in rifles, two mounted opposite each other inside the

forward deckhouse, two mounted atop the midship superstructure deck, and two in the after deckhouse. Each of these guns had a moveable steel shield 2in thick. Both the shield and the guns were worked by hand power. A tertiary battery consisted of seven 5pdr Driggs-Schroeder rapid-fire guns, four 1pdr Hotchkiss, four 1pdr Driggs-Schroeder, and four Gatling machine-guns. Four torpedo tubes, two each side on the berth deck, fired 18in Whitehead torpedoes.

Machinery

The machinery was built by N F Palmer, Jr and Co, the Quintard Iron Works, New York City, from designs furnished by the Bureau of Steam Engineering of the Navy Department. The contract price for the machinery was $735,000. The contract called for an indicated horsepower of 9000 for the main engines and the air and

Section view through the boiler room. Note the rectangular shaped boilers in their water-tight compartments, the coal bunkers near by, and the uptakes for the smokestacks. (US National Archives)

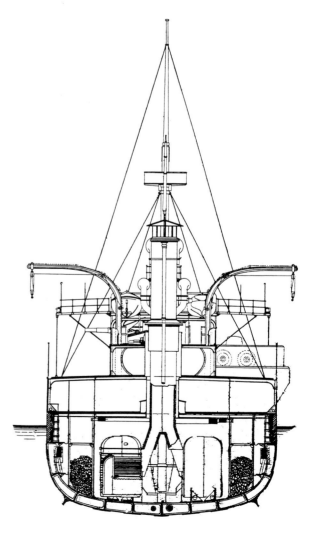

circulating pump engines, with a premium of $100 to be paid for each indicated horsepower in excess of the requirement and a penalty of like amount to be deducted for each horsepower below. While later contracts called for a specific trial speed, the horsepower designation was due to uncertainty as to the speed attainable with the hulls of the earlier US steel ships.

The two main engines were the modern triple expansion type, mounted in water-tight compartments separated by a fore and aft bulkhead. Within each engine steam was expanded against three pistons of increasing diameter to wring out as much energy as possible. The steam was then discharged to a condenser which converted it back to water. The low pressure pistons were the largest, some 88in in diameter. The pistons of each engine were arranged vertically and connected directly to one of the propeller shafts. Those shafts were 22ft long and 13in in diameter.

Lubrication of the engine components was accomplished by a complicated system of reservoirs and hoses built into the machinery. Distributing oil tanks were fitted on the sides of the cylinders, with pipes leading to

manifolds, adjustable valves, sight feed cups, journals and other moving parts of the engines.

Propellers were of manganese bronze, were four-bladed and 14½ft in diameter. They were true screws and had adjustable pitch. An unusual feature was that the blades were replaceable, with replacements carried aboard. One of these was recovered from the wreck and is on display at the Navy Yard in Washington DC.

The engines were fed by eight single-ended boilers of the horizontal return fire-tube type, with three corrugated furnaces in each boiler, for a total of twenty-four furnaces. Four boilers were mounted in each of two water-tight compartments, with boiler uptakes arranged to one of the two oval smoke stacks. Each boiler compartment was equipped with a forced draft system to maximize combustion.

In addition to the main propulsion engines, there were a total of fifty auxiliary steam engines which powered such equipment as ventilation fans, circulating pumps, refrigeration units and distilling pumps.

Her official speed trial was conducted on 17 October 1894, in Long Island Sound. Working against unfavourable wind and sea, she was credited with an average adjusted speed of 17.45kts. As was the practice, coal was specially selected, weighed, and bagged for the trial to optimize performance and as a means to determine consumption.

Smoke pours from the aft stack as Maine *prepares to get under way. Early steel ships were uncomfortable in warm weather. Here all available ports are open, including those for the Whitehead torpedoes, located just above the waterline.* (Naval Historical Center)

View of main deck looking forward taken at Bar Harbor, Maine, in 1895. The bridge wing is visible, as is the muzzle of the port amidship 6in gun. (Naval Historical Center)

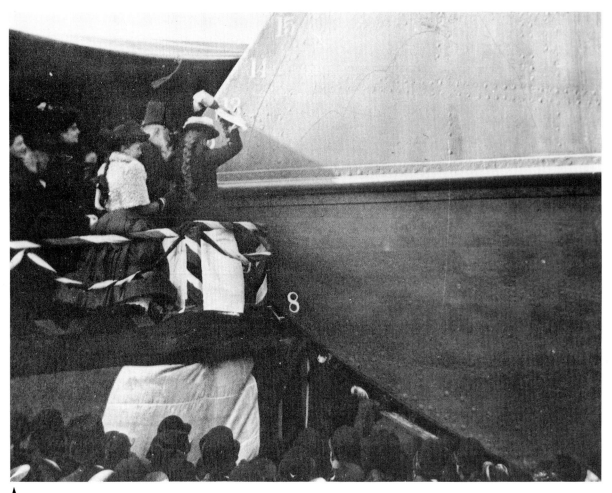

The granddaughter of Navy Secretary Benjamin F Tracy is poised to christen Maine *during the launching ceremony on 18 November 1890.* (Library of Congress)

Maine *with a steam launch (left) and cutter alongside. Just visible over the forward 10in turret is a vertical windsail, used to direct airflow to the decks below.* (Naval Historical Center) ▼

Photographers were allowed wide access to navy ships and crews in the 1890s and gathered many lighthearted shots. Here crew members pose in the seamen's mess. (From The American Navy)

Career and Destruction

In the two and a half years between her commissioning and her loss, *Maine* had her share of trouble. Three men had died when washed overboard in February 1897, and a year later she was intentionally driven into a pier at New York City to avoid a collision with a steamer. As tensions over Cuba mounted, *Maine* was sent to Havana on a 'friendly' mission, in reality to protect American interests there. Fearing trouble, Captain Sigsbee maintained a close watch at his anchorage, and shore leave was restricted. Nevertheless, on the night of 15 February 1898, two large explosions rocked *Maine* and she sunk in minutes in 36ft of water. Of her complement of 354 officers and men, 266 were killed.

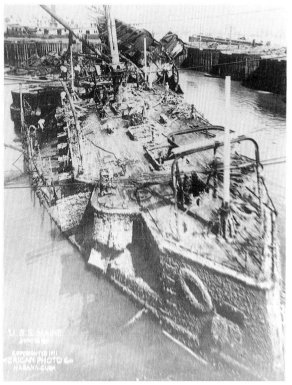

Stern of Maine *appears as the water is removed from the cofferdam, in a photo dated 26 June 1911. She was towed to sea and sunk the next year.* (US National Archives)

Wreckage of the aft portion of Maine *just a few days after the sinking. This mast is now mounted at Arlington National Cemetery, outside Washington DC. (From* The American Navy)

Workmen attempt to free a 6in gun from the wreckage. On the left is the funnel from a steam launch. (From The American Navy)

With Spain and the US already on the brink of war, the *Maine* incident was the last straw. A Navy Board of Inquiry quickly concluded that the explosions were caused by a 'mine' though it could not say by whom it had been set. War hysteria soon gripped the nation and President McKinley, having expended every effort to avert war, was now forced to declare it on 25 April. While the 'splendid little war' lasted but four months it resulted in greatly increased US influence in international affairs, particularly in the Pacific.

In 1911 a cofferdam was built around the *Maine* wreckage. Water was pumped out and at last the full damage could be examined. A second inquiry as to her loss again concluded that it had been caused by an external explosion. A concrete and wood bulkhead was constructed to seal off the damaged bow of *Maine*, and she was refloated, towed to sea and sunk.

In 1975 Admiral Hyman Rickover assembled a team of experts to re-examine the loss of *Maine*. They reviewed testimony, sketches and the vast array of photos available. Their conclusion was that *Maine* was destroyed by an *internal* explosion. The likely cause was spontaneous combustion of the anthracite coal in a coal bunker. Such fires can burn for hours with little smoke or heat detected. Bunker fires were an all too frequent occurrence on early US ships. Unfortunately for *Maine*, some of her bunkers were on shared bulkheads with magazines. In all probability, one such fire burned through the bulkhead into the forward 6in magazine and destroyed the ship.

Sources

The American Navy (Chicago, Belford, Middlebrook, 1898).

Conway's All the World's Fighting Ships, 1860–1905, Conway Maritime Press (London 1979).

Dictionary of American Naval Fighting Ships, Naval History Division, Navy Department (Washington 1959).

Journal of the American Society of Naval Engineers (February 1985).

Library of Congress, Washington DC 20540 (photos).

National Archives, Record Group 19, Cartographic & Architectural Branch, Washington DC 20408 (plans).

Naval Historical Center, Washington Navy Yard, Washington DC 20374 (for photos).

Hyman G Rickover, *How the Battleship Maine was Destroyed*, Naval History Division, Navy Department (Washington 1976).

Still Pictures Branch (NNSP), National Archives, Washington DC 20408 (photos).

Transactions of the Society of Naval Architects and Marine Engineers (1893 edition).

View of midship portion of the wreckage. Portions of the bow are folded over one of the boat cranes. (From The American Navy)

JAPAN'S PROTO-BATTLECRUISERS: THE TSUKUBA AND KURAMA CLASSES

Driven by capital ship losses during the war with Russia in 1905 Japan developed a powerful hybrid with the speed and protection of an armoured cruiser but the main armament of a battleship. Although almost immediately outdated by the advent of the *Dreadnought*, retrospectively they were seen as forerunners of the battlecruisers. One of the four ships was the first capital ship built in Japan and another was the first Japanese warship fitted with turbine propulsion so they are important steps towards the independence of Japan's shipbuilding industry. The problems encountered with this ambitious programme are outlined by Jiro Itani, Hens Lengerer and Tomoko Rehm-Takahara.

THE Japanese armoured cruisers *Tsukuba, Ikoma, Kurama,* and *Ibuki* are very significant ships in the history of Japanese warship building from several points of view. *Tsukuba* was the first domestically built capital ship, and completed in the remarkably short building period of two years, despite the fact that she was roughly three times bigger than the largest warship hitherto constructed in a Japanese shipyard and about four times heavier in displacement than the largest ship that her builder, Kure Navy Yard, had completed before.

The fundamental concept contained several outstanding ideas, the most unusual being the combination of battleship and cruiser characteristics. Contemporary armoured cruisers had four 20cm (8in) guns but the *Tsukuba* class carried four 30.5cm (12in) guns, making these ships the first cruisers to carry a battleship armament. Thus *Tsukuba* and *Ikoma* were ancestors of the battlecruiser, which appeared as the British *Invincible* a few years later.

The Naval General Staff required a fundamental rethink of armoured cruiser design, resulting in novel features like the abolition of the ram, fighting tops on the masts, and longitudinal bulkhead in the engine compartments, and also brought about several improvements such as better seaworthiness, improved habitability and reduced superstructures. Of course, many difficulties arose in the building of the hull as well as production of the engines, armament and armour plate, not to mention the shortage of skilled workers. All these problems were solved to a more or less satisfactory degree and the completion of *Tsukuba* proved the extraordinary progress which Japanese warship building had made during the previous ten years. It was also a sure sign that Japanese warship building would obtain independence within several years.

The succeeding class was orginally planned to be sisters but due to the rumour of new British warship construction the design was radically changed to introduce intermediate guns of 20cm (8in). Thus, the broadside power became four 30.5cm and four 20cm guns. Another feature was the adoption of the tripod mast in *Kurama*, but more remarkable was the turbine propulsion in *Ibuki*, which became Japan's first capital ship with this new machinery.

It was necessary to produce the main guns, intermediate guns and secondary guns and most of the armour plate in Japanese factories, and the effort required for the weapon production was relatively greater than even the step forward in shipbuilding, although the success was based, at least partly, upon the introduction of technology from Great Britain.

Not surprisingly, the role of the new armoured cruiser changed from mere assistance to the main battlefleet to forming part of the battle line itself, although the cruiser characteristics were not forgotten completely.

Outboard profile of Kurama. (Drawn by Michael Wünschmann)

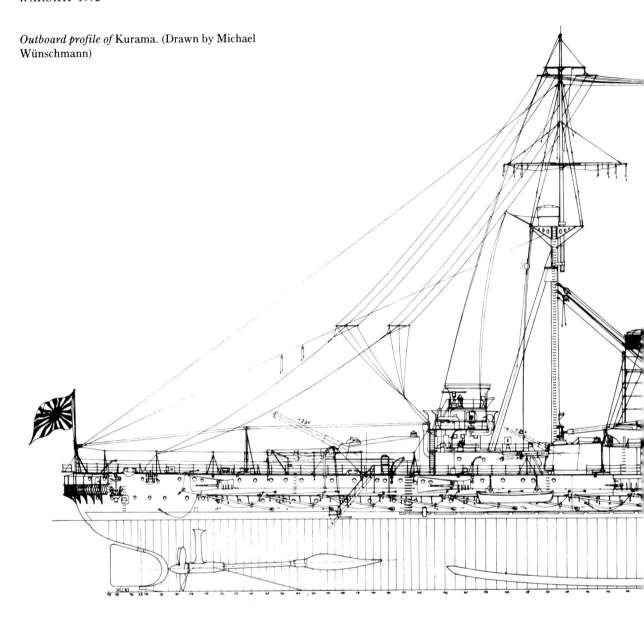

Deck plan of Kurama. (Drawn by Michael Wünschmann)

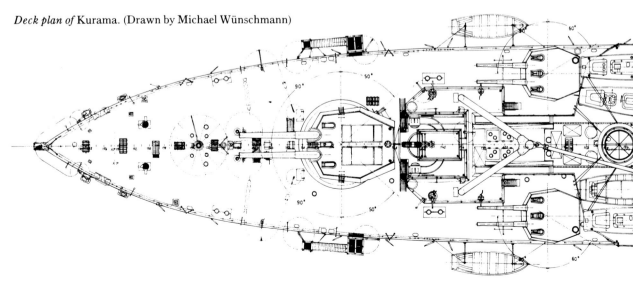

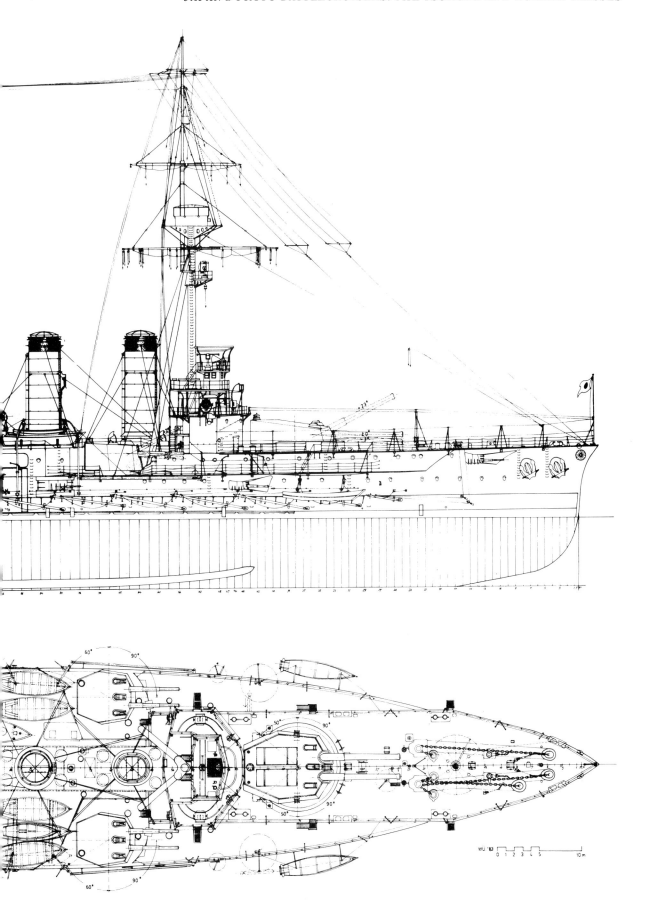

Tsukuba *off Kobe about 1912*. (All uncredited illustrations from the Hans Lengerer collection)

The 'Crisis of the Imperial Japanese Navy'

On the outbreak of the Russo–Japanese War of 1904–1905 the power of the Imperial Japanese Navy (IJN) and the Russian Pacific Fleet stationed in Port Arthur, Vladivostok and Jinsen (Chemulpo) was nearly equal but the Russian navy had fleets of almost the same power in the Baltic and Black Sea. Therefore the IJN had to destroy the Pacific Fleet before Russian reinforcements could arrive and could not afford to lose any capital ships in this fight because no increase in their numbers could be expected before having to face the Russian reinforcing squadron.

The first months after the outbreak of the war were marked by the blockade of the Russian fleet in the harbour of Port Arthur.[1] However, the course of the Japanese blockading fleet was always noted by the Russians and, on 14 May, the *Amur* laid fifty mines along a 1-mile line across the usual cruising course of the IJN ships. On the following day the battleships *Hatsuse* and *Yashima* hit the mines and sank.[2] This was a major disaster and one-third of the battleship strength was lost at one blow.[3] To make matters worse, the 2nd class cruisers *Yoshino* and *Miyako*, the gunboat *Oshima*, destroyer *Akatsuki* and torpedo boat *No 48* were lost between 12 and 17 May by accidents (*Yoshino*, *Miyako*,

Oshima) and mines. These six days were called 'The Crisis of IJN' and the losses were not reported to the Japanese nation.

At that time the decisive fleet battle had not yet been fought and although the First Fleet replaced the losses by the armoured cruisers *Kasuga* and *Nisshin*, it was absolutely necessary to supplement the battle line to oppose the powerful enemy fleet which would come from Baltic sooner or later. The completion and delivery of the battleships *Kashima* and *Katori* which had been ordered from Armstrongs and Vickers respectively could not be expected and during wartime it was impossible to purchase warships and ammunition from abroad because all likely sources were in countries which had declared neutrality. Thus, the building of capital ships to make up the losses could be done only in domestic shipyards and 'The Crisis of the IJN' forced the authorities into the domestic construction of large ships.

Roughly one month after the events which brought about the crisis, on 23 June 1904, Kure Navy Yard received the order to build two armoured cruisers but the sailing of the Russian 2nd and 3rd Pacific Fleets, composed of units of the Baltic and Black Sea Fleets, increased the order for more capital ships from Kure Navy Yard and Yokosuka Navy Yard (one battleship and one armoured cruiser from each yard) on 26 January (for the batleships) and 31 January 1905 (for the armoured cruisers). Four ships were armoured cruisers by classification but by nature they were transitional ships which embodied not only features of the later battlecruisers but also elements of the lightly armoured high-speed battleship like the *Regina Elena* class which was under construction in Italy at that time.

Kurama *about 1915. She differed from her sister most noticeably in her tripod masts and slightly taller and thinner funnels.*

The Third Period Naval Extension Programme

The First and Second Period Naval Extension Programmes after the Sino-Japanese War (1894–95) had authorised

the so-called 'Six-Six Fleet', namely a fleet whose nucleus was formed by six battleships and six armoured cruisers but also carried out the extension of shipyard building and repair facilities, thus achieving the preconditions for the domestic construction of large ships. In connection with the increase of the Russian Pacific Fleet, Navy Minister Yamamoto proposed the Third Period Naval Extension Programme to parliament. After some trouble[4] the

Armour and armament layout of Tsukuba *class.*

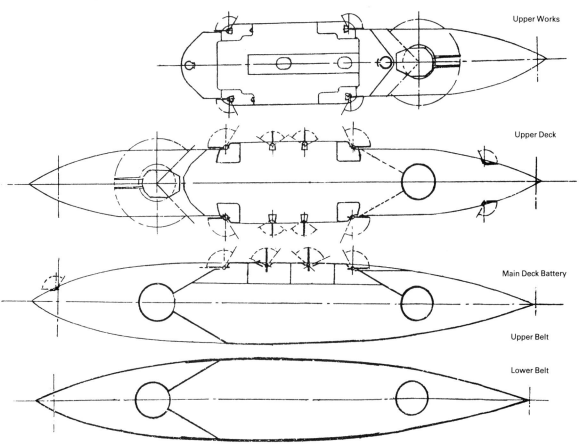

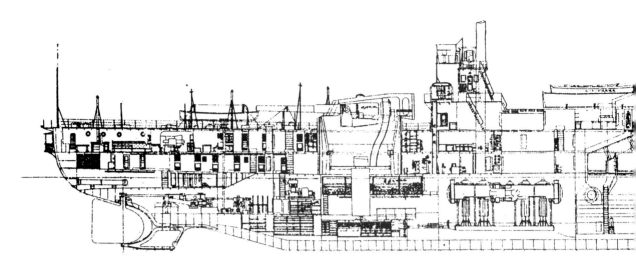

Profile drawing of Tsukuba.

programme finally passed the Diet on 3 June 1903. With a budget of roughly 100 million Yen, spread over ten years, three battleships, three armoured cruisers and some other ships could be built and the extension of the dockyards and other naval production facilities could be continued. The temporary names of the battleships were No 1 (later *Katori*), No 2 (later *Kashima*), and No 3 (later *Fuso*) and those of the armoured cruisers also No 1 (later *Ibuki*), No 2 (later *Haruna*) and No 3 (later *Kirishima*).

On 21 October 1903 the Navy Minister proposed the urgent purchase of two battleships under construction in Britain for Chile. One month later, on 20 November, the negotiations ended in failure but the IJN was able to buy two armoured cruisers instead which were under construction in Italy for Argentina. These ships became *Nisshin* and *Kasuga* which temporarily replaced the mined battleships *Hatsuse* and *Yashima*. At the same time the earlier completion of battleship No 2 (*Kashima*), *ie* the

Ikoma at Yokosuka in 1908.

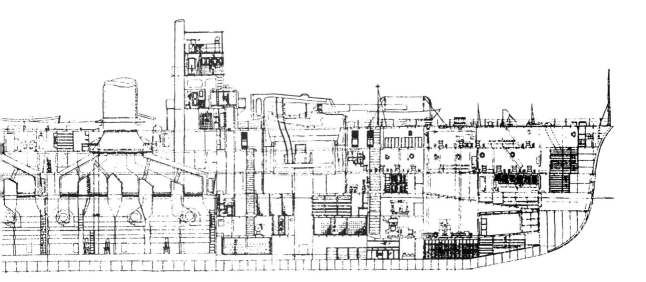

completion together with No 1 (*Katori*) in 1906 was proposed and this planning was agreed by the Finance Ministry on 22 December 1903. Both ships were ordered in Britain in the following month but it soon became evident that they would not participate in the war which broke out in the month following the order, because of the declaration of neutrality by Britain (even if they could be completed during the war).

1904 War Naval Supplementary Programme

Roughly one month after the outbreak of war a Temporary Special Budget Law was promulgated to last one financial year until the termination of the war.[5] A total budget of 48,465,631 Yen was provided and under the section Naval Complementary Expenditures two battleships, namely the *Ko* (later *Aki*) and *Otsu* (later *Satsuma*) and four armoured cruisers, namely the *Ne* (later *Tsukuba*), *Ushi* (later *Ikoma*), *Tora* (later *Kurama*) and *U* (later *Hiei*) could be built, besides forty-seven other ships.

Drawing on this budget, on 4 July 1904 Imperial authorisation was obtained for the urgent construction of the two armoured cruisers already ordered (23 June 1904); 859,060 Yen (divided into Weapon and Repair Expenditures and Shipbuilding and Repair Expenditures as Extraordinary War Expenditures) was allowed for the months of June and July out of the planned total of 25,279,765 Yen. The rest of the money (24,420,705 Yen) was to be requested on a monthly basis. In fact, the expenses to December 1904 (5,428,812 Yen as Naval Complementary Expenditures) did not get Imperial permission before 9 January 1905. On the last day of this month the 'Tora Go' armoured cruiser (later *Kurama*) was ordered from Yokosuka Kosho with the shipbuilding cost of 7,580,000 Yen (later revised) to be built from 1905 to 1907 under the same budget as before and also armoured cruiser No 1 (later *Ibuki*) was ordered from Kure Navy Yard with the same cost as *Kurama* (also later revised) as Armament Supplementary Expenditures to be built from 1905 to 1908.[6]

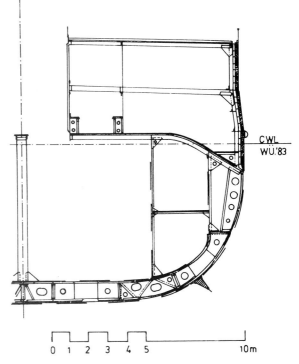

Midship frame section of Tsukuba. (Drawn by Michael Wünschmann)

The Design of Japan's First Capital Ships

The fundamental design of a warship was executed by the 3rd (shipbuilding) division of the Navy Technical Department. The process was that initially the substantive requirements of the Navy General Staff, namely offensive and defensive power, speed, radius and other elements were forwarded to the Navy Technical Department (NTD) whose chief ordered the 3rd division to carry out several sketch designs in close co-operation with the other divisions to produce the general arrangement drawings; then the documents were handed to the head of NTD who proposed them to the Technical Conference inside NTD. After discussions and inspections some aspects were usually re-cast with reference to contemporary counterparts in foreign navies, new technology, war and other lessons etc. The design which best incorporated the most advanced technology and superiority over foreign classes was submitted to the Navy Minister. He consulted the Higher Technical Conference and this body decided by lengthy discussions whether or not the proposal coincided with the views of the members and the tactical requirements. If no agreement could be obtained NTD was ordered to carry out the design again. In this case the whole procedure was repeated until the design was finalised and the construction of the ship was ordered.

Therefore, the shipbuilding division of NTD was in charge of the fundamental design of warships but the naval architects were not permitted to advance their own

concepts and in most cases several new designs were required by indirect order of the Higher Technical Conference. However, in the final analysis their skill decided whether or not the design was well-balanced and met effectively the tactical requirements of offensive and defensive elements on the minimum displacement.

Design of Tsukuba Class

The sinking of *Hatsuse* and *Yashima* occurred on 15 May 1904, the order for building *Tsukuba* and *Ikoma* was given to Kure Navy Yard on 23 June 1904 and the keels were laid on 14 January 1905 and 15 March 1905 respectively. Thus the fundamental design in the NTD and the preparation for building at Kure Navy Yard progressed at extraordinary speed. This was made possible only by the utmost effort of then Captain (later Vice-Admiral) Kondo Motoki[7] whose design team included several outstanding

Table 1. *GENERAL BUILDING DATA*

Item	Tsukuba	Ikoma	Kurama	Ibuki
Programme	1904 War Naval Supplementary Programme			1903 Third Period Naval Extension Programme
Budget	Extraordinary War Expenditures, section Naval Complementary Expenditures (*Rinji Gunji Hi moku Kantei Hosoku Hi*)			Armament Supplementary Expenditures (*Gunbi Hoju Hi*)
Official classification	——————— First Class Cruiser (Armoured Cruiser) (*Sōkō Junyokan*) ———————			
Classification from 28 August 1912	Battlecruiser (*Junyo Senkan*)			
Programme codename	Ne (rat) Go armoured cruiser	Ushi (ox) Go armoured cruiser	Tora (tiger) Go armoured cruiser	No 1 armoured cruiser
Building authorized	——————— 23 June 1904 ———————		——————— 31 January 1905 ———————	
Builder	Kure Navy Yard		Yokosuka Navy Yard	Kure Navy Yard
Laid down	14 January 1905	15 March 1905	23 August 1905	22 May 1907
Launched	26 December 1905	9 April 1906	21 October 1907	21 November 1907
Completed	14 January 1907	24 March 1908	28 Feburary 1911	1 November 1909
Building time	2 years	3 years	5 years 6 months	2 years 5 months
Removed from Navy List	1 September 1917		20 September 1921	
Fate	Sunk by magazine explosion, Yokosuka, 14 January 1917	——————— Scrapped under Washington Treaty provisions ———————		

Table 2. *PRINCIPAL DIMENSIONS*

	Tsukuba (Ikoma)		Kurama (Ibuki)		
Displacement, normal	13,750		14,636 (14,638)		
full load	13,692		15,595		
Loa	144.78m	475ft 0in	147.83m	485ft 0in	
Lwl (L)	137.16m	450ft 0in	144.30m	473ft 5in	
Lpp	134.11m	440ft 0in	137.16m	450ft 0in	
B max (B)	22.86m	75ft 0in	23.01m (22.98m)	75ft 6in	(75ft 4¾in)
Depth, moulded (D)	12.86m	42ft 2¼in	12.86m (12.88m)	42ft 2¼in	(42ft 3in)
Draught, average (d)	7.93m (7.95m)	26ft 0in (26ft 1in)	7.97m	26ft 1¾in	
Block coefficient (Cb)	0.562		0.560		
L/B	5.88		5.97 (6.10)		
d/B	0.347		0.346		
D/d	1.62		1.61 (1.65)		

people such as Eng Kaneda Wasaburo who had already designed as an exercise a battleship and a 1st class cruiser each with four main gun turrets arranged on the centreline[8] and Yamamoto Kaizō, later the chief of the fundamental design section.

In designing this class the team under Kondo showed real originality and it was surprising not only how rapidly the design was executed (although some work had already been done), but also how many new features it included. To mention the most important ones:

1. They were classified as armoured cruisers but they were very different from the 8in cruisers previously ordered from foreign countries, such as *Izumo* (Great Britain), *Yakumo* (Germany) and *Azuma* (France). Their role in the Combined Fleet made this class very important and they became frontline battlefleet units from the beginning. In order to overpower existing armoured cruisers the speed of the *Izumo* class had to be maintained but firepower had to be increased by going up to 12in guns. At the same time a large rise in displacement had to be avoided at all costs, so the thickness of the belt armour was made the same as *Izumo* class. Compared with the standard battleships of the time, the main armament was equal, secondary guns a little inferior, torpedo defence weapons superior, while the speed advantage of about 2.5kts partly compensated for the reduction of armour by 2in. Therefore despite their classification they were actually real capital ships and in concept prefigured the battlecruiser. In this regard it is no mistake to call them Japan's first domestically produced capital ships.

2. A raised forecastle deck was adopted to improve seaworthiness and make them drier.

The original launch of Tsukuba, *planned for 12 December, had to be hastily postponed due to the distortion of the launch way – Japanese inexperience in large ship construction was manifest in such details and greatly embarrassed the yard officials. The ship was eventually launched successfully on 26 December 1905, as shown here.*

3. The traditional ram bow was abandoned in favour of a curved, raked bow in which the fore-foot was cut away. The bow torpedo tube was also removed.

4. The superstructures were reduced as much as possible (one of the lessons of the Sino–Japanese War).

5. The living compartments and fittings were all specifically designed to meet Japanese requirements.

6. Stockless type anchors were adopted (these could be stowed in recessed hawse pipes).

Tsukuba *being fitted out in November 1906. The gantry crane in the background, over the berth where* Aki *was building, had only been recently erected; its absence had increased the difficulties of constructing* Tsukuba.

Tsukuba *off Kure about 1914. The middle deck 6in guns*
have already been removed.

Compared with the innovative design, there was nothing
new in the principal structure, fittings, arrangement of the
armour and armament or in the propulsion plant[9] and this
must be the explanation of their very rapid and comparatively easy fundamental design. Also the detailed design
and the production of the working drawings was left to
Kure Navy Yard shipbuilding division and drawing
office.

The Construction of Tsukuba and Ikoma

At that time the building of a large, roughly 14,000-ton
ship, took about three years, even in Britain. Therefore, it
was very ambitious to plan to complete these ships within
two years in Japan. The chief of Kure Navy Yard was
Rear-Admiral Yamanouchi Masuji and the chief of the
shipbuilding division was Commander Obata
Bunzaburo.[10] Under Obata Lieutenant-Commander
Yamada Sakuzō concurrently held the posts of chief of
building (*Kenzō Shunin*), chief of design (*Sekkei Shunin*)
and also chief of the hull construction section (*Senkoku
Shunin*). This means that the *Tsukuba* class was really a
one-man production and Yamada's achievements cannot
be overestimated.[11] One of the most famous naval
architects, Lieutenant (eventually Vice-Admiral) Hiraga
Yūzurū, was also involved in the early work.

At that time shipbuilding capacity was concentrated at
Yokosuka, Kure, and Sasebo Navy Yards. Yokosuka was
the most advanced in shipbuilding and Kure was the
centre of the weapon production; Sasebo and the civilian

shipyards had little or no experience of warship construction. Even though Yokosuka had not yet built a warship
larger than the cruiser *Matsushima*, these two ships
should have been constructed there, because of Yokosuka's incomparably greater experience in warship
construction,[12] the training standards and skill of the
workers, the existing facilities, and the number of
machine tools. However, at that time the result of the war
could not be foreseen and the authorities feared the
bombardment of Yokosuka by the Russian Second Pacific
Fleet. Thus, the order was given to Kure which was safer
in this respect. On the other hand, Yokosuka as well as
Kure were making every effort to improve their capacity
in building, repairing and converting the ships in preparation for war, while the extension of the berths and docks
and other shipbuilding facilities was already contracted
and under way. Thus *Tsukuba* was built on the newly
established 3rd berth which had been constructed from
August 1903 to November 1904. She was laid down on 14
January 1905, launched on 26 December of that year and
completed on 14 January 1907 after just two years, which
was exactly on schedule. The reason why *Ikoma* was laid
down two months later on 15 March 1905 was the
extension of the second berth, work that had begun at the
same time as the completion of No 3 berth. Because of the
end of the war and the imminent completion of the
battleships *Kashima* and *Katori* there was no necessity for
hasty construction and in her case construction took three
years (launched 9 April 1906 and completed 24 March
1908).

Sufficient numbers of skilled workers were a problem.
Some were drafted from Yokosuka (along with specialist
tools etc), and temporary unskilled workers were recruited
and the Yokosuka men trained them.[13] There was also
difficulty in obtaining the necessary steel. It is generally

said that these warships were constructed entirely from domestic material but in fact the steel production of Edamitsu Steel Works (later Yawata Seitetsusho) was only just getting under way and it was imported steel from the USA that was mainly used; it had been ordered in bulk and stored for the repair of damaged ships.[14]

A very serious detail problem concerning both personnel and material was the rivetting. At that time pneumatic hammers were not in use and rivetting by hand was not only very arduous but also very time-consuming work. As many as 1,300,000 rivets were needed up to launching, and to obtain so many rivets and not to exceed the schedule was a major difficulty. Fortunately rivets had also been ordered from USA in bulk but it was still necessary to produce them domestically in all sizes. As a result rivet makers were recruited and their rapid education was accompanied with many problems.

As far as the berths were concerned neither of them had gantry cranes and only No 3, in which *Tsukuba* was constructed, had derricks of 5 tons and 10 tons – No 2 berth, awaiting the laying down of *Ikoma*, had nothing. As an emergency measure shear legs made of steel were erected on both sides of this berth, equipped with 3-ton derricks which worked by motor-driven winches. This was the first time Kure installed electric machines. Another 'first' was the establishment of the inspection section in the yard, which was necessitated by the tight schedule; this section was given full independence. This section was also responsible for cost-effective subcontracting and since virtually everything was new attention had to be paid to every item and quite naturally it could not be achieved without trouble.[15]

These few examples demonstrate that the construction

of *Tsukuba* and *Ikoma* proceeded under great difficulty but it proved that Japan had learned much in a short period and was not far from complete independence from foreign shipyards. Manufacturing quality was to equal British products and since only a small number of items could be produced in civilian shipyards,[16] Kure Navy Yard not only had to build the hull, produce the armour, machinery, and armament, but were also forced to fabricate the host of wooden fittings, from masts to furniture decoration.

Skilful management[17] and the utmost effort of the work-force triumphed and *Tsukuba* was finally completed as scheduled even though the launching had to be postponed by an accident.

Ikoma's Period of Roll

Ikoma had a very short period of roll due to her excessive GM (metacentric height). Vice-Admiral Nagamura Kiyoshi measured the period of roll by an improvised method as roughly a mean of 6.6 seconds as compared to 8 seconds at least in similar ships and this meant that *Ikoma* showed all the disadvantages of the 'quick roller' which not only influenced the fighting capabilities but also the habitability.

In order to be able to propose countermeasures Nagamura calculated GM after the inspection of the weight distribution. The mean value of three calculations was GM = 1.3m in contrast to around 1m in other large ships at that time. As designed *Ikoma's* GM was planned to be 1.14m in full load condition but after completion proved to be 1.44m, *ie* the distance between M (metacentre) and

Table 3. *COMPARISON OF WEIGHTS*

	Tsukuba class	*Kurama* class	Difference
Hull and Fittings	5031	6105	(+) 1074
Protection	3547	3521	(−) 26
Armament	1719	2560	(+) 841
Machinery	2132	2078	(−) 54
Fuel	600	600	−
Equipment	663	731	(+) 68
Total	13692	15595	(+) 1903

Table 4. *STABILITY*

	Tsukuba class	*Kurama* class
Area of immersed midship section (m²)	161.36	171.30
Tons per inch of immersion (tons)	58.70	62.13
CB { below Lwl (m)	3.32	3.17
CB { abaft midship (m)	3.17	2.26
Centre of LWP abaft midship (m)	6.71	6.71
BM (m)	5.37	5.15
GM (m)	1.34	0.902
Longitudinal BM (m)	172.21	178.52
Moment to alter trim 1 inch (mkg)	443,827.33	511,346.07

Kurama in October 1907, a few days before launching. She was the only ship of the four built at Yokosuka Navy Yard.

G (centre of gravity) was roughly 26 per cent more than designed. As M depends on the shape of the ship its position remains constant after completion and therefore G was too low. In order to get a longer period of roll G had to be brought nearer to M by the reduction of weights in the lower part of the ship. This was achieved by the consumption of fuel and water stowed in the double bottom and lower and then upper bunkers while the coal in the side bunkers had to be consumed last under normal condition. These countermeasures were proposed by Nagamura and in addition the ship's boats on the upper deck could be filled with water in an emergecy. This was at best a palliative, since only radical redesign could change the period of roll. Nagamura's report was widely read in naval architectural circles and according to Vice-Admiral Kondo Motoki it was to have great influence on future warship design.[18]

Kurama at Yokosuka in 1913. The intermediate turrets are very evident amidships.

Change in Design for Kurama and Ibuki: Augmenting the armament

At the end of the nineteenth century the quality of armour was improved and its application became rather complicated by the protection of various areas of the hull with different armour thickness and also types in some cases. For the purpose of penetrating this intermediate type of armour, many navies adopted intermediate guns in their battleships. At the same time the cruiser grew in size and became more powerful, prompting the use of bigger calibre guns against it.

In 1902 the Royal Navy adopted the 9.2in (23.4cm) calibre for the intermediate guns and the Japanese surpassed this by going to 10in (25.4cm) in the battleships *Katori* and *Kashima* ordered from Britain. Following the trend of that time the design for *Kurama* and *Ibuki*, which were originally to be built as the sister ships of *Tsukuba* and *Ikoma*, was changed radically and intermediate guns of 8in (20cm) were adopted to be mounted in four twin turrets, one at each corner of the armoured citadel. Secondary guns were abandoned but the number of 4.7in (12cm) guns for defence against torpedo craft was increased by two. The changes in the armament inevitably required some alterations to the armour protection even though the thickness remained of the same standard as the *Izumo* class armoured cruisers.

The *Kurama* class was criticized as far from the new ideal of the all-big-gun *Dreadnought*, in which the Royal Navy not only abandoned the intermediate but also the secondary armament; but as pointed out already the Japanese aimed to have the same gun power as one pre-dreadnought and one older type armoured cruiser (of the level of the *Mikasa* and the *Izumo*) and the fitting of more 12in (30.5cm) gun turrets (even if single turrets were

considered) was quite impossible in a hull of that length. Despite the abolition of secondary guns the adoption of intermediate guns brought about an increase of more than 800 tons displacement and this in turn required additional power to maintain speed and to increase it a little in accordance with the trend of the time. Therefore the power-plant was revised to adopt the same type engines as the *Tsukuba* class but to increase the output by 2000hp to 22,500hp (aiming for an overload output of around 23,000hp). The number of boilers was increased, requiring three funnels instead of two as in their predecessors, resulting in a different appearance, as well as the change in the armament.

These modifications eventually necessitated a slight change of the main dimensions, and the displacement rose to 15,595 tons, an increase of 1903 tons compared to the *Tsukuba* class. In practice, a new class had appeared.

During construction the design was changed several times (some changes, mostly minor ones, will be mentioned later in the sections on armament and protection), the most remarkable items being the adoption of turbine propulsion in *Ibuki* and a tripod fore- and mainmast in *Kurama*.

The construction of Kurama and Ibuki

Kurama was the only ship among the four 'modern' armoured cruisers which was built by Yokosuka Navy Yard, the other three being constructed by Kure Navy Yard. At Yokosuka the building of the battleship *Satsuma* and the repair and conversion work on the captured Russian ships was given priority and other works had to be executed over and above the new construction; later the construction of the battleship *Kawachi* was favoured and thus progress on *Kurama* was extremely slow. Yokosuka Navy Yard had less experience in building capital ships than Kure and the secondment of engineers, foremen and workers in company with some equipment to

Ibuki at Kure in December 1915 after escort duty with the ANZAC convoys.

Kure Navy Yard for work experience on capital ships only reduced the number of skilled workers in Yokosuka at the time. The slow progress was also influenced by the appearance of the *Invincible* class battlecruisers in the year following *Tsukuba*'s completion which made these ships second class and inferior as soon as they were commissioned. This was not only a blow to the Japanese naval authorities but also paralysed efforts at Yokosuka for some time.

Due to these combined factors the time from laying down to launching rose from less than 12 months in *Tsukuba* and a little more than 12 months in *Ikoma* to 26 months and a period of 40 months was needed for the completion from the launching in contrast to a little more than 12 months and roughly 23 months in the case of *Tsukuba* and *Ikoma*. Thus, despite the fact that the laying down of *Ibuki* was 21 months behind *Kurama* the completion was 15 months behind *Ibuki*. She became the last ship of the six capital ships which had been laid down during the Russo–Japanese War and also the last big ship equipped with reciprocating engines, which had the largest output of any Japanese marine piston engines of the time.

During this extremely long building period *Kurama* was given various improvements which, besides those mentioned under 'Armament' and 'Protection', were mainly designed to give her a more modern appearance. The most visible change was the adoption of the tripod masts fore and aft which was a distinctive identification feature.

Ibuki was the last ship of the four 'modern' armoured cruisers, being roughly two years on average behind the other ships. The reason was that she had to wait for the launching of the battleship *Aki* whose building order had been given to Kure Navy Yard on 26 January 1905. After the launching of *Aki* in April 1907 she was laid down on 22 May and launched on 21 November of the same year. This was a record second only to the British battleship *Dreadnought* and in fact the IJN actively attempted to set a record for fast construction with *Ibuki*.

Five days after the launching of *Ibuki* it was decided to adopt the Curtis turbine as the main engines for her and

Aki and the requirement for 22,500hp for 21.25kts was changed to 24,000hp for 22kts. Even though *Aki* had been launched before *Ibuki*, the work on her was stopped for about five months[19] mostly in favour of the building of *Ibuki*. The fitting out of the latter preceeded that of *Aki* and *Ibuki* was completed only 30 months from laying down, to have the honour of being the IJN's first capital ship with turbine main engines; she needed only 45 per cent of the time which would be necessary to complete her sister *Kurama*.

The construction of *Ibuki* involved a remarkable reduction of the man-days required, largely resulting from the increased experience and technical expertise of work-force, overseers and management. The timely supply of materials also contributed – remarkable considering that not only the whole protective armour and all cast steel products for the hull were supplied by Kure Navy Yard Steel Division but also all cast steel products for engines and the shafts, while Yawata Steel Works (at that time called the Edamitsu Steel Production Mill) supplied the entire mild steel used in the construction of the hull. No building record could be expected when such material was imported and the achievement in the case of *Tsukuba* was made possible only by the punctual arrival of a large quantity of steel from the USA and a substantial stock of existing material.

General Arrangement of Tsukuba and Kurama classes

The general arrangement of the *Tsukuba* and *Kurama* classes is evident in the illustrations, so no lengthy explication is necessary, but the reader should note the following salient features when studying the drawings and photographs.

1. Replacement of the ram by a new bow shape (clipper stem).
2. Adoption of a raised forecastle deck.

Official profile drawing of Kurama.

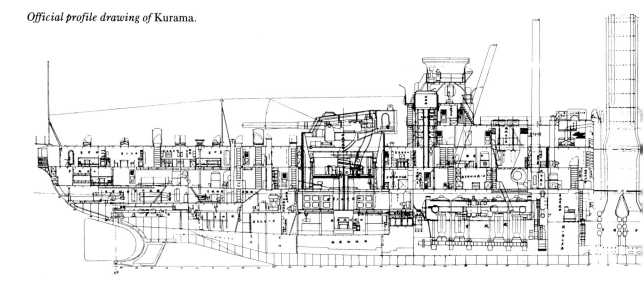

Tsukuba *showing several of her early modifications.*

3. Distinctive stern and rudder contour, especially stern casting.
4. Reduction of the superstructure to a minimum.
5. Adoption of tripod masts in *Kurama*.
6. No fighting tops on the masts.
7. Utilization of two struts only to support bridge wings in order to improve sight from conning tower.
8. Adoption of 45cal 12in (30.5cm) guns in twin turrets, thus having the same main armament as a battleship.
9. Several improvements in the mechanism of the turret, especially loading equipment.
10. Introduction of fire control gear for main and intermediate guns (later also for secondary guns).
11. Arrangement of most of the secondary guns in an armoured citadel.
12. Adoption of intermediate guns in *Kurama* class.
13. Maintenance of 4.7in (12cm) auxiliary guns as torpedo boat defence guns.
14. Reduction of fixed torpedo tubes to three from five.
15. *Kurama*'s domestically produced reciprocating engines had the largest power output of any in IJN warships.
16. Adoption of turbine propulsion in *Ibuki*.
17. Adoption of mixed fired boilers.
18. Abolition of the centreline bulkhead in engine and boiler rooms.
19. Reduction of the funnels to two in *Tsukuba* class but increased to three in *Kurama* class (incidentally, *Kurama* had funnels somewhat thinner and taller than *Ibuki*'s).

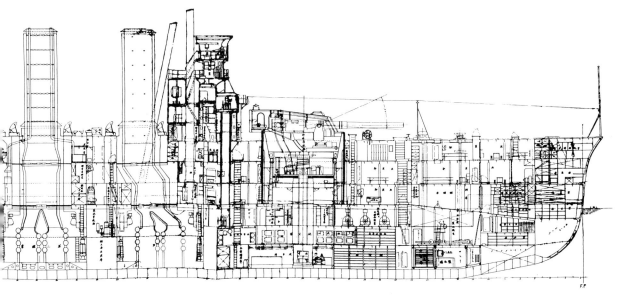

Kurama, *official upper deck plan*.

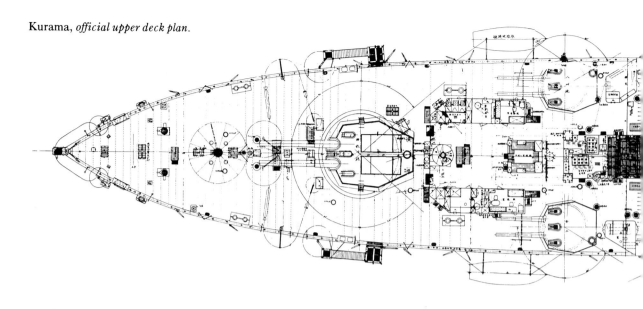

Kurama, *official middle deck plan*.

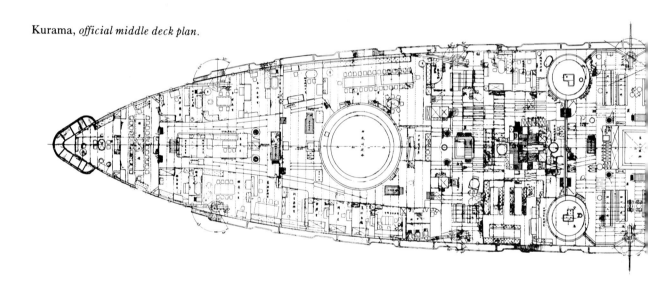

Kurama, *official lower deck plan*.

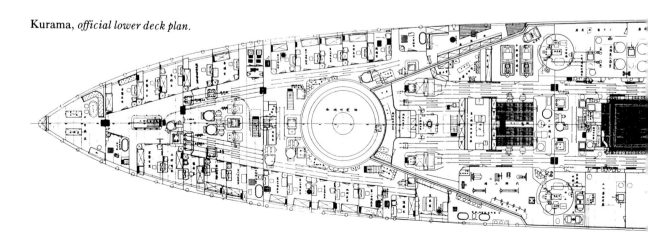

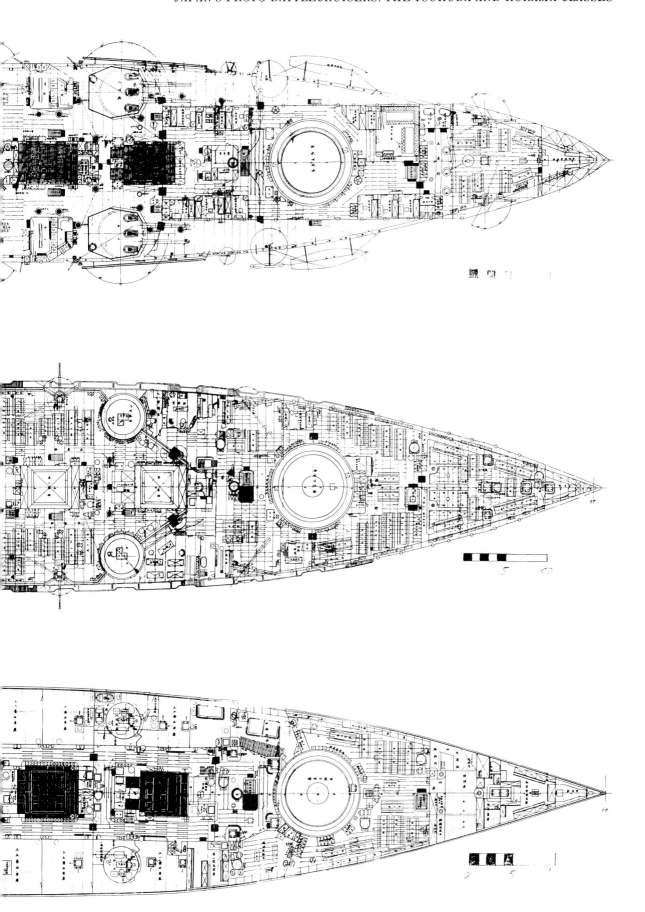

Table 5. *ARMAMENT*

	Tsukuba (Ikoma)		*Kurama (Ibuki)*	
12in/45cal (30.5cm) main guns	four Kure type		four type 41	
	(four Vickers type)		(four Armstrong type)	
8in/45cal (20cm) intermediate			eight type 41	
6in/45cal (15.2cm) secondary	twelve (later ten) type 41		(eight Armstrong type)	
4.7in/40cal (12cm) guns	twelve (later eight) Armstrong		fourteen type 41 (Armstrong)	
3.1in/40cal (8cm) gun	four type 41		four type 41	
3.1in/28 (8cm) Neho (HAG)	two type ?		four type 41	
47mm short gun	?		three	
47mm boat gun			(one)	
6.5mm Maxim MG	4	(3)	4	
35 year type rifle	?		269	
No 1 type pistol	?		59	
Mauser type rifle	?		Not decided when completed	
21in (53.3cm) TT hull side aft		(2)		
18in (45.7cm) TT hull side aft	2		2	
18in (45.7cm) TT stern	1		1	
No of torpedoes with warhead	?		6	
training	?		3	
14in (35.6cm) torpedo launcher for picket boat	1		1	
Electric generator 110v 800kA			8	(7)
110v 400kA				(2)
Air compressor			2	
36in (90cm) searchlight			2	
30in (75cm) searchlight	5		4	

Note:
The gun was designated according to the type of breech block.

20. No improvement of the armour protection over earlier armoured cruisers in order to increase the speed (in fact, 21kts was too slow for a modern cruiser of the period).

The main dimensions, hull shape (with the exception of stem and stern) and the arrangement of the armament – especially the secondary guns of *Tsukuba* class – were very similar to the British *Cressy* class. The Japanese ships had slightly thicker armour (and in a somewhat improved configuration), but instead of the single 47cal 9.2in (23.4cm) gun turrets fore and aft in the RN ships the IJN adopted 45cal 12in (30.5cm) twin turrets in those positions. This became possible by the adoption of more powerful Miyabara water-tube boilers, reducing their number from thirty to twenty for the same power. Accordingly the number of funnels was reduced to two from the four in the RN ships.

Main Armament

The IJN used four different calibres of 12in (30.5cm) guns, namely:
1. Six battleships from *Fuji* to *Mikasa* and three ex-Russian battleships had 40cal guns.
2. Six battleships from *Katori* to *Settsu*, and four armoured cruisers from *Tsukuba* to *Kurama* and two ex-Russian battleships had 45cal guns.

3. Two battleships (*Kawachi* and *Settsu*) had 50cal guns in the fore and aft turrets.
4. One ex-Russian battleship (*Iki*) had 30cal guns.
All were mounted in twin turrets.

A further analysis of the 45cal guns shows that four battleships (*Kashima, Katori, Satsukma,* and *Aki*) and the armoured cruisers used them in the fore and aft gun turrets in the prevailing standard arrangement while the later battleships *Kawachi* and *Settsu* positioned them as the sided turrets. These turrets, with a total of forty-eight 45cal 12in gun barrels were classified into several kinds by (i) the type of barrel and (ii) the type of breech. For the armoured cruisers in this study, four different types were used:

Name of ship	*Tsukuba*	*Ikoma*	*Kurama*	*Ibuki*
Type of barrel	Armstrong	Vickers	Armstrong	Armstrong
Type of breech block	Kure	Vickers	Type 41	Armstrong
Barrel length (m)	14.259	14.135	14.259	14.263
(cal)	46.8	46.4	46.8	46.8
Barrel weight (tons)	59.41	57.58	59.5	59.10
No of grooves	72	72	72	72
	gradually expanded,		equally	same as *Tsu-*
	1 rev in 30 cal		1 rev in	*kuba* class
			30 cal	

Note: The IJN classified the type of the gun according to the type of the breech block and thus four different kinds were used.

Ibuki *during gunnery trials.*

In general the barrels had the same structure and those which were constructed by the Gunnery Division of Kure Navy Yard for *Tsukuba* and *Kurama* were based upon the drawings supplied by the British Armstrong, Whitworth (Elswick) and Vickers (Barrow) companies, while the barrels for *Ikoma* and *Ibuki* were imported[20] and the same as used in the battleship *Katori* and *Kashima* respectively.

The Japanese 45cal 12in gun barrel was a half wire wound five layer type. The inner tube (1A) consisted of four parts (of which the first three from the breech end were wound by wire ribbons) connected by cannelured rings and divided into the rifled part and the chamber. Upon this tube was shrunk one more layer, divided into three tubes (2A to 2C) with one tube inside another and secured by cannelured rings in the same way as the inner tube (this process was made by 'freezing' 1A and heating 2A to 2C). The barrel was then placed on a very large lathe and revolved at a speed of 3.7 to 7.3m/minute and

flat steel wire of 3mm thickness and 12 to 13mm width was wound round. This ribbon was wound on from end to end at varying degrees of tension (sometimes amounting to 1800kg), and the process was rather difficult and time consuming. The thickness of the steel wire layers was different, corresponding to the pressure curve in the bore and was seventeen layers at the fore part near the muzzle at the fore wire securing ring and 95 layers (of ribbon) at the thickest part near the breech block.[21] Where the diameter changed, wire securing rings were used at the outer circumference with filling rings attached to 'A' tubes. After finishing this part, outer steel tubes 4A (the jacket) and 4B were shrunk on and then the barrel was machined externally in an enormous lathe. By this construction the radial strains on firing were overcome by the shrinkage of 'A' tubes upon the inner tube and by the wire wound at varying tensions around 'A' tubes. The longitudinal strains were taken by the large sections of 'A' tube and jacket which were connected by the breech ring.

At the rear of the jacket breech ring, the breech mechanism frame, shrunk collar, breech bush, and stop

Stern view of Ibuki *as completed.*

ring were fitted; the breech block which was mounted upon, and free to turn on, a carrier pivoted at the side of the breech. The interrupted threads on the breech block engaged with corresponding threads in the breech of the barrel and locked it. The swinging in of the breech block and the locking as well as the unlocking and opening were performed by hydraulic power in contrast to the handling of earlier guns, including those of the battleship *Mikasa*, that had been by hand only; in case of a breakdown hand power could be still used. This mechanism was of the single-movement type, *ie* the one action locked or unlocked the breech block, swung it in or out of the breech and actuated the firing gear in opening and closing operations.

The maximum range was roughly 22,000m using capped AP shell of about 400kg weight and 100.6kg of propellant.[22] This value was obtained by No X type barrel which had 245 litres volume of the powder chamber and barrel pressure 28.5kg/cm². The life of the barrels was regarded as 360 shells before the inner tube was worn out, but according to a post-war investigation the IJN had a tendency to restrict the use of guns[23] (mainly the result of the tight budget and this can also be seen by the provision of only one spare barrel per ship). By the time they were taken out of service an average of only 55, 42, and 37 shells had been fired by each gun of *Ikoma, Kurama,* and *Ibuki* respectively during the various fleet training manoeuvres. These low figures were instrumental in the decision to use the guns as army coastal batteries after the ships had to be decommissioned due to the Washington Treaty.

In theory improved arrangements allowed loading at high angles of elevation,[24] which allowed the barrel to remain in the line of sight and increased the rate of aimed fire. The gun was fired by means of an electric current which fired the primer which in turn ignited the powder charge. The firing could be done individually by each gun, but of course this was only an auxiliary method and the usual one was the simultaneous firing of all guns from one of the central positions by the mere pressing of a button when the line of sight moved through the target. Recoil supression, elevation and depression were performed by hydraulic power. Hand pumps were provided in the chamber below the turntable and connected to the hydraulic cylinders for manual run-in and run-out and these presses, which worked by a single ram working between them, were also used for hand elevating and depressing.

The operation of the turntable, trunk, guns and ammunition transport system required a large number of special auxiliary machines which operated mainly by hydraulic power, *ie* several hydraulic pumps working by steam power were mounted in separate compartments and connected to supply and exhaust pipes. Electric motors were still very rarely used. The power sources were duplicated in most cases. Nearly all of the turret operations had automatic and other checks; this was especially true for the ammunition hoisting and loading operations.

The turntable revolved on a roller path 7.0m in diameter, with roller bearings so arranged as to reduce the friction, and with the shell chamber under it were

surrounded and protected by the barbette, 8.3m in diameter, which extended from the protective deck to well above the upper deck.

The thickness of the armour was as follows (mm):

GUNHOUSE	*Tsukuba/Ikoma*	*Kurama/Ibuki*
Roof	38	
Front	244 (*Tsukuba*)	229 (*Kurama*)
Sides	229	
Aft	152	
BARBETTE		
Thickest part	178	

The guns had a traverse of 270 degrees and the weight of the turret was about 513 tons.

In 1920 the Imperial Japanese Army (IJA) requested the trial construction of a 15in (38.1cm) gun from Kure Navy Yard to equip a coast defence fort. Production was cancelled owing to the Washington Treaty agreement to scrap many capital ships; the turrets thus released were given to the IJA to be employed as coastal batteries. After a thorough investigation by IJA officers completed in August 1922, it was decided to use the turrets of *Kurama, Ikoma,* and *Ibuki* after the necessary modifications. (These were mainly to increase elevation to + 35 degrees from the former 23 degrees in order to obtain a maximum range of 26,600m; to change the recoil system from hydraulic to pneumatic; to insulate the interior of the gunhouse with asbestos cloth; and to instal diesel engines to replace the steam propulsion for hydraulic pressure pumps.) Eventually only four turrets were refitted of which three were installed as follows:

Ibuki	fore turret:	Omazaki battery
	aft turret:	Tsurumizaki battery
Ikoma	fore turret:	Sunosaki battery
Ikoma	aft turret:	reserved after refit

The turrets of *Kurama* remained unmodified along with the spare barrels.[25]

Intermediate Guns

Kurama and *Ibuki* adopted 45cal 8in (20cm) Type 41 guns in four twin turrets as the intermediate armament. One turret was placed at each corner of the armoured citadel, increasing the total broadside fire to four 12in guns and four 8in guns, or nearly 4.5 times as high as in the earlier armoured cruisers of the *Asama* class as seen by the following rounded figures:

	Weight of the broadside fire (kg)
Asama	453
Tsukuba	1542
Kurama	1996

Thus the broadside fire of the *Tsukuba* class was the equivalent of a *Shikishima* class battleship and that of *Kurama* class equalled the *Kashima* class because only two 45cal 10in guns could fire on each broadside in the latter ships.

The gun and its turret was much influenced by Armstrongs who had produced the guns and turrets for

Japan's earlier foreign built armoured cruisers. The barrel weighed 17.62 tons and fired a 115.3kg (254lb) shell at a muzzle velocity of 835m/s. The maximum elevation angle was 30 degrees, corresponding to a maximum range of less than 21,000m (23,000yds). Technical details of the mounting are sparse but resembled the Armstrong twin 8in/40cal, probably incorporating some simplifications, such as substituting manual for power operation of some functions. The protection of the parts below the gunhouse was provided mainly by the upper belt with the thickness increased to 6in (152mm) at those positions and the waterline belt 8in (203mm), so the thickness of the barbette at the exposed part was only 5in (127mm) and inside the citadel it was reduced to 2in (51mm).

Secondary Armament

The barrels of the 45cal 6in (15.2cm) guns were also of the wire-wound type manufactured after the British model. In contrast to the 45cal 12in barrels the wire only extended for a little more than one-half of the length of shell travel and at the muzzle end a solid steel tube (hoop) was shrunk over the inner tube to take the radial strains of firing. By

this the girder strength was increased and there was no fear of 'drooping' of the muzzle, which was the most serious disadvantage of the 12in gun barrel.

The secondary guns were mounted in a citadel battery, six on each broadside, four of which were mounted on the middle deck near to the waterline. This arrangement was imperfect since the guns could not be used in bad weather, and let in water. The secondary guns were eventually moved to the upper deck although only three could be accommodated and then only at the expense of the 50cal 4.7in (12cm) guns. The reduced armament was ten 6in/45cal (formerly twelve) and eight 4.7in/50cal guns (formerly twelve). Unfortunately no Japanese source is specific about the date of the modification but it seems to have been early in the Taisho Era (probably in 1913–14 before the outbreak of war).

Fire Control

When *Tsukuba* (accompanied by the cruiser *Chitose*) visited several European countries in 1907 she was fitted out in Britain with the most recent type of fire control gear manufactured by Vickers, based on the work of Scott,

Kurama, *official forecastle deck plan.*

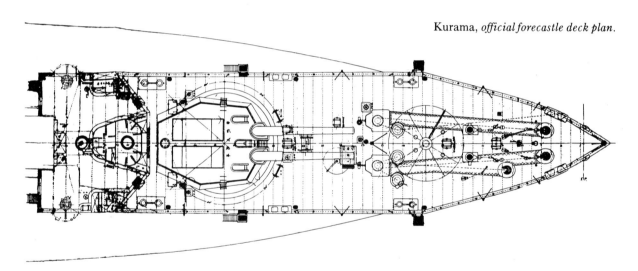

Kurama, *official superstructure deck plan.*

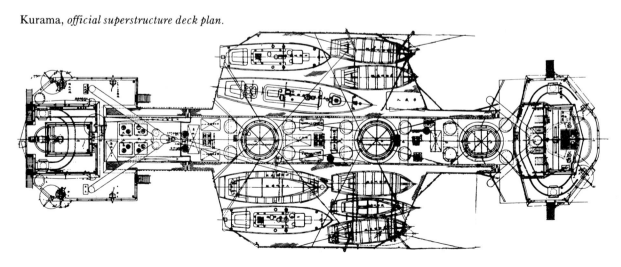

Kurama, *official sections drawings:*

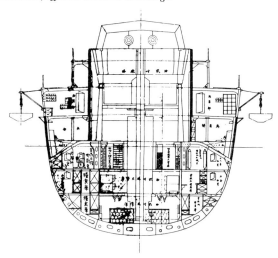

1. *Frame 37, at forward 12 in turret*

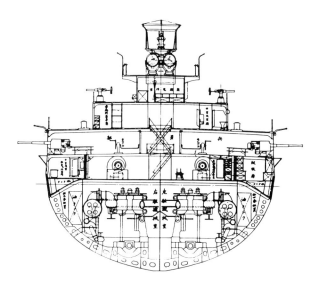

4. *Frame 140, at engine room*

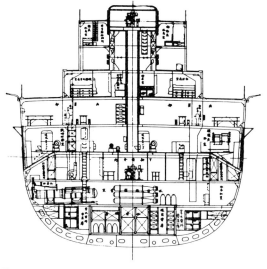

2. *Frame 47, at conning tower (note the space required by broadside torpedo tubes)*

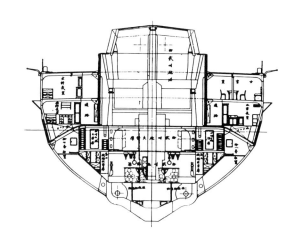

5. *Frame 154, at after 12in turret*

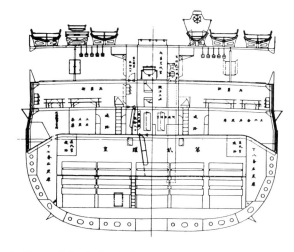

3. *Frame 109, at after boiler room*

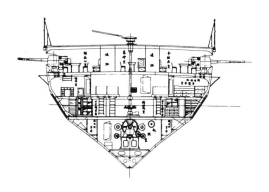

6. *Frame 174, at aftermost 4.7in battery*

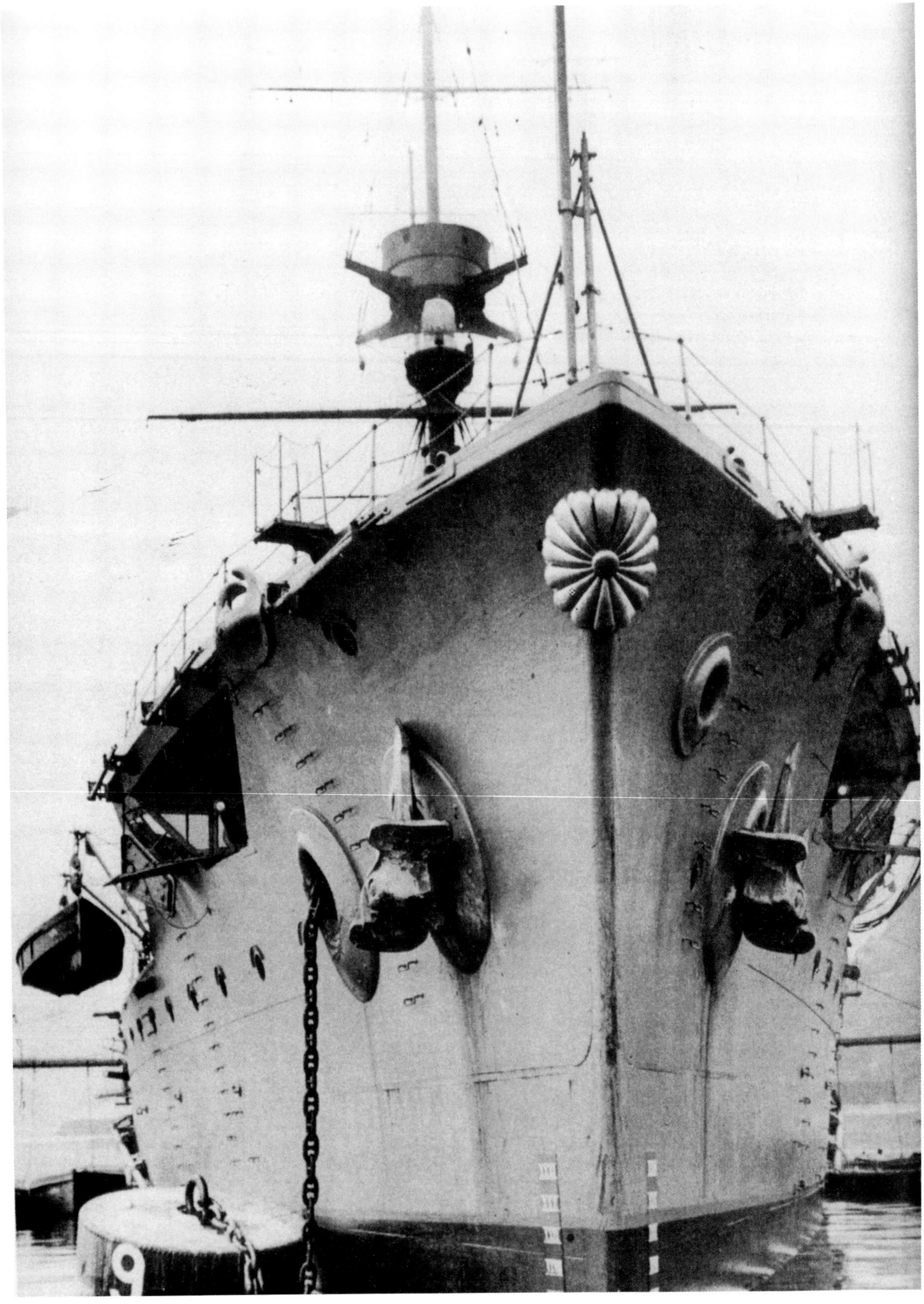

A close-up of the bow of Ibuki.

Dumaresq and Pollen. This, of course, was rather primitive equipment, but at the time it was a big step towards improving the hitting rate by introducing salvo firing and the transmission of centrally calculated firing solutions to the guns. According to a contemporary Japanese manual called *Naval Fire Directing Equipment*,

> the range calculated by the control station is transmitted to the gun side and the layer has only to adjust the needle to the requisite marking on the dial. No other action is necessary beyond matching the ends of two pointers. At the rear of the dial there are controls for adjusting powder temperature, the condition of the inner tube of the barrel [in order to determine the velocity of the shell, which became less as the tube was worn out] to adjust the range automatically and also the adjustment of the air density is included . . .

From this description it seems that the most important firing value – range – was given from the central fire directing gear but training still depended upon the individual layers. Firing of all guns was controlled by the gunnery officer who pressed the button when the target moved through his telescope sight. Transmission of firing data from the rangefinders and control stations, and central salvo firing implied radical improvement to the communication system (electric transmission instead of bugles, speaking trumpets, and voice pipes) and this was a great advance over the method used only two years earlier in the Battle of Tsushima.

In this context it is worth mentioning that *Ibuki* was not only the first turbine ship of the IJN but also the first capital ship which was designed with fire control instruments. A director was fitted on top of the conning tower when commissioned, allowing *Ibuki* to control the main and intermediate guns in salvo firing from the beginning (a rudimentary fire control system for the 4.7in guns was also fitted later). The system (with some unavoidable modifications to be usable by Japanese sailors) was the same as that which was beginning to equip British ships at that time and in this respect the efforts of Commander Hiraiwa Motoo, who was *Ibuki*'s chief gunnery officer, deserve mention.

Other Armament

The remaining armament principally comprised twelve 4.7in/50cal guns in the *Tsukuba* class (fourteen in the *Kuramas*), of which one was mounted in casemates at the bow and at the stern and the rest equipped with shields on the upper deck. The latter were removed or shifted when the position of the secondary guns was changed. In the case of the *Kurama* class the designed position of four guns placed outside the middle deck citadel in casemates was shifted to be nearer to the ammunition hoists immediately before the order for building was issued. At the same time it was also proposed to use the 4.7in magazines for 8in shells if there was some spare space because the stowage of the latter was a little short of required numbers. At the same time the number of 3in (nominal 8cm) guns was increased to four from two. These guns were later mounted on the roofs of the main gun turrets – a quite ineffective arrangement which was eventually abandoned, but it was a common trend of the time. One of the four Maxim machine-guns was positioned in each of the wings of the fore and aft bridges.

Up to the *Tsukuba* class capital ships were armed with five fixed underwater torpedo tubes but in the course of construction this weapon of dubious worth was reduced in number to only three. In *Ikoma* 21in (53.3cm) tubes were fitted on the forward broadside at middle deck level instead of the previous 18in (45.7cm) calibre but the tube located at the upper deck at the stern was still 18in, so *Ikoma* became the only ship to have two different calibres. The reason for the suppression of the after broadside tubes at the middle deck level was the extension of the magazines for the aft main gun turret. The five 30in (75cm) searchlights were located in each of the fore and aft bridge wings and one on a platform high up on the foremast.

Protection

The armour was on almost the same scale as that of previous armoured cruisers and that weakness was accentuated with the advent of the *Dreadnought*. However, it was a remarkable achievement that roughly three years after the start of the manufacture of armour plate at Kure Navy Yard, plates of sufficiently reliable quality could be produced in quantities nearly equal to requirements. According to various Japanese sources including notes from Vice-Admiral Kondo Motoki these plates were adopted for *Tsukuba* and the following ships, and a small amount of the armour ordered in the USA was used only in the first ship, *Tsukuba*. According to Vice-Admiral Nagamura Kiyoshi all armour plates and cast steel products were supplied by Kure Navy Yard Steel Production Division for *Ibuki* and later ships (in fact for *Ikoma* too) while the mild steel for the construction of the

Table 6. *WEIGHT OF ARMOUR*

	Displacement	Weight of armour	%	Weight of armour produced by Kure
Tsukuba	13,691	2049	14.96	2028
Ikoma	13,886	2068	14.89	2068
Kurama	15,594	2063	13.23	2063
Ibuki	15,088	2090	13.85	2090

hull and superstructures was provided by the Yawata Steel Mill.

The waterline belt had a thickness of 7in (178mm) amidships and was tapered to 4in (102mm) at the ends. The central battery was protected by 5in (127mm) armour (the protection of main and intermediate guns has been covered under armament). The flat of the protective deck was 1.5in (38mm) and this was increased to 2in (51mm) at the slopes but again reduced to 1.5in at both ends (in the *Kurama* class the thickness was 2in throughout). The thickness of the conning tower protection exceeded the maximum of waterline belt at 8in (203mm) and this was the thickest protection except the face and sides of the main gun turrets. The conning tower was modelled after

Midships details of Kurama *about 1915.*

that of *Katori* class battleships but by an order of the Navy Technical Department dated 10 March 1905 the screens fore and aft were abolished and the armour was to be fitted continuously to a height of 6ft (1.83m) and closed by a 3in (76mm) roof. In the *Kurama* class the communication tube under the fore conning tower was of 7in (178mm) thick armour between forecastle and main deck but this was reduced to 4in–2in between main deck and middle deck. All armour was of the so-called 'Krupp cemented' type.

In the *Kurama* class the length of the waterline belt was increased by two plates at the fore end and one sheet at the aft end. This in fact meant a real increase in the proportion of protected area even though the length of the ships had been increased by 10ft. In parallel with this the length of the 5in thick upper belt was increased by four sheets at the fore end. In both cases oblique bulkheads of

Ibuki *on full power trials.*

1in (25.4mm) thickness were placed between the fore edges of the armour plates and the barbettes of the main guns (the after bulkheads were already fitted in the *Tsukuba* class but for reasons not known to these authors there were no forward bulkheads at the level of lower and upper belts). This arrangement was intended to protect the vitals against shellfire from forward but it was quite insufficient to fulfil its purpose and was merely one more unintelligible measure in a piecemeal armouring scheme.

As the *Kurama* class were armed with 8in guns in twin turrets the thickness of the upper belt below the turrets was increasesd to 6in (152mm) and thus the barbette which was placed between the upper and middle deck was formed by only 2in (51mm) thick armour.

Inside the citadel the fitting of 1in (25mm) thick screens at both sides and fore and aft was given up in favour of 1in armour protection to the funnel casings. The alterations to the *Kurama* class in company with those concerning the armament brought about an increase in the displacement of 95 tons but at the same time the Navy General Staff reduced the requirement for the speed by 0.25kts to 21.25kts and this made the achievement of these and some other changes possible.

Machinery

Tsukuba, Ikoma, and *Kurama* were fitted with vertical four-cylinder triple expansion engines, the standard propulsion system at that time. The engines of *Tsukuba* and *Ikoma* were the first designed and produced in Japan to exceed 20,000hp. All ships were two-shafted and the steam for the engines was supplied by Miyabara type boilers working at a pressure of 16.8kg/cm^2, *ie* slightly

higher than in the *Katori* class.

The material of the engines was wrought steel and even the piston rods, connecting rods etc which had been imported from foreign countries in the past were also supplied by Kure Navy Yard Steel Division. Thus it must be emphasized that the engines were of entirely domestic production.

The *Tsukuba* class ships became the first to have a domestically produced forced lubrication system, even though this was fitted some time after completion. This system was first tried in the cruiser *Aso* in 1908 and became operational after some improvements (mainly the stopping of leakage from the pipe connections and reduction of lubricant consumption).

Ikoma was the first ship in the IJN which was fitted with oil-fired boilers. This boiler was experimentally built with mixed and purely oil fuel equipment and was tested in Kure Navy Yard in August to September 1906. The trials on the pressure and steam systems confirmed that the Miyabara boiler could increase the generated power by 10 to 15 per cent using the pressurized mixed burning system. Therefore this system was adopted and the boilers of *Tsukuba* were also modified for mixed firing. *Kurama,* of course, was equipped with these boilers from the first but the number was increased to twenty-eight (fourteen double-ended) in order to obtain about 10 per cent more power to offset the displacement increase and to obtain about 0.75kts more speed with an extra 2000hp.

Adoption of turbines for Ibuki

The intention of the Fourth Division of the Navy Technical Department (Engines) to adopt the turbine dates back to at least 1900. In a letter to Rear-Admiral Miyabara Jiro dated 19 April of that year A F Yarrow suggested applying Parsons turbines to some destroyers or

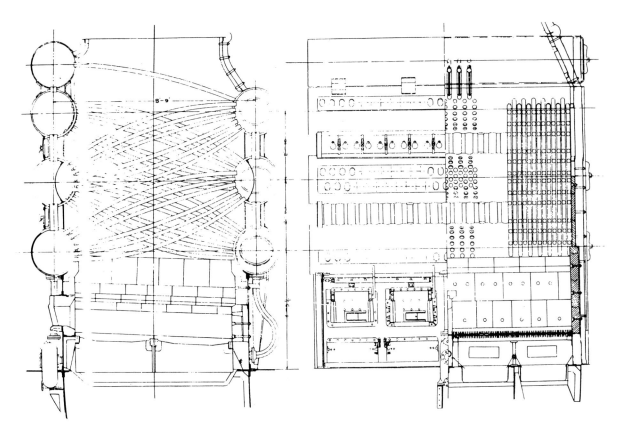

General arrangement of a Miyabara water-tube boiler as fitted to Tsukuba.

torpedo boats to be ordered from the British company. This proposal was inspired by the performance of the turbine-engined British destroyers *Viper* and *Cobra* but at that time the IJN wanted to await future development and the contract for the destroyers *Akatsuki* and *Kasumi* did not specify turbine propulsion. However, the Royal Navy completed the cruiser *Amethyst* with Parson turbines which demonstrated a great reduction in steam consumption at high speed when compared to piston engines. Therefore the British were considering applying the turbine to all warships including battleships to be built after 1905, while the American Curtis turbine was at sea in the passenger ship *Kaiser* of the Hamburg Amerika Line and later the steamer *Creole*. The US Navy intended to carry out comparative tests of the performance of these different propulsion systems using the cruisers *Birmingham, Chester* and *Salem* then under construction; they were fitted with reciprocating engines, Parson turbine and Curtis turbine respectively.

These factors prompted intense discussion about the adoption of the turbine in the IJN and in November 1905 the decision was taken to apply turbines to warships built in Japanese yards. Following this decision the main engines of the armoured cruiser *Ibuki* and the battleship *Aki* were ordered changed to Curtis turbines by the order of the Navy Minister dated 26 November 1905.

The reasons for the adoption of the turbine in outline were as follows:

1. Higher speed could be obtained at the same displacement.
2. The obvious advantages were already leading rival navies to adopt the steam turbine.
3. The disadvantage of higher coal consumption at speeds of less than 14kts compared to the reciprocating engine (as proved by the British experiments) would be more than offset by lower consumption at higher speeds.
4. Combining factors 1 and 2, when in action the turbine-driven ship would be able to steam for longer on the same amount of coal and could make higher speeds in order to gain the tactical advantage or retire safely before superior forces.
5. If turbines were adopted for *Ibuki* (and *Aki*) the weight and cost were calculated to be the same as compared to their sisters *Kurama* and *Satsuma* but speed would increase by nearly two knots (1.75kts) compared to *Kurama*'s 21.25kts (*Satsuma*'s 18.25kts).

At that time the performance of large turbines was not yet completely certain, so their adoption still involved some risk. Therefore the efforts of Rear-Admiral Miyabara who actively campaigned for the turbine are worthy of note. He wrote to his superiors four days before the final decision was made, and Miyabara's letter clearly shows how the officials responsible for naval machinery judged the risk and future development of the turbine (especially the Curtis design) and proves their far-sightedness. The main points were as follows:

1. The adoption of the turbine for future naval ships is the favoured option.
2. The most established turbine for marine use is the Parsons type.

3. The Curtis turbine has been developed only very recently so there is less operational experience available than for the Parsons type, but a study in detail of its structure suggests that in many points it is superior to the Parsons turbine. Therefore if this design is adopted it will undoubtedly achieve at least the same results as the Parsons turbine.

4. It may seem that the adoption of the Curtis turbine is risky but the Cunard Co adopted Parsons turbines for many ships in the Atlantic service when they were at a similar stage of development and it is believed that the risk is no greater now than then. When we consider the development of turbines, we note that the adoption of the water-tube boiler faced much opposition at the time but now cylindrical boilers have been removed from all the warships of the world; the turbine must be a similar case.

5. Fortunately the battleship and cruiser building at Kure are in the early stages so an engine change can be made without difficulty. If we miss this chance we have no other warships which can be equipped with the turbine and we will have to wait six to seven years until we can adopt this engine. Therefore the adoption of the turbine in these ships is highly desirable and for the reasons previously stated I believe the Curtis turbine is the most suitable.

6. The adoption of the Curtis turbine necessitates a small increase in the cost of the engine not exceeding 20,000 Yen per ship. I believe that the 40,000 Yen total can be squeezed from the budgets for other ships under construction, but for this amount of money we can

place turbines of 24,000ihp in each ship; in terms of space and weight they will cause no trouble and the change of design to the hull will be very small.

7. In case of the adoption of turbines in these ships, the engines will have to be ordered from the foreign countries. It is imperative to send the technicians together with the superintendents in order to study the production methods. The representatives will need to be trained in the handling of the engines at sea, so should be engineers with actual experience of the operation of main engines.

Later turbines should preferably be produced domestically. Therefore, preparations for home production should be made along with the training of personnel. It is quite evident that future warships will use the turbine, so the production problem should be addressed before even the technical problems of adopting the turbine.

On 1 June 1906 the contract for four main turbines and propellers for *Aki* and *Ibuki* (two for each ship) and the vacuum pumps, water pumps and patented condensers for *Ibuki* only was signed by the Japanese representative and the American Fore River Shipbuilding Co, Quincy, Mass, the price being $475,000. In accordance with Miyabara's suggestion (Item 7 in the précis of his letter) obtaining the licence for the Curtis turbine was proposed at the same time and the contract covering production rights was concluded exactly one month later (1 July) and for fees of $100,000 the IJN was able to produce this turbine at home.

By adopting the turbine the propulsion characteristics of *Ibuki* changed as follows:

Layout of Ibuki's *engine room.*

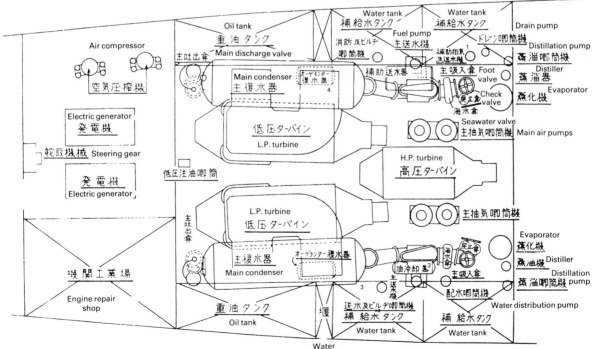

1 Auxiliary feed pump
2 oil cooler
3 fire extinguisher and bilge pump
4 Auxiliary condenser

	Decision in July 1905 reciprocating engine	*Decision in Nov. 1905 steam turbine*
IHP	22,500	24,000
SHP		21,600
rpm		255
Speed	21.25	22

Notes: 1. The increase of the speed is not as great as predicted but all Japanese sources agree on 22kts. Therefore the increase by 1.75kts may mean the overload power – see below.

2. In order to obtain a cheaper price it was decided to fit the same turbines in the battleship *Aki* and armoured cruiser *Ibuki*.

About half a year after the purchase of the turbines the trials of *Tsukuba* were concluded (on 24 November 1906). As her Miyabara boilers had proved to have remarkable spare power in steam generation it was calculated that *Ibuki*'s boiler could generate steam for about 29,000shp corresponding to 32,000 to 33,000ihp and it was thought possible to obtain 23kts without particular difficulties. In fact, this proved impossible, discussions with Fore River revealing that 'even if the turbine would generate 27,000shp (24,500ihp) at 270rpm by the sufficient supply of steam, the present condenser design has no surplus capacity beyond the 21,600shp contracted for, and even if the expansion of the condensers is planned the speed would not exceed 22kts'. Notwithstanding this failure the Navy Technical Department proposed to modify the turbine nozzles and the condensing system in order to improve the speed to 22.75kts, but this again proved pointless and the only modification carried out by Fore River after discussion in February 1907 with the Japanese superintendent in the USA was to change the propellers but the company still did not promise a speed of more than 22kts. On the other hand, the turbines were intended to develop 27,000ihp as maximum overload power, which should suffice to obtain a speed of nearly 23kts.

The *Ibuki* was powered by two Curtis turbines, each housed in a cast iron cylindrical casing with an outside diameter of 4.27m and overall length of 5.18m. The rotor was 3.66m in diameter; the length of the shaft was 8.30m and the total weight amounted to 180 tons. The casing was divided inside into a series of separate compartments by dished diaphragms and each compartment (or stage)

Table 7. *PARTICULARS OF MACHINERY*

	Tsukuba class	*Kurama*	*Ibuki*
ENGINES			
Type	Vertical four-cylinder triple expansion		Curtis turbine
Diameters of			
cyl (HP/IP/LP × 2)	1041/1626/1778mm × 2		–
Stroke	991mm		–
Design hp/speed (kts)	20,500/20.5	22,500/21.25	24,000/22.5
Actual hp/speed (trial)	23,260/21.1	23,081	28,977/21.16
	22,670/21.75 (*Ikoma*)		
No of propellers	2	2	2
Propeller rpm (design/actual)	150/147.7	150/150.6	270/265.6
BOILER			
Type	Miyabara water-tube boiler		
Number	20	28 (14 double-ended)	28 (10 double-ended and 8 single-ended)
Fuel	Coal only (changed)	Mixed firing and oil firing only	
Total area of			
boiler heating surface (m²)	4243.12	5804.5	5398.19
Weight of machinery			
(tons) (M)	2130	1880	2066
HP/M	9.62	11.67	11.6
Total area of machinery (T) m²	740.28	770.23	747.26
Area of ER (E)	229.77	264.31	232.13
Area of BR (B)	510.31	505.92	515.13
Ratio HP/T	2.77	2.72	2.99
HP/E	8.29	7.92	9.62
HP/B	3.73	4.14	4.33
Bunker (coil/oil) (tons)	1600	1868/288	2000/218
	1911/160 (*Ikoma*)		
Rudder area (m²)	24.55	24.36	24.36

Tsukuba *about 2 hours after the magazine explosion which sank her. It was caused by the decomposition of the propellant.*

contained one of the seven ahead and two reverse impulse wheels. The reverse wheels were mounted in the after end of the casing, and under ordinary ahead running they were in a vacuum in order not to waste power by steam friction. The construction was similar to the ahead wheels but the blades, of course, were reversed. Drain pipes which connected each stage with the next one were provided in order to allow the steam in any stage to pass to the next one of lower pressure to transform a part of its heat to useful work. The exhaust chamber drained to the condenser and the discharge was assisted by a small steam ejector. As the steam expanded in passing from stage to stage at diminishing pressures the lengths of the blades and also the arc of the nozzles was increased, thus giving greater area of passage in each succeeding stage. The pressure distribution was so arranged that one-fourth of the available steam energy was expended in the first stage and one-eighth in each of the other stages. The purpose of this arrangement was to keep the pressure in the shell as low as possible and it required the use of an expanding type nozzle in the first stage but all the other nozzles were of the parallel-flow type. This arrangement caused all the ahead wheels, except the first one, to operate under eight-stage conditions.

The Japanese regarded the advantages of the Curtis design as follows:
1. Small number of blades, large clearance around blades and strong mechanical construction of blading to make blade-stripping practically impossible.
2. Economy at reduced speed without cruising turbines by the use of valves on the nozzle openings of the diaphragms to maintain the proper steam pressure distribution at reduced steam flow (even though there was the unavoidable loss due to lower revolutions).
3. No full steam pressure subjected to the interior of the shell as the full steam pressure came on the steam chest only which was a comparatively small steel casting and the greatest pressure in the turbine shell was less than one-third of the working pressure, thus permitting the use of high steam pressure, large turbine diameter in comparison to the power and reducing expansion difficulties.
4. Low revolutions for given horsepower without sacrifice of economy or excessive weight, to allow the use of twin-screw arrangement instead of three or four screws and to obtain a higher efficiency of the propeller.
5. Absence of dummy pistons and their packings in order to eliminate the leakage of high pressure steam and to maintain economy without the necessity for adjustments.

The steam for the turbines was provided by eight single-ended and ten double-ended mixed-fired Miyabara boilers (17kg/cm^2 steam pressure) with superheaters.

During the engine trials steam measured 22 degrees F (above saturated steam) at the turbine inlet.

As proposed in Rear-Admiral Miyabara's letter of 22 November 1905, Lieutenant-Commander (Eng) Shigemura Kiichi, who worked in the Engine Division of Kure Navy Yard, was ordered to the USA and Britain in January 1907 to study the production process and turbine operations aboard actual ships. Unfortunately he was not allowed inspection facilities aboard *Creole* and could only experience the machinery as a passenger. On the other hand, he was able to study turbine structure and operation aboard the cruiser *Amethyst*. Armed with this detailed knowledge he returned to Japan in June 1908 to be mainly in charge of fitting the engine of *Ibuki*. He became her chief engineer on 11 October 1909, roughly two months after the first full power trials on 12 August at which *Ibuki* did not reach the expected speed. At that time the maximum speed was only 20.865kts with 27,353bhp and 252rpm of the propellers and the average values of the 6-hour trial were 27,142bhp, 250.2rpm with a steam consumption of 6.858kg/hp/hour.

Therefore, Kure Navy Yard were directed by the Navy Technical Department to change the propellers (which were newly designed by Fore River, reducing the diameter by 1ft) after several experiments in the model basin of Mitsubishi Nagasaki; to expand the throat of the turbine nozzles and to increase the height; and to reduce the number of tubes of the condenser and to expand the area of holes of the plates in the upper section. After carrying out these improvements the trials were repeated and on 23 June 1910 at the full power trials the following results were obtained:

STEAM PRESSURE		
(kg/cm^2)	*23 June 1910*	*12 August 1909*
Boiler	18.88	18.76
Main Steam in ER	17.18	17.29
Chest of turbine	16.24	16.18
VACUUM IN MAIN CONDENSER (°F)		
Starboard top	27.975	26.2
Starboard bottom	29.25	28.65
Port top	27.95	16.525
Port bottom	29.05	28.5
PROPELLER SPEED (rpm)		
Starboard	265.075	252.15
Port	265.05	251.13
POWER (bhp)	28,977.05	27,353.0
SPEED (kts)	21.16175	20.8675

Notes

[1] The passive role of the Russian naval forces only changed to offensive operations for a short period when Vice-Admiral Makarov replaced the former C-in-C. But after his death on 13 April 1904 when his flagship *Petropavlosk* sank with the loss of 649 men after touching two mines laid by *Koryu Maru*, the Russian fleet returned to sitting out the war inside the port again.

[2] This tragedy happened one day before the navigation course was to be changed by the order from the HQ of the Combined Fleet.

[3] It was mistakenly supposed at first that the ships were torpedoed by a Russian submarine which was the rumour at that time.

[4] The Diet was dissolved in December 1902 because it was unwilling to approve the new land taxation increase which was to provide the finance for the armoured ships in the programme.

[5] This law ran until 31 March 1907 and the special accounting ended on 30 November 1907 with the transfer of 1,706,742 Yen to the general finance to be used followingly.

[6] The shipbuilding costs of *Tsukuba* and *Ikoma* rose to roughly 20,220,000 Yen and those of *Kurama* and *Ibuki* were still higher. Unfortunately the authors lack definitive data about engine, weapon, and administrative costs and therefore cannot give the exact building costs. If any person among the readers knows the details the authors ask him to share his knowledge by writing to Conway Maritime Press. The data about budgets and costs are based upon *Kaigun Gunbi Enkaku* (literally 'History of the Naval Armament'), pp98ff.

[7] Baron Vice-Admiral Kondo Motoki held the post of the chief of the fundamental design section in the NTD for ten years from 1900 to 1909 and after that he became the chief of the Navy Hull Form Experimental Station (*Kaigun Kankei Shikensho*) for thirteen years and during that time he also served the NTD as the authority on design and shipbuilding.

[8] Kaneda's proposal unfortunately did not dispose the turrets in a superfiring arrangement and his design was rejected by the authorities as being inconvenient. It is thought that the tacticians paid little attention and overlooked the possibilities of superfiring turrets.

Shipbuilding in Meiji Era (1868–1912) can be characterized as a time when naval architects made strenuous efforts to respond to earlier designs but if they varied from the model they mainly concentrated upon improvements to the armament (*ie* a large calibre, more guns) so that it was practically impossible to be ahead of other countries. It was a period of imitation rather than originality.

[9] In this respect the design was almost a straight imitation of British practice but this is quite natural considering the technology of ships ordered in the past combined with the training of naval architects sent to foreign countries.

[10] Dr (Eng) Obata was later promoted to Rear-Admiral.

[11] Yamada (eventually Rear-Admiral) was educated in Britain and worked in the shipbuilding division of Kure from the beginning of his career. He was a very skilful engineer and before the construction of *Tsukuba* and *Ikoma* he had already built the cruiser *Miyako* and gunboat *Uji* under Obata. He was rather more than an assistant to Obata and such famous engineers as the previously mentioned Yagi Ayao and Shiraya Chozaburo or Suzuki Nakami and Yamagata Asakichi were his students.

[12] On the other hand Kure was in the lead for repair and conversion experience, having been the repair base for the Combined Fleet (not yet the official term at that time) in the Sino–Japanese War, with assistance from Yokosuka; in preparation for the Russian war many commercial ships were taken up and converted at Kure. Furthermore the urgent repair of damaged ships (as in the Chinese War Kure was mostly in charge of repairs requiring docking) became a responsibility after the outbreak of the Russian conflict. Therefore Kure had the self-confidence to be able to construct the first capital ships in Japan.

[13] The secondment was dual purpose, in that the skilled workers gained experience in the construction of large ships in preparation for future building at Yokosuka.

[14] For the construction of these two ships about 10,000 tons of steel of many scantlings were necessary but in this respect the rather simple and conventional construction was advantageous.

[15] As soon as Obata had made up his mind to begin the construction after full consideration of the problems he went to Kawasaki and Mitsubishi and inspected the facilities and capacities with the intention to use both shipyards as the contractors for various metalwork.

[16] *Ikoma*'s protective deck, which was ordered from Mitsubishi's Nagasaki shipyard in order to meet the completion schedule. The deck was assembled in Nagasaki, then dismantled and transported to Kure to be finally mounted at the berth by the workers from Mitsubishi Nagasaki.

This was the first time a civilian shipyard carried out such work for warships and Mitsubishi Nagasaki judged it a great honour. On the other hand, this example showed the progress in the great civilian shipyards and proved that they would be ready to take up the building of large warships in the near future.

[17] Too close an imitation of British practice had disadvantages, as did lack of experience. Problems included:

1. The windows of the admiral's cabin were too high, the position having been adopted from the British built ships without considering the shorter stature of the Japanese.

2. The quarterdeck was often wet because it drained very badly even though sufficient sheer was given not only to the forecastle but also to this deck. The reason was that drainage was arranged forward of fittings instead of aft of them.

3. With regard to a more serious failure refer to the section on the rolling of *Ikoma*.

[18] Nagamura lectured about his experiments and was told by the then Captain Takarabe about an episode he experienced when he brought home a destroyer built in Britain. Takarabe was nervous of heavy weather likely in the long voyage to Japan and ordered all the fittings which could be removed from the upper deck, including the boat davits, to be stowed low down in the ship in order to lower G and improve the stability. But the ship rolled very hard after leaving port and he was forced to return to consult the top men of the shipyard. He was right that G came down because of the shifting of the fittings from the upper deck to the bottom thus increasing GM and this condition would continue until the fittings were returned to their original position. Once refitted, the destroyer pursued her voyage with a 'soft' (long) period of roll without any difficulty.

This experience confirmed Nagamura's experiments and was in accordance with his proposals to improve *Ikoma*'s condition in this respect.

[19] This was caused primarily by the fact that the turbines for *Aki* would be late and the completion of *Ibuki* first would allow her use as the experimental ship for turbines instead of the more important battleship.

[20] There are many contradictions in Japanese sources about the origin of the gun barrels. Some authors judge that all barrels were constructed by Kure Navy Yard, others state that most of the barrels were imported, but these authors believe that half were manufactured in Japan and half imported from Britain, based upon the fact that the types of barrels and breech blocks each coincide in *Ikoma* and *Ibuki* (in the case of the latter ship authorities like Fukui Shizuo and Niwada agree that imported barrels were mounted) while in the cases of *Tsukuba* and *Kurama* the modified Japanese type breech blocks were used. There are also indications that the capacity of the Gunnery Division was insufficient to manufacture all the barrels and turrets needed for the capital ships.

[21] Up to 180km of steel wire were used in the construction of one gun barrel.

[22] Smokeless powder called 'ribbon type powder' consisted mainly of gun cotton, nitric acid, and phosphoric acid with the addition of nitro-glycerine to form the shape of a ribbon.

[23] Before their removal from the list by the Washington Treaty provisions the continuous firing of about 100 shells from the fore and aft turrets of *Aki* was carried out in order to obtain precise data about the life of the gun barrel, especially the degree of wear under extreme load conditions and influence upon 'fluttering' of the muzzle and, hence, dispersion of the shells; this was to be able to decide wartime countermeasures.

[24] The elevation range of the twin turrets of the four ships was from − 3 degrees to + 23 degrees but in fact + 5 degrees was the normal fixed loading angle even though it was possible to load up to + 13 degrees.

[25] Fourteen 45cal 30.5cm twin turrets and six spare barrels were transferred to the IJA in total of which eight turrets and all spare barrels were not refitted.

THE SVERIGE CLASS COASTAL DEFENCE SHIPS

Never before or since 1912 has a western nation's citizenry used mass demonstrations, including a march on a royal palace, to force an unwilling government to strengthen naval defences. These activities caused the fall of a prime minister and his government, but initiated public subscriptions that more than covered the construction costs for the first of a series of three armoured coastal defence ships for the Royal Swedish Navy. The resulting heavily armed ships were to be the kernel of the fleet for some twenty-six years. The history of these three *Sverige* class coastal defence ships is outlined by Daniel G Harris.

I n 1873, the Swedish parliament united the high seas and inshore fleets that had been separated in 1866.[1] In 1882, after nine years of discussions, the parliamentary defence committee laid down the navy's responsibilities as including the protection of the coast, the defence of the islands of Gotland and Åland, the prevention of enemy landings, and the engagement of the enemy in open waters. To meet these responsibilities, the committee recommended the fleet should be strengthened with eight armoured ships and thirty-four torpedo boats. The committee proposed the construction of eight armoured ships be carried out over fifteen years. In 1884, the parliament voted funds for the first armoured ship, *Svea*. The 1890 and 1893 budgets provided funds for three more vessels. In 1896, the revised defence plan increased the fleet's quota of armoured coastal defence vessels from eight to eleven. The four 3415-ton *Dristighet* series were launched in the years 1900–1903. The launch of *Oscar II*, an enlarged *Dristighet*, took place in 1905.[2]

The 1901 defence committee's report to parliament not only confirmed the 1882 responsibilities but added the breaking of any blockade of Swedish ports and neutrality patrols of territorial waters, in addition to seeking out and destroying an enemy on the high seas. The committee believed seaborne invasion was the greatest threat to Swedish sovereignty. It emphasized that any new construction must be able to navigate the confined waters of the skerries and fight an enemy's strongest and fastest ships. It also recommended the sizes of any new vessels be limited so that the fleet could have several.

The 1904 and 1906 committee's recommendations stipulated that any new ships' armament must be compa-

rable to those of the largest foreign warships, and be able to pierce armoured cruisers' armour. The main armament should be forward; it should include two underwater torpedo tubes, and armour of sufficient thickness over the waterline, turrets, decks, conning tower, boiler and engine rooms. Triple bottoms in certain areas, a well-developed cellular system, and heavy water-tight doors ought to give the vessels good resistance to damage. New construction should have steam turbine engines and a speed equal to, or higher than, all existing or projected foreign battleships. Moreover, the new vessels were to have a radius of 3000 miles at economical speed and be able to use the restricted channels of the skerries.[3] The 1906 plans changed earlier policies; the navy was now to have a new larger class of armoured seagoing vessel.

The 1909 committee proposed new coastal defence ships be 7500 tons in displacement, have a speed of 21kts, be armed with four 28cm (11in), four 19.4cm (7.6in), four 37mm guns, and two 45cm (18in) torpedo tubes. The committee recommended 200mm (7.9in) armour for the waterline, conning tower and main turrets, 150mm (5.9in) for the secondary armament, 100mm (3.9in) for the citadel and 30/40mm (1–1½in) for the decks. The new ships' high speed would give tactical freedom in action with foreign battleships. The proposed vessel was to be a combination of an armoured coastal defence vessel and an armoured cruiser. The committee's report contained five alternative designs, in tonnage ranging from 6440 to 7500 tons and speeds from 18kts to 23kts. The committee's final proposal was the so-called design 'F': length 120m (393.7ft), beam 18.6m (61ft), draught 6.8m (22.3ft), tonnage 6800, to be armed with four 28cm, and eight

Sverige *as completed 1917.* (Otherwise uncredited illustrations by courtesy of the Krigsarkivet, Stockholm)

15cm guns, and have a speed of 22.5kts. The committee stressed that seagoing vessels were essential to enforce neutrality, to prevent trade blockades or enemy hegemony over Swedish territorial waters, and to destroy or delay enemy landing forces. The report reduced the calibre of the proposed ships' secondary armament from 19.4cm to 15.2cm (6in), since it regarded 15.2cm guns as perfectly adequate for repelling enemy torpedo vessels.

The Naval Staff held Russia to be the most likely enemy, believing that Russia wanted harbours on the Norwegian coast and to control the Sound, the Belts, southern Sweden and Norway. The rivalry between Britain and Germany might allow Russia to achieve those goals, so in the Staff's view Germany's interest was to oppose any major powers' attempt to gain control of Sweden. It, therefore, saw no threat from the large German navy because it believed Germany would gain nothing from Sweden's seizure. In fact, in 1910 some unofficial defence staff discussions took place with Germany.

The Political Background

In 1911, the 'russification' activities in Finland, and the tensions between Germany and Russia raised Swedish concerns. The conservative government obtained parliamentary approval for the allocation of about 4 million kroner (£200,000, US $1 million) to begin the construction of one 'F' type coastal defence vessel; its total cost was not to exceed 11,686,000 kroner (£580,000, US $3 million). It placed orders with Bofors for the 28cm guns, but in the 1911 elections the conservative government lost power to the liberals, a party intent on social reforms led by Karl Staaf, who disliked both the army and the navy. Staaf's dislike of the navy is rumoured to have begun as a result of seasickness while on board a warship in the Gulf of Bothnia.

In December 1911, the new liberal government, under Prime Minister Karl Staaf, decided to annul the Bofors contract, and to cancel construction of the first 'F' ship, proposing to use the funds for social reforms. The King,[4] Gustaf V, in a rider to the cabinet's decision to cancel the 'F' ship construction, expressed concern about the government's delay in increasing naval strength. The King's action caused discussion, and a campaign for the defence forces. In January 1912, the famous Swedish explorer, Sven Hedin, wrote the pamphlet *A Word of Warning,*[5] of which 850,000 copies were circulated; it added to the public indignation with the Staaf government's decision. On 26 January 1912, the Reverend Manfred Björkquist proposed a public collection of funds to pay for the new ship. The Armoured Ship Society formed a day later and made an appeal to all Swedish men and women to contribute an amount at least equal to their 1911 tax assessments to cover the 'F' ship's cost of construction. By the beginning of May 1912, the appeals had collected 15,021,530 kroner; (£751,000, US $3,755,000); the Reverend Björkquist's committee contribution was 360,000 kroner (£18,000, US $90,000). The Society promised to turn over the funds to the crown provided that the keel of the new ship was laid down before the end of 1912. The total number of contributors was 125,000. One poor widow sent all she had, a silver cup – it was later kept in a glass case in the admiral's cabin on board *Sverige,* and is now in the Stockholm Maritime Museum.

Sverige as modified: general arrangement drawing dated 15 July 1933.

On 21 May, the government received parliamentary approval of the gift acceptance legislation without debate. Royal consent to the 'F' ship act and approval of the draughts followed on 29 May 1912. The new ship's name was to be *Sverige* (Sweden) because it represented the whole nation. The Association stipulated that the surplus funds were to be used for additional vessels of the same class. The Björkquist committee required its gift to be used for a naval air arm.

In 1913, the Staaf liberal government agreed with public opinion that a rearmament programme was desirable but took little action. Early in 1914, 31,000 farmers and the student body marched on the Royal Palace in Stockholm to pledge support for any new defence plans. Gustaf V addressed the crowds urging the government take immediate action to reinforce the fleet and the army.[6] The Monarch's speeches caused a constitutional crisis, the Prime Minister's and the government's resignation, the dissolution of parliament, and a special general election. The election issues were the strengthening of the fleet and the

longer service for army conscripts. As a result, a conservative government replaced Staaf's liberal administration. The new cabinet, influenced by the tensions in central Europe and between Britain and Germany, ordered two more *Sverige* class ships, two destroyers and other small craft.

Construction

There was great public interest in the progress of the first 'F' ship, *Sverige*, since its costs were to be defrayed by the public's subscription. All parties were determined that the ship should be built in Sweden, and of Swedish materials. The Scottish yard of William Beardmore & Co had obtained a set of the drawings and offered to build the ship, but the Swedish Admiralty was unable to consider Beardmore's proposals under the terms of the public collection act.

The Naval Material Board's initial problem was that no Swedish shipyard had ever built so large a naval vessel or even a merchant ship of similar tonnage. The Board invited tenders from Kockums of Malmö, Lindholm of Göteborg, Finnboda Bergsund of Stockholm, the Karlskrona Royal Dockyard and Göteborg's Nya Verkstad, later to be known as Götaverken. All yards with the exception of the last made no offers. The Royal Dockyard stated it would have to construct a new slip but even so it could not meet the deadline for the keel laying.[7] At this moment, the managing director of Götaverken, Hugo Hammar, moves to centre stage.

Hugo Hammar (1864–1947), had started life as a metal worker and shipbuilder, and had worked in British, French and American naval shipyards. He had built four armoured ships at the Lindholm yard, and taken part in the discussions about the 'F' type ship, which he favoured. He was prepared to take risks, had energy, self-confidence and foresight. Hammar believed the construction of *Sverige*, and any sister vessels, would help to expand Swedish yards, especially Götaverken, and encourage the development of new techniques: 'We should not copy other nations' work – it is easy to put one's self into a lower class because one does not care to take risks. We must take the lead in technical problem solving'. Before 1912, Hammar's yard had never built a ship of over 2000 tons.

Launch of Drottning Victoria *at Kockums, Malmö, 15 September 1917. Note the timber backing for the waterline armour and outlet for the underwater torpedo tube.*

It had neither drydock nor a fitting-out quay. It lacked all types of equipment and technical personnel. Nonetheless, he proposed, with the full support of Götaverken's staff, to build the ship. The yard's staff, gathered at the station to see Hammar leave for negotiations in Stockholm, shouted 'Don't come back without that contract'!

Negotiations with the Naval Board took a long time. It demanded any offer should state a price per kilo, the method used at the beginning of the century. Hammar rejected it. 'You cannot bid for a complicated large vessel like kilos of butter. No such complicated vessel has ever been built in Sweden.' The four yards finally agreed to co-operate to build *Sverige* with Hammar's Götaverken becoming the main contractor. The subcontractors, Kockums, were to deliver the turbines, Finnboda Bergsund the boilers and auxiliary machinery, Lindholm all deck machinery and the steam steering gear. Domnarvet was to deliver the plate and profiles; four other companies were to supply the electrical equipment, pumps, auxiliary turbine generators and diesel engines. W G Armstrong of Newcastle-on-Tyne was to supply the underwater torpedo tubes. On 4 November 1912, the Naval Board, after much bargaining, accepted the syndicate's bid of 6,216,500 kroner for the hull, boilers and machinery. Götaverken included no part of the costs of the new slipway, additional equipment or insurance in its bid. The

syndicate estimated its net profit from the ship's construction would be ½ of 1 per cent.

Bofors contracted for the guns, turrets and armour plate, but it subcontracted with the American Carnegie Steel Corp for the deck and vertical armour. The highly-competitive American prices gave a saving of about 800,000 kroner (£40,000, US $200,000). Since Bofors had never made 28cm guns and turrets, it had to modernize its buildings, purchase a large forge press, new machinery and find new proving grounds. Its total outlay was about 6 million kroner (£300,000, US $1,500,000). The negotiations between Bofors and the Naval Board took time, the latter pressing for lower prices and suggesting, for patriotic reasons, Bofors should be willing to make no profits on the guns and armour.

A British concern offered Bullivant's patent anti-torpedo nets. It sent a blueprint to show the installation of the equipment, mostly steel booms attached to the hull, and the stowage of the nets. No records show the acceptance of Bullivant's proposal.

Prior to the start of construction, trials to determine the final hull form, using two models in ⅟₃₆ scale at three different waterlines, took place in the North German Lloyd Line's testing tank at Bremen. These trials established the hull resistance, studied the effect of trim, and determined the position of the bilge keels. The final lines adopted, according to the late Captain (E) Ivar Hult's papers, coincided with the proportions and co-efficients of contemporary armoured cruisers.

The Naval Board laid down that the hull was to be built of steel with a tensile strength of 42–48 kilograms per mm^2 and 21 per cent elongation. Moreover, the steel for the keel, keelson, inner bottom's midship strake, the main deck for one-third of the vessel's length midships and the main deck stringers were to have a tensile strength of 52–62 kilograms per mm^2 and 18 per cent elongation. The longitudinal stress on the main deck was 1046 kilograms per cm^2. The space between each frame up to the main deck was 1.0m over the whole ship's length. Below the armoured deck, the space between frames was much less; above it, both frames and beams were also fewer but of heavy profiles. Only alternative stringers of the double bottom were made water-tight. Lap-joint riveting was used for the shell plating, the armour's skin, and the decks. The Naval Board's specifications required one or two water-tight compartments to be tested after launch by filling them with water to a height of 1m above the waterline.

Sverige's underwater protection consisted of water-tight transverse bulkheads that below the armoured deck divided the vessel into thirteen compartments: also the cell-divided double bottom extended up to the armoured deck and to a depth of 1.2–6.8m (4–22.3ft). The coal bunkers were well protected but the turbine rooms had no

Sverige's commissioning ceremony, 1917. (Sjöhistoriska Museum, Stockholm)

other protection than the double bottom's wing cells. Other compartments had only that protection given by the interior bulkheads. It is probable the Swedish Naval Board knew of the German Navy's trials to improve underwater protection from mines and torpedoes, but no extra underwater protection could be given to *Sverige* and her sisters because the fire-lined hull form derived from the speed requirement did not lend itself to heavy underwater protection.

Bolts attached the armour with a wooden backing to the shell plating of the hull and citadel. The armoured deck comprised an upper layer of nickel alloy steel and a lower of ordinary ship's plate riveted together. The turret's armour plates were scarf-jointed with butt straps which gave a considerable weight saving. The armour was about 20 per cent of the ship's standard displacement.

At midday on the 12 December 1912, the Association's delegates witnessed the laying of *Sverige*'s keel at Götaverken's yard in Göteborg – the terms of its gift were met. *Sverige*'s construction continued throughout 1913. The fitting of the deck armour began in January 1914, but the outbreak of the First World War delayed the launch until May 1915. Since Götaverken had no dry dock, the four propellers were mounted on the four tail shafts before the launch. The propellers were cast steel because, owing

Sverige showing laying of armoured deck at Götaverken Göteborg 1914.

to the war, the British manufacturer was unable to deliver the bronze.

King Gustaf V, Crown Prince Gustaf Adolph (later Gustaf VI), Crown Princess Margaret, daughter of the Duke of Connaught, other royal family members, and the Armoured Ship Association's council attended the launch on 3 May 1915. The King's speech, thanking the Association for its patriotism and the staff of Götaverken for its fine work, ended: 'May this ship, which shall now glide out onto the billows and shall carry Sweden's name and flag, meet expectations and follow the traditions of the Swedish Navy – May good luck always follow *Sverige*'. The King gave the signal, the successful launch took place and those present sang the national anthem 'Du Gamla Du fria' (Thou old, Thou free).[8] Thereafter, the fitting of the belt armour engines, boilers, upperworks and armament began. Götaverken had to hire 50- and 20-ton pontoon cranes for this work.

A few days after the launch, the keels of *Gustaf V* and *Drottning Victoria* were laid at the Götaverken and Kockums yards. The wartime conditions delayed the completion of *Sverige* until June 1917. Material shortages caused steel piping to replace copper wherever possible.

Sverige left Göteborg for Karlskrona at the beginning of June. She was piloted through a German minefield at the southern entrance to the Sound, and on arrival she was docked at Karlskrona for bottom cleaning, and final inspection. The inspectors found that at full load, the vessel displaced 90 tons less than calculated, and drew

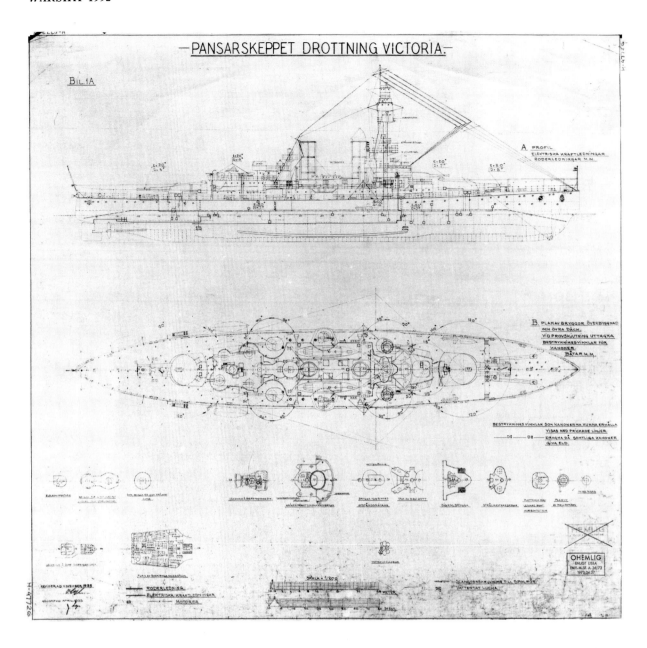

Drottning Victoria, modifications: originally dated April 1933 and revised November 1935, but including wartime alterations.

10cm (3.9in) less both fore and aft. She arrived in Stockholm on 13 June 1917. At 11 am on 14 June 1917, King Gustaf, wearing an 1850 admiral's jacket, accompanied by Queen Victoria, the cabinet and senior defence officers, took formal possession of the ship from the Association on the ship's quarterdeck.

Drottning Victoria and *Gustaf V*, both laid down in 1915, differed from *Sverige*, being 1m (3.3ft) longer and had icebreaking bows. Queen Victoria launched *Drottning Victoria* at Malmö on 15 September 1917. The launch photograph shows the position of one of the two underwater torpedo tubes, and the wooden backing for the yet to be fitted belt armour is also visible. Kockums

placed a stand near the end of the slipway so that when launched, the hull passed by the queen. She gave the ship a silken flag in the colours of her home state of Baden, Germany. The Queen stipulated that this flag was only to be flown in battle. Late in 1944, this nearly happened.

On 18 January 1918, Götaverken launched *Gustaf V* in the presence of the Crown Prince. America's entry into the First World War delayed the completion of the two ships until 1919 and 1922 because neither the armour plate ordered from Carnegie nor the Westinghouse floating-frame gearing for the turbines could be delivered.

In 1919, some parliamentarians suggested *Drottning Victoria* and *Gustaf V* be converted to merchant vessels for the Göteborg – London trade. The idea died when the Naval Material Board pointed out that the removal of the armour would make the ships unstable and gave further information about the implications of the proposed conversion.

THE SVERIGE CLASS COASTAL DEFENCE SHIPS

Sverige, *May 1942 after reconstruction.*

Sverige was fitted as flagship. All three ships had
innovations for the comfort of the crew, including reading
room and bastu (sauna).

Drottning Victoria, *1935 after first reconstruction.*
(Courtesy of Naval Museum, Karlskrona)

Machinery

The Parliamentary Defence Committee had stipulated
that the new armoured coastal defence ships' engines were
to be steam turbines. Three different types were available
– the American Curtis or Westinghouse, or the British
Parsons. The Curtis action turbine gave direct drive, the
Parsons was a reduction-geared turbine, and the Westinghouse was a floating-frame reduction-geared turbine. The
Naval Board of Administration had some experience with
German-built AEG Curtis turbines installed in the small
destroyers *Hugin* and *Munin* built in 1911. Although

Motala Verkstad offered Parsons geared turbines, the lack of equipment in Sweden to cut the large gears, and a noise problem were reasons for rejection. As a result of its earlier experience, the Board chose Curtis direct-drive 20,000shp turbines coupled to four shafts, which gave *Sverige* a maximum speed of 22.5kts. The four three-bladed propellers of 2.34m diameter turned at a maximum of 430 revolutions per minute. Twelve coal-fired Yarrow-type boilers installed in four boiler rooms provided the steam.

The twelve boilers had 3000m^2 of heating surface and 66.7m^2 grate area, the working pressure was 18kg per cm^2, and the maximum allowable blast pressure was 60mm water column; 270 kilos of coal per km^2 of grate area gave 132 tons of steam power. Each boiler had two oil burners for high speed running; the fuel oil tank held about 100 tons. A separate boiler provided steam for the electrical generators, auxiliary machinery, heating, etc. The propulsion equipment was in two compartments separated by a longitudinal bulkhead. Each was divided by an athwartships bulkhead into two sections. The fore contained the turbines, the aft the condensers. The four rooms contained a high pressure turbine and a built-in

reverse turbine or a low pressure one with its reverse turbine. The high pressure turbines were connected to the outer shafts and the low pressure to the inner shafts.

The Navy's engineering branch reviewed the choice of engines for the two sister ships and decided in favour of geared turbines. Thus, *Drottning Victoria* and *Gustaf V* had Westinghouse turbines that, through floating-frame gearing with reduction of 17.23 to 1, gave the two propeller shafts 200rpm. The turbines' revolutions per minute were about 3450 that resulted in smaller size, less weight and greater economy. As a result, the power was increased to 22,000shp to provide a maximum speed of 23.5kts. The two ships using geared turbines carried the same quantity of coal and oil as *Sverige*, but at a speed of 14kts burnt less fuel and had an increased range of about 560 miles.

A programme to replace some of the three ships' coal-fired boilers began in 1935. Two Penhoët oil-fired boilers replaced six coal-burning of *Drottning Victoria*. In 1937, two Penhoët oil-burners replaced six of *Gustaf V*'s coal-fired and in 1938, four oil-burning boilers replaced all *Sverige*'s coal-fired.

Two diesel-driven generators installed forward provided 88kw power and two turbine-driven aft produced 100kw. All deck machinery, the ventilating, turret-turning equipment, and ammunition hoists were electrically driven. Steam from the main boilers supplied steam

Sverige. *Bofors drawing of the 28.1cm turret for* Sverige. (Sjöhistoriska Museum, Stockholm)

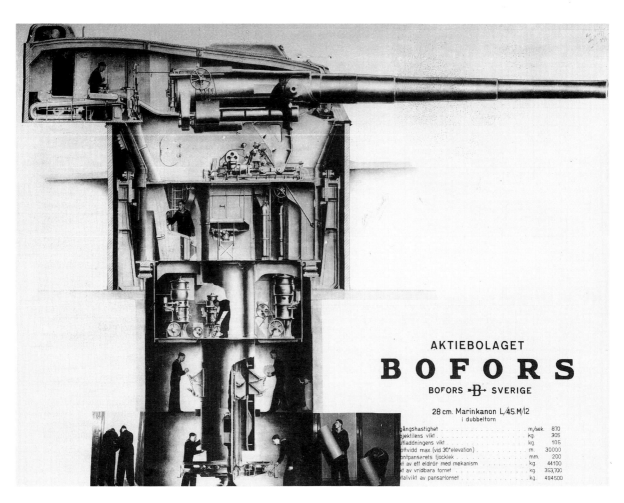

AKTIEBOLAGET

BOFORS

BOFORS ⟶B⟶ SVERIGE

28 cm. Marinkanon L/45.M/12
i dubbeltorn

gångshastighet	m/sek.	870
bjektilens vikt	kg.	305
utladdningens vikt	kg.	105
ottvidd max. (vid 30°elevation)	m.	30000
ontpansarets tjocklek	mm.	200
kt av ett eldrör med mekanism	kg.	44100
kt av vridbara tornet	kg.	353,700
talvikt av pansartornet	kg.	494600

Sverige. *Preparing a 28.1cm gun for firing. Note the separate breech block.*

to the two steering engines, one to port and the other to starboard, which operated the rudder through connecting shafts.

In the original design, the ships' fuel was 665 tons of coal and 100 tons of oil, to give a radius of 910 miles at 22.5kts and 2720 at 14kts. The machinery's total weight in *Sverige* was 923 tons or 13.5 per cent of the total displacement. The figures for the other two ships were 864 tons or 12.5 per cent of total displacement.

The Armament

The original armament was four 28.3cm (11.15in) guns in twin turrets, one forward, one aft; two 15.2cm (6in) in a twin turret forward, six 15.2cm in single gunhouses on the broadside amidships; two, later increased to six, 75mm guns; two 57mm field guns and two 6.5mm machine-guns. The Naval Material Board held that a 28.3cm shell could damage the largest battleship. The rate of fire of the 28.3cm guns was about four rounds per minute. The 28.3cm guns, made by Bofors, comprised a forged core and three layers of cast jackets and recoil brake. The break block was similar to existing guns but Bofors designed a new breech mechanism. The barrel rested in a recoil jacket fitted with a brake.[9] Electric motors connected to hydraulic oil-filled gearing, known as Janney control, provided the elevation and training movements. The speed of elevation was 5° per second. The speed of training was 4° per second. A reserve mechanism and hand-operated equipment were available.

The 28.3cm guns fired a 350kg (770lb) projectile. In the magazine, Armstrong pattern overhead grabs and trollies carried the shells to the hoists. The charges comprised two 50kg (110lb) bags of propellant, which were moved by hand in cartridge boxes to the hoists. Electric motors operated the hoist mechanism. The Naval Board had flash-proof doors installed in the magazines as a result of

studying the British Navy's losses at Jutland. It decided that shells would be high explosive rather than armour piercing since it was cheaper and more effective against unprotected targets. The maximum range at 18-degree elevation was 19,600m (21,400yds), the muzzle energy being 11,500 metric tonnes.

The 15.2cm 50-calibre guns comprised a forged barrel with a shrunk-on jacket. Muzzle velocity was 850m (280ft) per second, shell weight 45.4kg (100lb), and the maximum range at 15-degree elevation was about 16,000m (17,500yds). The recoil mechanism was on the upper side of the cradle and was combined with other equipment; in the twin turrets, both guns lay in a common cradle. The 15.2cm guns had a special type of screw breech block. In the single 15.2cm mounting, elevation and training was by hand, but in the twin turrets electric motors provided the power for the elevation and training. The hoists could lift ammunition at the rate of eight rounds per minute. In 1912, the highest rate of fire for the 15.2cm guns was about five to six rounds per minute.

On completion, *Sverige* had one 3m and one 2m rangefinder. The gunnery officer had the 2m rangefinder, range indicator and range clock in the fore top, but unfortunately, the 2m rangefinder proved unreliable at ranges of over 7000m (7650yds). Communication with the turrets was by telephone or by voice pipes. The electric order transmitters were the Danish Schepelers torque coil system. That system was later replaced by a moving coil system.

It was clear from the developments in gunnery during and after the First World War that the maximum range of the 28.3cm guns was inadequate. Increases in the angles of elevation could bring greater ranges, but the cost to improve the ship's turrets was too high. Nonetheless, during the 1930s, improvements in the ammunition enabled the ranges of the 28.3cm guns to be extended to 25,000m (27,300yds) and the 15.2cm guns to about 19,000m (20,750yds). It was never possible to adapt the 15.2cm guns to an anti-aircaft role.

Consideration of director-firing and new rangefinders began in 1921. Two years later, tenders came from Barr & Stroud of Britain, Giradelle of Italy and Hazemeyer of the Netherlands, this last being the one accepted. Hazemeyer became the supplier of fire control equipment throughout the three ships' lives. Originally, Barr & Stroud had supplied the coincidence rangefinders, but Zeiss stereoscopic equipment replaced them during the 1930s.

The modern fire control equipment required the replacement of the foremast with a tripod mast. The upper part carried the director tower, rangefinder and periscope; the central section a 4m rangefinder, and the lower part the communications equipment. All three ships had the changes made between 1924 and 1930. Central fire control for the 15.2cm guns was added during the Second World War.

In 1938, two Hazemeyer stabilized twin 40mm AA Bofors automatic guns, similar to those fitted to the Dutch cruiser *de Ruyter*, replaced *Gustaf V*'s forward 15.2cm turret; Hazemeyer also provided the fire control. Two twin Bofors 40mm guns also replaced the other two ships' 15.2cm midship guns during the Second World War. Director control towers for anti-aircraft guns were erected

Gustaf V, *1945 showing bridge complex and fore top.*

Gustaf V, *May 1942 after reconstruction. Note the coat of arms on the stern.*

on the quarterdeck along with two twin 40mm high-angle guns.

The 45-degree angle underwater torpedo tubes were removed from all three ships in the mid-1920s. The torpedo room was unprotected and therefore a weakness in the hull. If it was hit, flooding could upset the ship's stability. Combat centres took over the vacant space.

At the end of the three ships' service lives, the armament of each was as follows:

Four 28.3cm in twin turrets	All three ships
Two 15.2cm in twin turrets	*Sverige* and *Drottning Victoria*
Four 15.2cm in single gunhouses	*Sverige* and *Drottning Victoria*
Six 15.2cm in single gunhouses	*Gustaf V*
Four 75mm AA twin mountings	All three ships
Six 40mm AA twin mountings	All three ships
Four 25mm AA twin mountings	All three ships
Three 20mm AA single mountings	All three ships

In 1943, a subsidiary of L M Ericsson AB had developed an early type of radar which was installed on *Drottning Victoria*'s forward director. It used the long waveband and proved ineffective for navigational purposes. In 1946, British radar was installed on *Gustaf V*.[10]

Tactical Deployment

Until 1938, the Naval Staff believed the Soviet Union to be the probable enemy. After the 1938 seizure of Austria, the cabinet compelled the Defence Staffs to consider possible German aggression but the Naval Staff felt vindicated by the 1939 Soviet attack on Finland. In the years between the two wars, the Navy directed its planning at meeting the threats posed by the Soviet *Kirov* cruisers and the modernised First World War *Marat* class battleships.

Prior to 1941, the defence strategy was a first line of mines and large submarines operating just outside territorial waters. The aircraft-carrying cruiser *Gotland* and destroyers were to be the second line between the minefields and territorial waters. This group was a reconnaissance force, with *Gotland*'s seaplanes providing distance intelligence. The group was to report back to the main fleet, the three *Sverige* class ships. When details of the enemy's approach were received, the three armoured ships and their anti-submarine escort would put to sea to meet them. To provide concentrated fire-power, the three ships were always to operate together. The Navy believed the *Sverige* group, using smoke screens and the tactics of concentration, could damage the Soviet *Marat* class battleships or the German pocket battleships.[11] One authority[12] agreed that the size, speed and sea-keeping qualities of the three ships inspired Swedish tactical thinking to move away from operations only in the skerries to the open waters, and, consequently, the building of small seaworthy craft as escorts. Beginning in 1940, the active fleet began to specialize in night fighting. Late in 1940, two *Sverige* class ships and destroyers took part in exercises to defend Gotland from a 'southern'

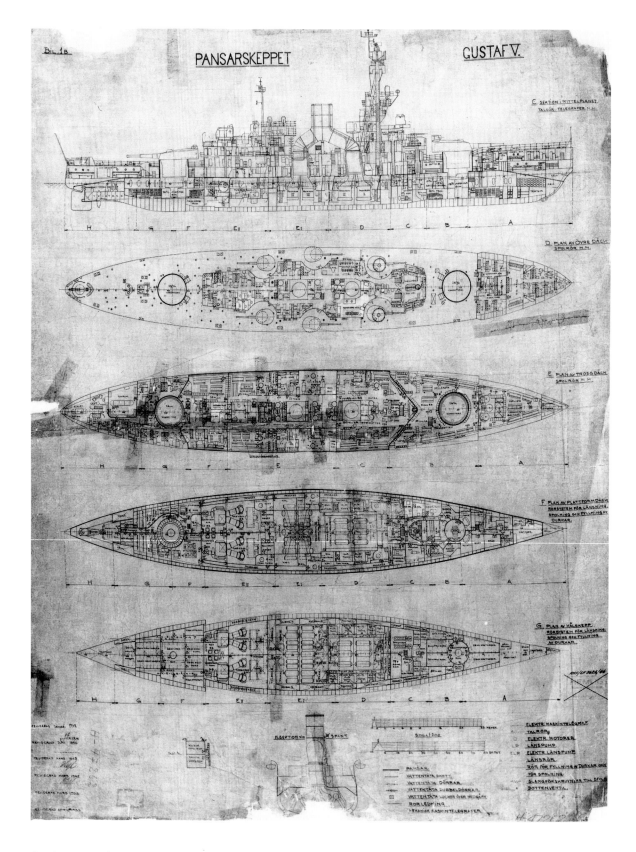

Sverige, *general arrangements and decks, revised*
September 1933 and January 1936, but including wartime
alterations.

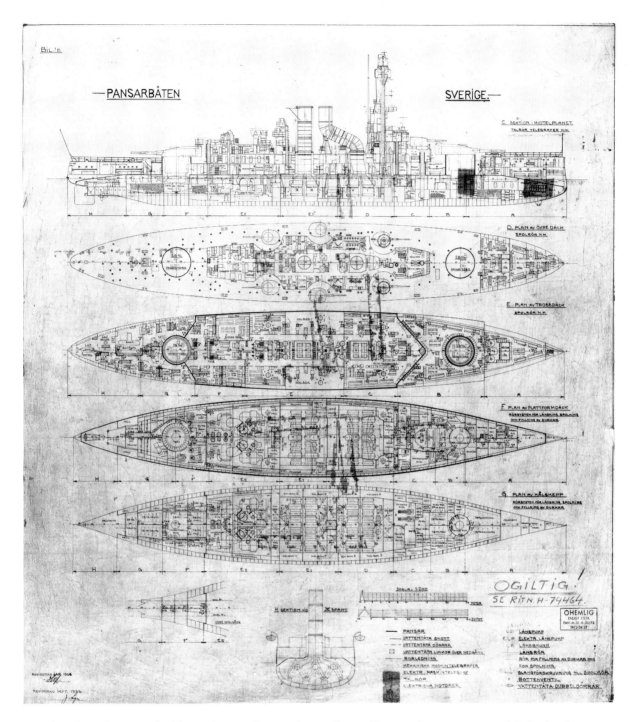

Gustav V, general arrangements and decks showing various stages of modifications from 1933 to January 1948.

Service Careers

The activities of the British, German and Russian navies in the Baltic in the summer and early autumn of 1917 prevented *Sverige*'s full speed trials in open waters. She

invading force. In 1941, the idea took root of aggressive task forces comprising cruisers, destroyers and motor torpedo boats to seek out and destroy an enemy in the open sea. Thereafter, the three ships were to be a second line of defence and back-up to the cruiser-led forces.

was stationed at Karlskrona, the principal Swedish naval base for the winter of 1917–18. In February 1918, a delegation from the Åland Islands (part of Finland) petitioned Gustaf V to reunite the islands with Sweden, for protection from the Russian garrisons and Finnish red guards. Fighting between Finnish defence forces and the red guards had begun. Public pressure forced the Swedish government to act. It sent *Sverige*, *Oscar II*, three other vessels and 500 men to maintain order, arrange a truce

Drottning Victoria *at sea, 1945. Camouflage painted but with white neutrality stripes.*

between the combatants, to evacuate Swedish citizens and others who wished to leave. Both ships landed troops and seamen which took possession of some Russian equipment. After some negotiations, the Russians agreed to leave the islands. At the beginning of March, the German battleships *Rheinland* and *Westfalen* and the icebreaker *Hindenburg* arrived at Eckerö, probably at the request of the provisional Finnish government. The force began operations against the red guards and the Russian garrison. The Stockholm government ordered its forces to return to Swedish waters when relations with the Germans became difficult.[13]

In 1923, *Sverige* with *Drottning Victoria* and *Gustaf V* and two destroyers visited Sheerness to coincide with the announcement of Crown Prince Gustaf Adolph's and Lady Louise Mountbatten's engagement. During a visit to the Swedish ships, Lady Louise Mountbatten inscribed her name on *Sverige*'s aft 28cm turret. *Sverige*, and the accompanying vessels, later sailed to Rosyth for an official visit to the Royal Navy. During an inter-service regatta, using British boats, *Drottning Victoria*'s crew of southern Swedes won a 2-mile rowing contest.

Sverige made official visits to Helsinki, Copenhagen, Reval, Riga and other Baltic ports during the 1920s, and to Kiel in 1937. Changes made to *Sverige*'s silhouette prior to the Second World War included a tripod mast with director fire control and rangefinder, replacing the foremast. A short signal mast replaced the main. During the 1930s, the fore funnel was rebuilt and bent aft to prevent smoke from affecting the bridge. In 1945, *Sverige* was the host ship to a British naval visit; relegated to harbour service in 1947, she was scrapped in 1953.

In 1921, *Drottning Victoria* was finally ready for service. The Westinghouse Company sent an engineer to be present at the machinery trials because there had been some difficulties with the American-supplied gearing.

During the full power steaming trials, 22.5kts was attained. At that speed, the rudder was put over from hard a starboard to hard a port which took 19.2 seconds. The reverse took 18.5 seconds. A similar manoeuvre using the hand steering gear put severe strain on the mechanism. The rudder's maximum effective angle was 35 degrees.[14]

In the 1920s and 1930s, *Drottning Victoria* accompanied *Sverige* on visits to foreign ports in the Baltic and its approaches. February 1929 was one of the worst winters on record. Most of the Baltic was frozen, the Sound was blocked by pack ice, and many merchant vessels were unable to move. In addition, there was a shortage of icebreakers. Since *Drottning Victoria* had an icebreaking bow, the Naval Command sent her to the southern Baltic to free shipping, and thereafter to the Bay of Danzig to break a passage through the ice for a convoy of about twenty vessels inbound for the Stockholm area. The ship's attempt to free a vessel at the entrance to the Kalmar Sound failed because she could only break ice by battering. Neither *Drottning Victoria* nor *Gustaf V* thereafter acted as icebreakers for merchant vessels.

Drottning was Sweden's representative at King George VI's 1937 coronation review. She escorted the Finnish coastal defence vessel *Ilmarinen* to Britain because the latter, built for the skerries, had poor sea-keeping qualities.[15] *Drottning Victoria*'s silhouette changed between the two wars, when a tripod replaced the pole foremast, and twin 40mm anti-aircraft guns replaced two of the single turret 15cm guns. The fore funnel was fitted with a clinker screen. She left the active fleet in 1950 and was scrapped in 1960.

Gustaf V was ready for service in 1922. An engineer from Westinghouse also attended her machinery trials although the Motala Works had manufactured the turbines. Like her sisters, *Gustaf*'s silhouette changed in the 1920s and 1930s. In addition to new masts similar to the two sister ships, the two funnels were trunked into a single smoke stack. *Gustaf V* made a 3-month cruise to the

Gustaf V, *1945. Note the additional anti-aircraft armament. Ship has been painted with camouflage to blend in with the physical features of the skerries. Vessel has the white neutrality stripes.*

Drottning Victoria *in 1945. Note the primitive radar 'mattress' on the fore top.* (Sjöhistoriska Museum, Stockholm)

Mediterranean in the winter of 1933–34, calling at Plymouth, Gibraltar and Malta, as well as Italian, Spanish and North African ports, during which the ship encountered a Force 10 storm in the Atlantic and a Force 9 storm off Syracuse. A boiler explosion killed ten of her men in 1940. Withdrawn from the active fleet in 1948 with the advent of the *Tre Kronor* class cruisers, she survived until scrapped in 1958.

The three ships proved good sea-boats. As built, the rolling period was 11 seconds with a 1.23m metacentric height. Rebuilding increased the rolling period to 13 seconds and reduced the metacentric height to 1.0m. The maximum rolling angles in heavy seas encountered were

18–20 degrees. *Gustaf V*, in the previously mentioned Force 9 storm in the Mediterranean, developed a 25-degree roll. The pitching and rolling movements were slow, but ideally, the ships ought to have had greater freeboard; the forecastle in heavy weather was very wet.

The only time the three ships put to sea for action was in the late summer of 1944, when a German force was sighted approaching Swedish territorial waters and believed to be intending to occupy Åland or attack Sweden. The sight of the three ships may have caused the Germans to turn away, and steam to the Finnish mainland. The German opinions about the three ships are interesting. In January 1940, Admiral Raeder, at a conference with Hitler about future plans, stated he had to keep some large units in the Baltic because of the three *Sverige* class ships. In March 1943, General Bamler completed plans for an attack on Sweden, which required the German navy to destroy the Swedish ships before any landing on the east coast could take place.[16] The respect extended to the Soviet navy: a 1946 Russian naval journal stated that the three *Sverige* class ships were of great importance for the defence of the skerry areas of the Baltic.

In 1946, Mr Edwin Sköld, defence minister during the Second World War and a member of the Swedish labour party, stated 'Many times during the war was I thankful we had the three ships – during the inter-war years, they strengthened our position in the Baltic. All that time, until the end of the Second World War, our Navy was a match for both the German and Soviet Navies because we had those three ships'.

Conclusions

The Swedish people's determination to defend their nation forced a government to listen, and act to increase defences – a rare occurrence even in democracies. The three ships' construction brought about the expansion of Swedish engineering and shipbuilding industries, and provided a first line defence against invasion of the Swedish coasts during the Second World War. From these points of view they may be regarded as the most successful ships the Swedish Navy possessed before the new concepts of fast light forces operating in open waters and the recognition of air power took away their role.

Table 1. *SVERIGE CLASS TECHNICAL SPECIFICATIONS*

Construction

Builders	*Sverige*	Götaverken, Goteborg
	Drottning Victoria	Kockums, Malmö
	Gustaf V	Götaverken, Goteborg
Final Authorization	*Sverige*	May 1912
	Drottning Victoria	June 1914
	Gustaf V	June 1914
Contracts Signed	*Sverige*	September 1912
	Drottning Victoria	September 1914
	Gustaf V	September 1914
Laid Down	*Sverige*	December 1912
	Drottning Victoria	May 1915
	Gustaf V	May 1915
Launched	*Sverige*	3 May 1915
	Drottning Victoria	15 September 1917
	Gustaf V	31 January 1919

Design data

	Sverige	*Drottning Victoria* *Gustaf V*
Displacement (Full Load)	7688	7663
Length overall	119.72m (392ft 9in)	120.9m (396ft 8in)
Max beam	18.63m (61ft 1in)	18.63m (61ft 1in)
Max draught	6.25m (20ft 6in)	6.25m (20ft 6in)
Design speed	22.5kts	23.2kts

Armament as built (All three Ships)
Four 28.3cm (11.1in) guns in two twin turrets
Two 15.2cm guns (6in) in one twin turret
Six 15.2cm guns (6in) in single turrets
Six 75cm (3in) guns
Two 45cm (18in) torpedo tubes at 45° to hull
Four hand-operated searchlights
Two field guns and two machine-guns

Table 1. *SVERIGE CLASS TECHNICAL SPECIFICATIONS (Continued)*

Armament 1948

Sverige	Gustaf V
Drottning Victoria	
Four 28.3cm guns in two twin turrets	Four 28.3cm guns in two twin turrets
Two 15.2cm guns in one twin turret	
Four 15.2cm guns in single turrets	Six 15.2cm guns in single turrets
Four 75cm AA in twin mountings	Four 75mm AA in twin mountings
Six 40mm AA in twin mountings	Six 40mm AA in twin mountings
Four 25mm AA in twin mountings	Four 25mm AA in twin mountings
Three 20mm AA in single mountings	Three 20mm AA in single mountings
Four 8mm machine-guns	Four 8mm machine-guns
Fitted with paravanes	Fitted with paravanes

Armour (All three Ships)

Main deck	40mm (1.6in)	
Main turrets	200mm (7.9in)	
Secondary turrets	125mm (4.9in)	Note: The turbine room's only
Conning tower	175mm (6.9in)	protection was the double
Waterline	200mm (7.9in)	bottom.
Citadel	100mm (3.9in)	

Machinery

	Sverige	Drottning Victoria / Gustaf V
Boilers	12 Yarrow coal-fired* (all replaced by 4 Penhoët oil-burning 1938)	12 Yarrow coal-fired* (6 coal-fired replaced by 2 Penhoët oil-burning 1935/37)
Engines	Curtis direct drive turbines 20,000shp	Westinghouse geared turbines 22,000shp
Propellers	Four 3-bladed, 430rpm = speed 22.5kts.	Two 3-bladed, 200rpm = speed 23.2kts.
Fuel	As built – coal 665 tons, oil 100 tons. * (1938 – oil 596 tons)	As built – coal 665 tons, oil 100 tons. * (1937 – coal 350 tons, oil 350 tons)
Radius of Action	910nm at 22.5kts. 2720nm at 14kts.	910nm at 23.2kts. 3280nm at 14kts.
Complement	443	427

Cost per ship

	13,450,000 kroner (£6,725,000; US $33,515,000)	14,202,000 kroner (£7,101,000; US $35,505,000)

Note:

Bofors (the armament manufacturer), Götaverken and Kockums made claims for extra compensation for their losses incurred by the three ships' construction. The courts, in 1923, awarded:

Bofors	about £16,700, US $ 83,500
Götaverken	£45,000, US $225,000
Kockums	£64,650, US $323,250

Notes

[1] In 1866, the Minister for the Navy recommended that the service be divided into two separate forces, the Royal Navy and the Royal Skerries Artillery. The new force was responsible for the defence of the inner waters and fixed defences. Its fleet comprised four 250-ton monitors [armed with one 24cm (9.5in) gun, and able to pass through the Göta canal system, having a speed under steam of 6kts and 1.5kts when operated by hand-cranked propeller] and sailing gunboats. Its officers had to wear exotic uniforms including a shako! The force became part of the Navy again in 1871.

Sources: G Grandin, *Amiralitets Historia*, Vol 3 (Malmö 1977); G Halldin, *Svenskt Skepps Byggeri* (Malmö 1963).

[2] In 1902, a prelate and politician, P Waldenström, attacked King Oscar II in the press for christening *Ära* (Honour) with a bottle of champagne. Waldenström held christening a ship was sacrilege. He caused such a furore that to avoid upsetting the feelings of the religious, the christening of crown-owned ships with wine or water ceased and has never resumed.
Source: J Wedin, *Amiralitets Historia*, Vol IV (Malmö 1980).

[3] Parts of the Swedish Baltic and west coast skerries are shown as blank spaces on published charts. These are defence areas, prohibited to all shipping, that contain passages known only to Swedish naval officers.

[4] Swedish kings attended cabinet meetings having two votes until 1975. The practice continues in Norway.

[5] Sven Hedin's pamphlet's opening sentence read 'Like a heavy darkening fog in the dark days of fall, awareness of an insidious worry is spreading over Sweden . . . In 1809, we lost Finland, in 1905, Norway. Now it's Sweden's turn. It concerns our people, our freedom . . . our dear old Sweden, our farms, fields, villages, and our cities . . . Japan has thwarted Russia's drive in the Pacific – Russia's desire for an ice-free port would be to open a corridor across Northern Sweden and Norway, the latter too weak to resist.'
George Kish, *The Life of Sven Hedin* (Ann Arbor 1984).

[6] Sven Hedin wrote the speech Gustaf V delivered in the palace yard to the farmers and students. The King promised Sweden's defences would be increased.

[7] A retired warrant officer owned the land needed by the royal dockyard for the new ship. When asked the price, he replied if the Crown wanted the land to increase the nation's naval defence, it would cost nothing.

[8] The Swedish Women's Defence League gave the ship a silk ensign with a box made from the mainmast of the old frigate *Vanadis*, the second Swedish naval vessel to sail round the world.

[9] The Naval Material Board had difficulties with Bofors about the inspection and testing of the 28.3cm guns. Its staff was familiar with French practice but had little knowledge of the British standards used by Bofors.

[10] Source: Cdr S Olow, RSWN (ret).

[11] Source: Cdr C Fredholm, RSWN (ret).

[12] Source: the late Captain M Hamar, RSWN.

[13] Sweden, until 1948, regarded any foreign occupation of the Åland islands to be 'a pistol pointed at the heart of Sweden'. Although the islanders wished to join Sweden, Finland maintained the islands were an integral part of its territory. The dispute was referred to the League of Nations for settlement, and its decision favoured Finland, which agreed, however, that Swedish would be the island's official language.
(Sources: W R Mead, *The Åland Islands* (London 1975); S Carlson, *Svensk Historia* (Stockholm 1970); *Svenska Flottans Historia*, Vol 3 (Malmö 1945).

[14] F H Chapman 1721–1808 determined that the best angle to turn a ship quickly in practice is 35 degrees having regard to the effects of the line of flow.

[15] Source: a Swedish naval officer who was part of *Drottning Victoria*'s complement. In 1941 *Ilmarinen* hit a mine off the island of Ösel, capsized and sank in seven minutes with the loss of 271 men.

[16] The late Admiral S Hson Ericson, *Klart Skepp* (Stockholm 1949).

Sources

Naval Defence Policies and Plans
A Berge, *Sakkunskap och politisk rationalitet* (Stockholm 1987).
J Olofsson, *Försvaret till Sjöss* (Stockholm 1984).
B Steckzen, *Klart Skepp* (Stockholm 1949).
A Sandström, *Pansarfartyg at Sveriges Flotta* (Borås 1984).
B Åhlund, *Från Vanmakt till Sjömakt* (Stockholm 1989).
Y Schoerner, *Svenska Flottans Historia*, Vol 3 (Stockholm 1945).

The Politics
(Manuscript)
Chief of Naval Staff's Memo of 9 January 1907, Royal Military Records Office

(Published)
S Carlsson, *Svensk Historia* (Stockholm 1961).
O Lybeck, *Svenska Flottans Historia*, Vol 3 (Malmö, 1945).
A Sandström, *op cit*.
F D Scott, *Sweden: the Nation's History* (Minneapolis 1977).
B Steckzen, *op cit*.
A Åberg, *Svenksa Historia* (Stockholm 1978).

The Construction
(Published)
G Halldin, *Svenskt Skepps Byggeri* (Malmö 1963).
G Halldin, *Klart Skepp* (Stockholm 1949).
I S Hult, *Klart Skepp* (Stockholm 1949).
F Wedin, *Amiralitets Kollegiets Historia* (Malmö 1980).
Y Schoerner, *Svenska Flottans Historia*, Vol 3 (Malmö 1945).

(Unpublished)
Bullivant's Offer re Anti-Torpedo Nets, Royal Military Records Office.

The Machinery
(Published)
I S Hult, *op cit*.
G Halldin, *Svensk Skepps Byggeri*.

(Unpublished)
K M F Skepps Bygnads Rapport 339–341, 1921 and 1922.

The Armament
M Hammar, *Klart Skepp* (Stockholm 1949).
F Wedin, *op cit*.

Tactical Use
H Hammar, *op cit*.
I S Hult, *op cit*.
A Holmquist, *Flottans Beredskap, 1938–1940* (Stockholm 1972).
S Ekman, *Stormakts Tryck – S* (Stockholm 1986).
Små Stats Politik
J Oloffsen, *Försvaret till Sjöss* (Stockholm 1984).
Svenska Flottans Historia, Vol 3 (Malmö 1945).

Careers
S Carlson, *op cit*.
S H Ericson, *Knopar, på Logg – Linan* (Stockholm 1966).
I Hult and B Jacobson, *Klart Skepp* (Stockholm 1949).
Svenska Flottans Historia, Vol 3 (Malmö 1945).

AFTER THE DREADNOUGHT

The genesis of *Dreadnought*, authorised in 1905–06 and completed in 1907, and of her battlecruiser companions, the *Invincibles*, is well-known, but the story behind her immediate successors, the 'First Generation' dreadnought battleships and battlecruisers, has suffered comparative neglect. They have had a bad press, and, in any case, have been regarded as simply *Dreadnoughts* and *Invincibles* Mks II, III and IV. In fact, the story is much more complex and looks simpler and more logical in retrospect than it was at the time. Keith McBride explains.

THE course of events was much affected by politics and economics; warships are, in the last resort, political instruments. For most of the period since the Naval Defence Act of 1889, Conservative governments had been in power. The brief Liberal government of 1892–95 had continued a policy of intense naval construction, and Gladstone's long and distinguished career had ended with him being forced out by his colleagues over the Spencer Programme of 1893 onward. The Conservatives had extended their term in power in the 'khaki election' of 1900 and could, in theory, go on until 1907 before the next General Election. In practice, governments normally timed elections for the sixth year. The *Dreadnought/Invincible* programme of 1905–06 was authorized a year before this.

Balfour, the Prime Minister, chose to hold on until almost the last moment, against his colleagues' advice, and the election of January 1906 resulted in a famous Liberal victory. The 1906–07 Naval Estimates were due to come before Parliament in March 1906, and the planning for them had already been done. In view of the time element, the new government accepted their predecessors' immediate plans, including the authorization of three more dreadnoughts, but were not prepared to commit themselves to four big ships a year for future years. Furthermore, a vicious economic slump set in during 1906, discouraging expenditure, causing distress, strikes and riots in many countries, and giving added bite to the First World War when it came.

The Bellerophon Class

The three 1906–07 ships, the *Bellerophon*s, were, in fact, a close development of *Dreadnought*, but they might have been very different. In their 'Cover' are details of 'X4', a 22,000-ton project of December 1905, carrying *Dread-*nought's ten 12in guns, a mixed 4in and 12pdr anti-torpedo armament, and having a speed of 25 knots. She appears to represent the First Sea Lord, Sir John Fisher's ideal of the all-conquering battlecruiser. Presumably she proved either too costly or impracticable, and vanished from the papers without further trace. The 4in guns reflect tests against the old destroyer *Skate*, which showed the 4in to be the smallest effective stopper of torpedo craft.

The ships actually built were less ambitious; they were designed, like *Dreadnought*, by J H Narbeth. The 12pdrs disappeared, being replaced by sixteen 4in (the *Invincibles* were caught in time, and the same change was made in them), while rig and armour were considerably altered. Two high tripod masts were fitted, the foremost being ahead of the fore funnel, thus avoiding the smoke interference experienced by *Dreadnought*, whose smoke was supposed to pass under the fore control top and above the after one. The new arrangement was better for radio, too. The side armour was thinned from 11in to 10in, probably reflecting experience in the Russo–Japanese War, where, it is believed, no armour thicker than 6in was pierced. The barbettes were thinned similarly, to 10in on the sides and to 5in 'amidships', *ie* on the fore and aft sectors. Below the level of the main belt, they were reduced from 4in to 3in. The internal magazine bulkheads were reduced from 2in to 1½/1in; in compensation, the turret roofs and the bow and stern armour were thickened and internal anti-torpedo armour was provided for the machinery spaces. These changes suggest concern over descending – not yet 'plunging' – shell at long ranges. The result was a slight increase in displacement. As *Dreadnought*'s machinery was repeated, there was a nominal reduction of ¼kt in speed, which was hardly noticeable, and coal supply was slightly less.

It is interesting to note that the US Naval Attaché asked for details of *Bellerophon*'s armour; these were supplied.

Table 1. *Dreadnought Battleships And Projects 1904–9*

	Dreadnought	*'X4'*	*Bellerophon*	*'F'*	*St Vincent*	*Neptune* ('K2')	*Hercules* ('K5')
LBP (ft)	490	580	490	500	500	510	510
LOA (ft)	526	623		?	536	545	546
Breadth Ext (ft–in)	82	83	82	83–6	84	85	85
NLD							
fore perp	26–6	27–6	27	27 (mean)	27	27	27
aft		27–6	27		27	27	27
Disp NLD (tons)							
('Legend')	17,900	22,500	18,600	19,700	19,250	19,900	20,000
Sinkage							
(tons per inch)	70		70		73	76	76
Freeboard NLD (ft–in)							
fore	28	30	28	30	28	28	28
min	16–6	23 Amid	16–6		16–6	16–6	16–6
aft	18	17	18	17–2	18	18	17–6
Deep load							
draught (full							
bunkers & OF)	31				31	31	31
Depth Amid	43	50–6	43–6		43–6	43–6	43–6
Axial gun height							
fore	31–6	32	31–6	33	31–9	31–9	31–6
amid	22–6	29	22–6	22	23–3	23–3	23–0
'X' turret					23–3	29–3	31–6
'Y' turret	23	29	23	29	23–3	21–3	22–0
SHP	23,000	45,000	23,000	25,000	24,500	25,000	25,000
Measured mile speed							
NLD	21	25	20.75	21	21	21	21
NLD Coal (tons)	900	1000	900	900	900	900	900
Bunker max (tons)	2700	3000+	2700	?	3000	2900	3000
Oil max (tons)	1000	1000+	800		900	800	800
Complement							
(private ship)	770		780		724	697	708
Armament	10–12in Mk X	10–12in Mk X	10–12in Mk X	10–12in Mk XI	10–12in Mk XI	10–12in Mk XI	10–12in Mk XI
(rounds per gun)		80	80	80			80
	24–12pdr (300)	8–4in (200) 18–12pdr/8cwt (300)	16–4in	16–4in	20–4in BL (200)	16–4in BL (150)	16–4in BL (164)
Torpedo tubes	4–18in	3ft	3–18in	3–18in	3–18in	3–18in	3–21in
(torpedoes)					(9 beam, 5 stern)	(9 beam, 5 stern)	(7 beam, 6 stern)
Armour (in)							
Side fwd	6	6	6/7	2	7/2½	7/2½	7
Side amid	11/8/7	11	10	10	10	10/8	11/8
Bulkheads	11/8	?	8	8			
Side aft	6/5/4	5	5		2½	2½	Nil
Side height	+8½ft (11)	+8ft	+8½		+8½ft	+8½ft	+8½ft
above and below							
waterline at NLD	+4ft/−2ft	−5ft/−5ft	−5ft	−5ft	−5ft	−5ft	−5ft
Height of							
protective deck	?	+2ft			+2ft/−5ft	+2ft	+2ft
Barbettes	11/8	11/4		8	9/5	9/5	11–4
Turret faces	11	11		11	11	11	11
CT fwd	11	11	11/8/3	11/8	11/8/3	11	11
aft	8			1½		1½	3
Signal tower		8		3		3	11
Communication tube							
fwd	5	5	5	5	5	5	5
aft	4	4	4	4	4	nil	3
Machinery		2/1½	2/1½	2/1½	2/1½	2/1½	Nil

Table 1. *DREADNOUGHT BATTLESHIPS AND PROJECTS 1904–9 (Continued)*

	Dreadnought	'X4'	Bellerophon	'F'	St Vincent	Neptune	Hercules
Magazines/shell rooms	3/2		3/2/1	3	1/2/3	1/3	1/3
Uptakes/vents					1½/1	1/1½	1/1½
Upper deck					Nil	Nil	Nil
Main deck ends		¾ all	¾	1½ fwd	1½/¼	1¼	1½
Middle deck	1¾/2¾	1¾/2¾/4	1¾/4	?	1¾	1¾	1¾
Lower deck, fwd	1½/4	1½	1½/2/3	?	1½	1½	2½/1¾
aft	1½/4	1½	8	?	3	3	4/3
Upper part of belt	8	8					
WEIGHTS (tons)							
Water (10 days)	60				63	63	64
Provisions (4 weeks)	40				40	40	41
Officers' stores & slops	42				42	42	43
Men and effects	82				90	90	92
Running total	(224)				(235)	(235)	(240)
Masts & rigging	113				145	147	102
Anchors & cables	115				117	121	121
Boats	48				50	50	50
WO stores (4 months)	90				90	90	90
Torpedo nets	60				45	47	47
Group total	(426)				(445)	(455)	410)
Running total	(650)	(750)	(688)	(700)	(680)	(690)	(650)
Armament	3100	3210	3140	3300	3520	3570	3610
Machinery	2050	3550	2056	2250	2200	2190	2300
Legend (NLD) coal	900	1000	900	900	900	900	900
Armour & backing	5000	6540	5389	5670	5500	5700	5490
Hull	6100	7350	6245	6780	6350	6750	6950
Margin	100	100	100	100	100	100	100
Total	17,900	22,500	18,518	19,700	19,250	19,900	20,000
Cost	£1,813,100		£1,765,000	£1,950,000	£1,820,000	£1,890,000	£1,860,000

Notes

NLD = Normal load draught, sometimes called Navy List draught or Legend.

The Controller noted that, although they were more secretive than in the past, the Americans always gave a fair exchange of information.

The Way Ahead – 1906

Technical progress was rapid on many fronts; gun ranges in particular were increasing in parallel with progress in fire control and torpedoes. In 1905, 6000yds was thought of as the practical limit of accurate gunnery, with 9000yds being dreamed of. Fire control was succeeding the era of the hyper-trained gunlayer, as that had succeeded the period of fighting tops, ramming and boarding. From the gunnery standpoint, there seemed to be three ways ahead: more guns of existing type, longer guns or guns of larger calibre.

The 'bigger gun' idea led to the production of designs to incorporate a revived and much longer 13.5in gun, firing 1250lb shell like its 1889 predecessor, but with cordite propellent. Both 45- and 50-calibre versions were considered. In November 1906, sketch designs for ships with eight guns in four turrets following the *Invincible* layout, were produced, but rejected as the guns' ranges exceeded that of practical fire control, 'Unless Mr Pollen's apparatus proves efficient'. Despite this decision, work on the 13.5in apparently continued.

'More guns' led to the development of the triple 12in turret, in both 45- and 50-calibre forms; the first details date from November 1905. The 50-calibre version required a 29ft diameter roller path against 28ft or 28½ft for the shorter gun. Everywhere except in America, it was taken for granted that superfiring was impracticable because of blast effects, ruling out one way of carrying more turrets. To get round this, the British armament firms even went beyond the infamous double-decker turrets of USS *Kentucky* and *Georgia*. Their masterpiece was a double-decker with five 12in, two up and three

Bellerophon *about 1916. The overall similarity to*
Dreadnought *is disguised by wartime additions to the*
superstructure. (All uncredited photos CMP)

St Vincent *and her 12in sisters lying in Scapa Flow.*
(NMM)

down. It was offered to Russia and Japan in 1908, but wisely rejected. The hull stresses would surely have been tremendous. To be fair, it should be compared with a superfiring pair of a triple and a twin turret. It is (just) possible to imagine *Cavour*s with such turrets fore and aft; as for USS *Nevada*, the imagination boggles.

Though the quintuple remained on paper, the triple found considerable favour.[1] For 1907–08, an early proposal was for one in 'X' position in the proto-*St Vincent*, making an 11-gun main armament. A number of 'J' designs were considered in late 1906. 'J7', with four triples on the centreline, foreshadowed the Russian dreadnoughts and *Dante Alighieri*. At what the Controller reported as 'a lengthy discussion' by the Board of Admiralty in December, the struggle was between 'J6', with one triple forward, one amidships and one aft, and 'F', with triples fore and aft, and twins *en echelon* amidships, all with 50-calibre 12in ('J1' to 'J5' were much like her). The latter was victorious, on the ground of her better end-on fire. Broadside fire had priority, but the 'J's were felt to overemphasize it. At the same time, a series of super-*Invincible* 12in 50-calibre battlecruisers were considered, most with 9in or 10in side armour and some of up to 21,400 tons. One of these was selected, with 'F', early in 1907, and design work on them went ahead for several months.

The St Vincent *class were generally similar to the proceeding* Bellerophon*s but introduced the 50-calibre 12in guns. This is* Vanguard *as completed.* (NMM)

The Mark XI – The Longer Gun

Apart from being 5ft – five calibres – longer, the 50-calibre 12in, designated the Mk XI, weighed 66½ tons against the 58-ton 45-calibre Mk X. It used a heavier and longer charge – 270lb against 260lb – throwing the same 850lb shell at a muzzle velocity of 2850 feet per second, against 2735. The 50-calibre 12in BXI twin turret required a 24½ft diameter roller path against 23½ft for the 45-calibre BVIII. The gun gained a reputation for rapid wear and poor shooting, causing opinion to shift towards the 13.5in, with its lower muzzle velocity and a heavier shell, in a similar-sized mounting.[1]

The Battlecruisers That Never Were

Designations given to the battlecruiser studies varied, but one set of sketch designs, put to the DNC on 20 November 1906, included 'A', 'B' and 'C', all 550ft between perpendiculars against *Invincible*'s 530ft, and with the echeloned turrets amidships spaced out to permit cross-deck fire. Eight 45-calibre 12in, as in *Invincible*, were carried; the secondary armament was to be either twenty 12pdr with 300rpg or sixteen 4in QF with 100. In 'B' and 'C', 200ft of the side belt was to be 9in and 'C' was to have 4in stern armour as well – *Invincible*, not yet completed, had none. The speed of 'A' and 'B' was to be 24½kts, 'C's 24¼kts, all on the same 41,000shp as the earlier ship. Displacements, including 100-ton margin, were 17,250 for *Invincible*, 18,100 for 'A', 18,500 for 'B' and 18,900 for 'C'.

H.M.S VANGUARD.

Table 2. BATTLECRUISER PROJECTS 1906–8

	Invincible	'A'	'B'	'C'	'A'	'B'	'D'	'E'	Indefatigable
Date submitted		20 Nov	20 Nov	20 Nov	21 Nov	21 Nov	22 Nov	6 Dec	Mar 1908
LBP (ft)	530	550	550	550	560	560	565	565	555
Breadth (ft)	78½	79	79½	80	81	81	81	83	80½/80
NLD fwd (ft)	25	25	25	25	?	?	25	?	25–1
aft (ft)	27	27	27	27	?	?	?	?	26¾
mean	26	26¼	26½	26¾	?	?	27	27	26½
Legend disp (tons)	17,250	18,100	18,500	18,900	19,700	19,900	20,700	21,400	18,750
Sinkage (tons per inch)	69.8	?	?	?	?	?	?	?	75
Freeboard NLD (ft)									
fwd	30	32	32	32	33	33	30	30	32
aft	22	21	21	21	22	22	22	21	21
mean	17⅙	28	28	28	29	29	28	29	28
SHP	41,000	41,000	41,000	41,000	41,000	41,000	43,000	48,000	43,000
Speed, measured mile natural draught NLD	25	24½	24½	24¼	24	24	24	25	25
NLD coal (tons)	1000	1000	1000	1000	1000	1000	1000	1000	1000
Bunker max (tons)	3000	3000	3000	3000	3000	3000	3000	3300	3000
Armament	8–12in/45	8–12in/45	8–12in/45	8–12in/45	8–12in/50	8–12in/50	8–12in/50	8–12in/50	8–12in/45
(rounds per gun)	(80)	(80)	(80)	(80)	(80)	(80)	(80)	(80)	(80)
	20–12pdr (300rpg) or 16–4in (100)								
Torpedo tubes	5–18in	5–18in	5–18in	5–18in	5–18in	5–18in	5–18in	5–18in	3–18in

ARMOUR

	Invincible	'A'	'B'	'C'	'A'	'B'	'D'	'E'	Indefatigable
Side height above and below waterline at NLD	+7¼ft/−4ft	+7¼ft/−4ft	+7¼/−4	+7¼ft/−4ft	+7¼ft/−4ft	+7¼ft/−4ft	+7¼ft/−4ft	+7¼ft/−4ft	+7ft/−4ft
Protective deck height at NLD	+1ft/−4ft	+1ft/−4ft	+1ft/−4ft	+1ft/−4ft	+1ft/−4ft	+1ft/−4ft	+1ft/−4ft	+1ft/−4ft	+1½ft/−4ft
Side (* 9in over 200ft of length)	6/4	6/4	9*/6/4	9*/6/4	9*/6/4	10/6/4	10/8	9	6
Turrets	7	?	?	?	?	?	7	7	7
Stern	Nil	Nil	Nil	4	6/4	6/4	4	1½	2½
Splinter protection	2	2	2	2	2	2	?	2	?
CT	10/6	10/6	10/6	10/6	10/6	10/6	?	10/6	10/6
CT tube	4/3	4/3	4/3	4/3	4/3	4/3	?	4/3	+
Signal tower	3	3	3	3	3	3	?	?	4/3
Magazine	2½	2½	2½	2½	2½	2½	2½	3	2½
Armoured decks main fwd	¾	¾	¾	¾	¾	¾	?	1½	1/2/3
Under fwd & mid barbettes, lower CT crowns	1/2	1/2	1/2	1/2	1/2	1/2	?	1/2	1/2/3
Lower deck (flat/slopes) fwd	1½/1	1½/1	1½/1	1½/1	1½/1	1½/1	1½/1	1½/2½	1½/2½
amid	1½/1½	1½/1½	1½/1½	1½/1½	1½/2	1½/2	1½/2	1/2	1½/2
lower	2½	?	?	?	1½/2/2½	1½/2/2½	1½/2/2½	1/1½/2	1/1½/2

Table 2.   *BATTLECRUISER PROJECTS 1906–8 (Continued)*

	Invincible	'A'	'B'	'C'	'A'	'B'	'D'	'E'	Indefatigable
Date submitted		20 Nov	20 Nov	20 Nov	21 Nov	21 Nov	22 Nov	6 Dec	Mar 1908
WEIGHTS (tons)									
Water (10 days)	70								
Provisions (4 weeks)	40								
Officers' stores & slops	45								
Men and effects	90								
Masts & rigging	130								
Anchors & cables	115								
Boats	55								
WO stores	65								
Torpedo nets	50								
Group total	(600)	(680)	(700)	(700)	(720)	(720)	?	(720)	(680)
Armament	2440	2600	2600	2600	2780?	2780?	?	2780	2540
Machinery (inc 90 eng stores)	3300+	3420	3420	3420	3450	3450	3500	4100	3650
Legend Coal	1000	1000	1000	1000	1000	1000	1000	1000	1000
Armour/ Backing	3460	3600	3860	4180	4500	4650	5150	5200	3800
Hull (inc barbette framing)	6200	6700	6820	6900	7150	7200	7450	7500	6980
Margin	100	100	100	100	100	100	100	100	100
Legend disp	17,250	18,100	18,500	18,900	19,700	19,900	20,700	21,400	18,750

Note:

Some figures, especiailly for 'D' and for certain freeboards, seem doubtful.

Neptune *as completed with flying bridges over the midship's turrets.* (NMM)

These studies were sent back to be adapted for a longer side patch of 9in armour and 50-calibre 12in guns, and the next group were sent to the DNC on the 21st. This time there were two, 'A' and 'B', 560ft long and 81ft in beam, draught being unaltered. 'A' was of 19,700 tons, with 9in side armour, while 'B' had 10in and was of 19,900 tons. Powerplant remained the same and speed fell off to 24kts. Armament weight went up by 240 tons, and armour by over 1000 tons.

Yet another study appeared on the 22nd: 'D' of 20,700 tons and 565ft length, with 10in and 8in side armour and 24kts speed. Apparently the loss of speed was considered unacceptable, because in December, 'Battlecruiser E' appeared, prepared in accordance with the decisions at the meeting of 22 November. 'E' was as long as 'D' but 2ft wider, and power was boosted to 48,000shp to regain a speed of 25kts. Her displacement was 21,400, 24 per cent larger than *Invincible*. Armour, however, was thinned to 9in, still much more than in the 1905–06 projects. 'E' and battleship 'F' were formally accepted by the Board of Admiralty at a meeting of 12 February 1907.

'F' – Triple and Echelon Turrets

'F' was of 19,700 tons, with ten 50-calibre 12in guns disposed in triples fore and aft and twins *en echelon* amidships, giving a ten-gun broadside. Her armour was on the *Bellerophon* scale; its layout was changed during development, and she was to steam at 21kts on first 24,250shp and later 25,000shp. Cost was forecast as £1.95 million. The only illustration I have found is a boat stowage plan, which is very like *Neptune*, and only shows part of the ship.

The St Vincent Class

In July 1907, there was an abrupt change. The Board rejected triple turrets and, very late in the annual design and building cycle, ordered a modified *Bellerophon* with 12in 50-calibre guns to be designed, the task falling on E N Mooney and A M Worthington. The battlecruiser was cancelled entirely. Instructions were given that the 'F'

drawings were to be preserved with careful notes, in case they should be wanted again.

The new design, which became *St Vincent*, was enlarged to 19,250 tons to incorporate the bigger barbettes, power was increased to 24,500shp to make up any loss of speed, and the 4in battery was increased to eighteen, some on turret tops, to give adequate coverage. Armour was as in the *Bellerophons*, but the belt extended more fore and aft, past the end magazines, which had to be enlarged to take the bigger charges required by the new gun.

Deck armour and the forward bulkhead were improved. Three ships were included in the 1907–08 programme, though *Vanguard* was delayed pending the outcome of the Hague Conference.

1908–09, Low Water Mark – Neptune and Indefatigable

For 1908–09, funds were shorter than ever and there was strong opposition to the armaments race. Critics pointed out that no other country yet had a dreadnought or battlecruiser in service – the first German one appeared in 1910. Hence, only two ships were authorized. Design 'K1' had been developed by Mooney and Worthington, and was in a sense 'F' with three twin turrets on the centreline instead of two triples. With the two echelon turrets, they at last gave a full ten-gun broadside, at the cost of much blast damage. For the first time, a superfiring turret was included (aft), but only as a way of getting it in on a limited length. The Admiralty still used sighting hoods like prompt boxes on the turret roofs, which were very exposed to blast. Stops were fitted to the turret to prevent axial fire.

On being shown 'K1', Reginald McKenna, the new First Lord, minuted, 'Approved subject to being under

The final 12in ships to join the fleet (excepting the commandeered Agincourt) *were the battlecruisers* Australia *and* New Zealand *in 1912–13.* Australia *is seen here passing Nelson's* Victory *in Portsmouth Harbour.* (Courtesy of Vic Jeffery)

The last in the line of 12in dreadnoughts, Hercules *completed in August 1911. The after turrets were superfiring but the main mast was abolished and the fore was once again positioned abaft the funnel.*

20,000 tons'. 'K1' was therefore shortened by 10ft, one bulkhead cut out of the engine rooms, and the main deck amidships thinned from 1½in to 1¼in, becoming 'K2', of 19,900 tons – at least on paper. She was a handsome ship, and the first battleship to have cruising turbines and to carry a director. The Navy was a bit ruffled by Reginald McKenna at first, though they came to appreciate his virtues.

One battlecruiser, the first since 1905–06, was authorized in the same year, design 'A', which became *Indefatigable* (undoubtedly named after Sir Edward Pellew's giant frigate). She was designed by W T Davis, and showed the effects of shortage of money. As far as can be determined, she followed the layout of the unbuilt 1906–08 ships, with her turrets spaced out to give a true eight-gun broadside, but her 12in were the old 45-calibre Mk Xs, her side armour was 6in, as in *Invincible* (though there was no 4in) and she was of only 18,750 tons.

In one way the slump helped; it enabled the Admiralty to drive prices down. *Neptune* was £87 a ton, the cheapest British battleship ever, and *Indefatigable* £82, making her £200,000 cheaper than the smaller *Invincible*. In the same year the Germans laid down four ships, which led to some unease; Austria and Italy were starting to build dreadnoughts, too. The Admiralty therefore planned four for 1909–10.

The Colossus Class – The last 12in Dreadnoughts

The four ships were to include a new battleship and battlecruiser with what was described as '12in "A" guns' – the 45-calibre 13.5in, now ready for service – and two modified *Neptunes* (again by Mooney and Worthington) to design 'K5'. (I do not know what 'K3' and 'K4' were like, or why 12in ships were planned alongside 13.5in.)

Perhaps because the Germans had gone to 12in guns in their 1908 *Helgolands*, armour policy was changed. The side and the outer halves of the echelon barbettes were thickened to 11in, the bow and stern armour and the internal screens to the machinery spaces being removed to compensate. The lower deck was thickened fore and aft, which cost a lot of weight. The machinery spaces were better subdivided, and the rig considerably changed. The mainmast was abolished and the foremast again set aft of the fore funnel, bringing back the smoke problem. The fore and aft positions of the echelon turrets were reversed. The hydraulic turret machinery was worked by swashplate engines, which gave smoother movement. Considerable internal redesign had to be done at the last moment, to get in the new 21in torpedoes and their tubes.

Most of these changes were due to Admiral Jellicoe, by now Controller. He was deeply impressed by the new torpedo, considering it as a British 'first', giving the possibility of getting in a devastating opening blow, from beyond the range of accurate gunfire – an idea which recurs in his memorandum on tactical policy of 17 October 1914.

The two 'K5's were named *Hercules* and *Colossus*. With these ships, and the slightly modified *Indefatigables*, *Australia* and *New Zealand* of 1910, the development of the British 12in dreadnought came to an end. (*Agincourt* was, in the nicest possible sense, *sui generis*.) They were built down to a price, and it showed. None had an upper belt, such as was then thought necessary, and their armour was kept down by the demands of 21kts speed and limited displacement. All were good sea-boats, their machinery was good and they steamed well. They were

Australia *passing through the Suez Canal in 1919.*
(Courtesy of Vic Jeffery)

never really tried by gunfire, which was probably
fortunate. The German and American ships were probably better, though their navies were not under the same
pressure to produce large numbers of ships.

As they were commissioned, they joined the Home
Fleet, which was to become the Grand Fleet. Initially,
they formed the 1st Battle Squadron, *Neptune* being Fleet
Flagship for a long time. However, she was succeeded by
Iron Duke as soon as the latter commissioned.

War Experience

All nine battleships and two *Indefatigable*s were present
at Jutland, and the *Colossus*[2] in particular did some very
good shooting, which suggests that the 12in Mk XI
50-calibre gun was better than its reputation. She was the
only Grand Fleet battleship to be hit by gunfire, suffering
two hits in the superstructure. The shells set off some 4in
ammunition boxes, but these vented as they had been
designed to, and there was no explosion. The 6in
protection of the German secondary batteries was much
praised, but in several cases this was pierced, with
devastating results. The loss of *Indefatigable*, two other
battlecruisers and two armoured cruisers to explosions
showed the vulnerability of British ships, though this was
due more to the volatility of British cordite than to design

faults, as was emphasized by the later loss of *Vanguard*.
Had the unbuilt battlecruisers been present instead, they
would have had the same menace within them.

It may be noted that British deck protection was much
the same as that of German ships, which suggests that
long ranges did not come as a complete surprise to British
designers. However, in general, it looks as if the planners
and designers did not see quite far enough ahead. At
Jutland, 4in proved ineffective against daylight destroyer
attacks from about 8000yds. By 1918, all these ships were
obsolete, showing the rapid and costly pace of development, which was exceeding the resources of all but the
super-powers of the day. Many were scrapped before the
1921 Washington Treaty.

Notes
[1] There was an illustrated article on the 50-calibre triple in the
1913 *Brassey's Naval Annual* (reprinted 1970).
[2] This may have helped her Captain, A D P R Pound, on the way
to becoming First Sea Lord. Midshipman 'Mr Johnson' of the
Collingwood ascended the throne in 1936.

Sources
ADM 138/251 & 251A: *Indefatigable* Ship Covers.
ADM 138/255/230 'Battlecruiser E' & 'Battleship F' Cover.
ADM 138/324/224 *Australia & New Zealand.*
ADM 138/325/224A *Indefatigable, Australia & New Zealand.*
ADM 138/319/225 E & F.
ADM 116/1012 & 1013A: Warship Design 1905–11.

THE LE HARDI CLASS

The inter-war French navy is most closely associated with large and spectacular super-destroyers or *contre torpilleurs*. The smaller *torpilleurs d'escadre* were both fewer in number and technically less impressive. John Jordan looks at the change in French thinking on destroyers in the early 1930s that produced the moderate-sized *Le Hardi* class.

I N contrast to the other major participants in the First World War, France laid down no vessels in the destroyer/torpedo-boat category after the outbreak of hostilities, and so desperate was the shortage of shipyard capacity that the *Marine Nationale* resorted to the expedient of ordering twelve *Kaba* type destroyers 'off the shelf' from Japan in 1917.

The result of this hiatus in construction was that whereas Britain and the United States ended the war with large numbers of modern flotilla craft in service and on the building ways, the *Marine Nationale* needed a crash programme of construction to provide escorts for its existing battle fleet of seven dreadnoughts. Thus twelve *torpilleurs d'escadre* of the *Bourrasque* class were authorized in 1922, the new vessels being completed between 1926 and 1928. They were large, three-funnelled ships with a heavy gun armament comprising four single 130mm (5.1in) Model 1919 guns, and a torpedo armament of six 550mm (21.7in) in two triple banks. They were known in the *Marine Nationale* as the *1500 tonnes*.

The *Bourrasque* class was quickly followed by the fourteen-strong *L'Adroit* class (also designated *1500 tonnes*), authorized in three separate batches in 1924 (six ships), 1925 (four) and 1926 (four). The design was fixed and approved fully two years before the first of the *Bourrasque*s entered service and, apart from the substitution of the improved 130mm Model 1924 for the original guns, the *torpilleurs d'escadre* of the second series were little modified.

Unfortunately the *1500 tonnes* design proved defective in a number of respects. Too much had been attempted on the displacement; metacentric height was inadequate, with resulting stability problems. Shortly after completion the ships of the first series had the height of their funnels reduced by 1.5m (5ft) in order both to save topweight and to reduce their distinctive silhouette. The layout of the fuel tanks and the proximity to the bow of the forward 130mm gun mountings combined to concentrate weight forward, and the relatively fine lines and light construction of the bow section proved inadequate to cope with these stresses, with the result that individual ships suffered structural damage in heavy seas.

Table 1. *TWO DESIGNS WHICH INFLUENCED THE LE HARDI CLASS*

	Navigatori (Italy)	*'Special Type' (Japan)*
Laid down:	1927–28	1926–30
Completed:	1929–31	1928–32
Displacement:*	1654t standard	1750t standard
	2010t full load	2057t trials
Dimensions:	107.7m oa × 10.2m × 3.4m	118.4m oa × 10.4m × 3.2m
	353ft 4in × 33ft 5in × 11ft 2in	388ft 6in × 34ft 1in × 10ft 6in
Machinery:	4 boilers; 2-shaft	4 boilers; 2-shaft
	geared steam turbines	geared steam turbines
	50,000shp = 38kts	50,000shp = 38kts
Oil fuel:	630t	500t
Armament:	3 twin 120mm (4.7in)/50	3 twin 127mm (5in)/50
	2 single 40mm, 2 twin 13.2mm AA	2 single 13.2mm AA
	2 triple 533mm TT	3 triple 610mm TT
	2 DC throwers	18 DCs
	(54 mines)	
Complement:	173	197

* True displacement was almost certainly in excess of these figures, but they are representative of the open-source data available to the *Marine Nationale* during the early 1930s.

Trombe, *of the* 1500 tonnes *series, photographed shortly after her completion. Note the height of the bridge structure and the funnels (the latter would subsequently be shortened in order to reduce the silhouette).* (Marius Bar, 26 March 1928)

The performance of the 550mm torpedo constituted a major improvement on the earlier 450mm models, but the 130mm Model 1919 gun was less successful, and the Model 1924 had similar defects. The impressive theoretical range of 18,500m (20,250yds), at 36 degrees of elevation, was achieved at the expense of excessive height of the trunnion. The gun was therefore difficult to load at angles greater than 15 degrees, resulting in a slow rate of fire (4/5rpm for the Model 1919, 5/6rpm for the Model 1924). Moreover, in spite of the sacrifices made to enable the gun to engage targets at long range, fire control was accurate only to 10–11,000m (11–12,000yds) a single optical rangefinder with a 3m (9.8ft) base being initially provided.

The designed speed of 33kts was barely attained on trials, and in service the *1500 tonnes* had difficulty sustaining 28–29kts in formation. This problem can be attributed to French inexperience with geared turbines, which were trialled for the first time in *Enseigne Gabolde*, a torpedo boat of prewar design completed postwar as a trials ship. Endurance also proved to be much lower than anticipated, due to the high fuel consumption of the main propulsion machinery and the auxiliaries. Wartime commanders estimated maximum radius at 1500nm at 15kts, only half that designed and barely adequate for even the Mediterranean.

The New Construction Programme

Many of the defects of the *1500 tonnes* became apparent as soon as the ships entered service, although it was only in 1938 that serious concern was expressed about their

Fleuret *running her speed trials in March 1940 off Toulon. A maximum speed of 40.2kts was attained during these trials, the fastest recorded speed for any unit of the class. Note the open mounting for the after rangefinder and the absence of a protective shield around the twin 37mm Model 1933 mounting.* (Marius Bar, 20 March 1940)

stability and remedial measures undertaken, and it took wartime operations to demonstrate the full extent of their endurance problems.

Even by the early 1930s, when the last units of the *L'Adroit* class were still fitting out, the basic design was already viewed as obsolete in the light of new tactical concepts and technological developments. Following the accession of Vice-Admiral Durand-Viel to the post of Naval Chief of Staff a new generation of surface ships was being projected. The new designs would combine high speed with high-performance artillery allied to sophisticated fire control systems. The cruisers and flotilla craft would also have a much reduced silhouette in order to make them less easy to identify and to hit. In architectural terms they would therefore be very different to their predecessors.

The most important ships of the new programme were the fast battleship *Dunkerque* (authorized 1931), and the light cruisers of the *La Galissonnière* class, the first pair of which was authorized in the same year. The designed speed of the former was 29.5kts while the latter ships, which were intended to operate in conjunction with the new battleships, had a maximum speed of 31kts. The service speed of the *1500 tonnes* (28/29kts in formation) gave them a more than adequate margin over the elderly 21kt dreadnoughts of the *Courbet* and *Bretagne* classes, but was clearly insufficient if they were to keep pace with the new battle squadrons. This was highlighted in a report on the *L'Adroit* class presented in June 1932 by the *Commission Permanente des Essais de la Flotte* (CPEF),

which went on to establish the following criteria for the next series of *torpilleurs d'escadre*:

- a sustained speed of 34–35kts at normal load, in order to ensure a 3–4kt margin over the ships they would be expected to accompany
- a smaller silhouette, to be obtained by suppressing the mainmast, and by reducing freeboard, the height of the superstructures, and the number of funnels
- greater initial stability (the metacentric height of the first series had turned out at 0.36m and that of the second series 0.45m, as against a designed GM of 0.58m)
- a reinforced bow section
- improved habitability
- the ability to launch torpedoes close to the ship's axis, a distribution of tubes which would ensure coverage of all four quarters at night, and a launch system which would permit both prepared and quick-reaction firings
- replacement of tripod masts, which had been found to be subject to vibration, and a firm seating for the rangefinders, of which there should be two
- a different layout of the fuel tanks to secure less weight in the bows at full load.

These recommendations were fully accepted by the French Naval Staff, which requested the authorization of the first of the new *torpilleurs d'escadre* as part of the 1932 Programme. This request was duly approved, but it would be a further two years before detailed design work could be completed. For in contrast to the *contre-torpilleur* programme, which had been continuous and

Table 2. *LE HARDI CLASS BUILDING DATA*

Name	Builder	Laid down	Launched	In service
1932 Programme				
Le Hardi	A C Loire	20.5.36	4.5.38	6.40
1935 Programme				
Fleuret*	F C Méditerranée	18.8.36	28.7.38	7.40
Epée*	F C Gironde	15.10.36	26.10.38	7.40
1936 Programme				
Casque	F C Méditerranée	30.11.36	2.11.38	end 40
Lansquenet	F C Gironde	17.12.36	20.5.39	1941
Mameluk	A C Loire	1.1.37	18.2.39	end 40
1937 Programme				
Le Flibustier*	F C Méditerranée	11.3.38	14.12.39	
Le Corsaire*	F C Méditerranée	31.3.38	14.11.39	1941
1938 Programme				
L'Opiniâtre	F C Gironde	1.8.39		
L'Intrépide	F C Méditerranée	16.8.39	26.6.41	
Le Téméraire	F C Méditerranée	28.8.39	7.11.41	
1938 bis Programme †				
L'Aventurier	F C Gironde	4.8.39		

* On 1 April 1941 these four units were renamed in honour of *torpilleurs* of the *1500 tonnes* type lost in the spring of 1940. New names were as follows: *Foudroyant* (ex-*Fleuret*); *L'Adroit* (ex-*Epée*); *Siroco* (ex-*Le Corsaire*); *Bison* (ex-*Le Flibustier*). It was also proposed that *Lansquenet* be renamed *Cyclone*, but the change of name was never officially sanctioned.

† Five ships were to have been authorized under the 1938 *bis* Programme: *L'Aventurier*, *L'Eveillé*, *L'Alerte*, *L'Inconstant*, and *L'Espiègle*. Only *L'Aventurier* was subsequently ordered, the remaining ships being replaced by four *contre-torpilleurs* of the *Mogador* class.

Table 3. *CHARACTERISTICS OF THE LE HARDI CLASS (AS DESIGNED)*

Displacement:	1772 tons standard
	1936 tonnes normal
	2417 tonnes full load
Length:	110.70m pp, 117.20m oa (363ft 2in, 384ft 6in)
Beam:	11.10m (36ft 5in)
Draught:	4.20m full load (13ft 9in)
Complement:	41 officers, 146 men
Machinery:	Four Sural-Penhoët pressure-fired boilers, 35kg/cm^2 (500psi), 358°C
	Parsons/Rateau geared steam turbines for 58,000shp
	(66,000shp max); two shafts each with one HP turbine
	(4490rpm), one MP turbine (4490rpm), one LP turbine
	(3230rpm) and one cruise turbine (9000rpm); speed 38kts
	max
	Oil fuel 470 tonnes; 790nm at 36kts, 2760nm at 20kts
Armament:	Six 130mm (5.1in) Model 1935 semi-automatic guns in three twin
	pseudo-turrets (1020 AP shells, 60 starshell, plus 193
	practice rounds)
	Two 37mm Model 1925 semi-automatic AA guns in single
	mountings (2960 rounds), four 13.2mm Model 1929 Hotchkiss
	AA guns in twin mountings (9600 rounds)
	Seven 550mm (21.7in) torpedo tubes in one triple and two twin
	mountings
	Two racks each for six 200kg (440lb) depth charges; Ginocchio
	towed AS torpedo; Type C sweep gear
Fire Control:	Two 5m (16.4ft) rangefinders forward (one for torpedo FC), one
	5m rangefinder aft

Profile and plan views of Le Hardi *as designed. The drawings are based on the official plans approved in April 1936, shortly before the ship was laid down at Ateliers Chantiers de la Loire. Note the tentative configuration of the quad 37mm Model 1935, and the ramp for the Ginocchio ASW torpedo directly above the stern. Note also the configuration of the 130mm* pseudo-tourelles, *the twin booms for handling the ship's boats (to be replaced by cranes), and the position of the twin 13.2mm Hotchkiss AA guns.* (Author)

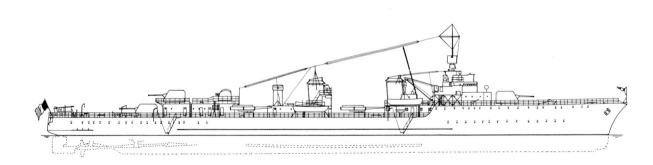

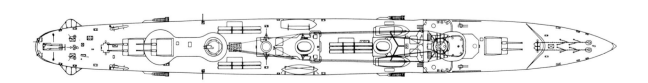

Epée *off Toulon in March 1941, shortly before she was renamed* L'Adroit. *She has the after (4m base) rangefinder in an open mounting, and two single 13.2mm Browning heavy machine-guns on the quarterdeck. She has a single depth charge 'tunnel' on the port side of the stern, and what appears to be the launching apparatus for the Ginocchio ASW torpedo to starboard. The twin davits are for handling the Type C minesweeping floats.* (Marius Bar, 4 March 1941)

developmental, with successive batches of six ships incorporating incremental improvements, *torpilleur* design had been virtually frozen since 1922, when the twelve *Bourrasques* had been authorized.

Technological advances made during this period included German-pattern quick-firing guns with horizontal sliding breeches, boilers operating at higher steam pressures allied to lightweight turbine machinery, the increasing use of welding and light alloys for superstructures, and superior fire control arrangements which combined advanced stereo rangefinders with a central transmitting station. It was desired that all of these features be incorporated in the new *torpilleurs*.

The new design also had to take into account developments abroad, as there was little point in meeting the above criteria if the resulting ships were inferior in military terms to their likely opponents. The latest destroyers to enter service with the Italian navy, the 'Navigatori', displaced 1654 tons standard and were armed with six 120mm (4.7in) guns in twin mountings. The Japanese 'Special Type' destroyers of the *Fubuki* class were even more powerfully armed, with six 127mm (5in) guns in twin mountings and three triple banks of torpedo tubes (see table).

Thus the *Le Hardi* design grew in size from an initial proposal for a vessel of 1300/1400 tons standard armed with four 130mm in twin mountings (*ie* a faster, more technologically advanced variant of the *1500 tonnes*) to a much larger type with a standard displacement of 1772 tons and six 130mm guns in twin mountings.

In terms of architecture the new *torpilleurs* would incorporate many of the features introduced by the

Inboard profile of Le Hardi, *also based on the official plans of 1936, and showing the location of the major machinery, magazine and operational spaces.* (Author)

Key:
1 130mm Magazine ('A' mounting)
2 130mm Starshell magazine ('A' mounting)
3 Navigation bridge
4 Operations room
5 Radio room
6 Radio transmissions (fwd)
7 Radio transmissions (aft)
8 FC transmitting station
9 37mm Magazine
10 130mm Magazine ('X' mounting)
11 130mm Magazine ('Y' mounting)
12 Depth charge magazine
13 Emergency steering position
14 Depth charge chutes

Le Hardi *as she appeared in December 1941. Single 25mm Hotchkiss mountings (not visible) have been fitted forward of the bridge, and the twin 13.2mm Hotchkiss mountings relocated to the quarterdeck. Single 13.2mm Brownings are fitted on platforms projecting from the sides of 'X' 130mm mounting. The Ginocchio ASW torpedo installation has been suppressed.* (Marius Bar, December 1941)

contre-torpilleurs and the *Le Fantasque* class. The latter had been authorized in 1930, and were originally to have had the distinctive four-funnel configuration of their predecessors of the *2400 tonnes* series, together with the square bridge structure and tripod masts of the latter ships. Redesigned to conform to the new principle of reduced silhouette (the 1930s equivalent of the 'stealth' characteristics currently in vogue for aircraft and surface ships), the *Le Fantasque* class were to emerge with two short, broad funnels and a low, rounded bridge structure (intended to make it difficult to assess the angle of approach) topped by revolving structures incorporating the DCT and optical rangefinders and the distinctive *mât de flèche*, the radio aerials being strung between the yardarms of the latter and outriggers projecting from the second funnel.

This configuration would be adopted for all subsequent prewar destroyer and torpedo-boat designs: the *contre-torpilleurs* of the *Mogador* class, the *torpilleurs d'escadre* of the *Le Hardi* class, and the *torpilleurs légers* of the *600 tonnes (La Melpomène)* and *1010 tonnes (Le Fier)* classes.

Armament

The 130mm/45 Model 1935 gun adopted as the main armament of the *Le Hardi* class had a German-pattern horizontal sliding breech. Unlike its dual-purpose counterpart installed as secondary armament in the *Dunkerque* class, it was housed in a low-angle mounting loadable at its maximum elevation of 30 degrees and was capable only of surface engagements.

The guns were housed in fully-enclosed twin mountings, or *pseudo-tourelles*: a single mounting on the forecastle, and two superimposed mountings aft. This arrangement facilitated the adoption of a low, streamlined bridge and reduced the stresses on the hull structure forward. The after mountings enjoyed excellent arcs, 'X' mounting being able to fire within 20 degrees of the ship's axis on forward bearings because of the suppression of the tripod mainmast of earlier designs.

In order to secure a high rate of fire much new technology was incorporated into the new 130mm mounting, including semi-automatic loading and power ramming. This was to have unfortunate results, and the complexity and fragility of the mounting was much criticised following gunnery trials and war experience (albeit limited) with the first units completed. Theoretically the 130mm Model 1935 was capable of 14/15rpm, but the power rammers were prone to breakdown and the electrical firing mechanism frequently malfunctioned, so that this figure was rarely achieved.

The provision of 1020 AP and HE shells (plus 60 starshell in a separate magazine serving the forward gun mounting) was somewhat inferior to that for British destroyers of the period (generally 200/250rpg) but substantially greater than that for the German Type 1934 destroyer, which was provided with only 120 rounds for each of its five 127mm single mountings.

In spite of the reduction in elevation maximum range remained at 19,000m (20,750yds), and the ability of the ships to engage surface targets successfully close to their maximum theoretical range was greatly enhanced by the provision of a modern fire control system comprising two stereoscopic 5m (16.4ft) base rangefinders (one of which was incorporated into the DCT). The official design drawings show the after rangefinder in an enclosed housing similar to that adopted for the *contre-torpilleurs* of the *Fantasque* and *Mogador* classes, but the first three ships entered service with a 4m (13ft) base rangefinder in a simple open mounting. For the first time in a French *torpilleur* there was a centralized transmitting station, located at main deck level close to the after 130mm mountings (see drawing).

Anti-aircraft provision was the subject of some debate. Initial proposals included two single 37mm Model 1925, then a uniform armament of four twin 13.2mm Hotchkiss, before a final decision was made in favour of the new twin 37mm Model 1933 semi-automatic mounting plus two twin 13.2mm Hotchkiss. The absence of a mainmast provided an excellent position for the twin 37mm mounting at the forward end of the after deckhouse. The magazine was adjacent to the after 130mm magazines (see drawing). The 13.2mm Hotchkiss were initially to have been located at forecastle deck level abeam the bridge structure, as on other contemporary French flotilla craft. However, this position was abandoned as unsatisfactory, and on completion the guns were relocated atop the short superstructure deck forward of the bridge.

The seven 550mm torpedo tubes, in one triple and two twin mountings, were of the then-standard Model 1928 first installed in the *contre-torpilleurs* of the *2400 tonnes* type. The forward (triple) mounting was located on the centreline between the twin funnels, and could fire at

angles of 30 degrees either side of the beam; the after (paired) mountings, which were located close to the deck edge, could fire within 20 degrees of the ship's axis on forward bearings, and within 25 degrees of the axis on after bearings, thereby meeting the 1931 CPEF recommendations regarding night firings under unprepared conditions. For long range firing under normal daytime conditions fire control was provided by a specially-adapted rangefinder with a 5m base, which was incorporated into a rotating circular housing directly above the DCT.

Anti-submarine provision was on a par with other contemporary French flotilla craft, but was to prove wholly inadequate. The operational philosophy of the *Marine Nationale* envisaged that high speed and manoeuvrability would provide adequate protection for naval vessels against most submarine and aerial threats; hence the emphasis on offensive surface engagement capabilities at the expense of defensive weaponry. There was no French counterpart to the British Asdic sound-ranging apparatus. The *Le Hardi* class was to be provided only with two depth charge racks, located in 'tunnels' beneath the quarterdeck and discharging over the stern, each of which could hold six 200kg (440lb) depth charges. The racks could be reloaded from a magazine located immediately abaft the quarterdeck 130mm mounting (see drawing). In contrast to British practice there were no depth charge mortars to provide a broad-area pattern, and the first three ships (*Le Hardi, Fleuret* and *Epée*) were in the event completed with only a single DC rack to port holding eight depth charges (later ships reverted to the original plans).

Mameluk as she appeared in April 1941. The anti-aircraft armament is identical to that of Epée, *with twin 13.2mm Hotchkiss forward of the bridge and single Brownings on the quarterdeck. Note the enclosed housing for the after rangefinder, which appears to have a 5m base as in the original design plans. (Marius Bar, 8 April 1941)*

The *Le Hardi* class was also to have had the ingenious Ginocchio anti-submarine torpedo, which was also intended for installation aboard the *torpilleurs légers* of the *600 tonnes* type. This was to have been accommodated on an angled ramp aligned with the ship's axis directly above the stern (see design drawing). However, the only photograph in the author's possession which shows the weapon installed is the one of *Epée* taken in March 1941, in which the launch apparatus is angled out over the starboard quarter of the stern. This serves to explain the single depth charge 'tunnel' (to port) of the first three ships; the Ginocchio torpedo was abandoned for later units.

Mechanical minesweeping gear, which was also a feature of the *1500 tonnes* and contemporary British destroyers, was fitted. The Type C floats, served by twin davits, were moved from their designed position on either side of the quarterdeck 130mm mounting to the stern.

Hull and Propulsion Machinery

The hull, some 10m (33ft) longer and 2m (6.5ft) broader than that of the later *1500 tonnes*, was altogether more robust and seaworthy, and was regarded by the *Marine Nationale* as an unqualified success. It nevertheless accounted for only 29 per cent of the trial displacement due to the adoption of welding and the extensive use of light alloy for superstructures. When completed the ships were slightly overweight, displacement at normal load being 1982 tonnes (*vice* 1936 tonnes designed) and at full load 2577 tonnes (2417 tonnes designed).

The *1500 tonnes* had been fitted out with a mix of Parsons, Rateau and Zoelly turbines. The last had proved less successful in service than the other two types, and were therefore abandoned by the *Marine Nationale*. *Le Hardi, Mameluk, Casque, Le Corsaire, L'Intrépide* and *Le Téméraire* were to have Parsons geared turbines, and the remainder Rateau–Bretagne. Designed horsepower was 58,000shp for a speed of 38kts, with a maximum of 66,000shp specified for trials at Washington displacement. In spite of a doubling of ship horsepower as compared with the *1500 tonnes*, the machinery accounted for only 33 per cent of trial displacement, and the weight/power ratio was only 18kg/hp (in the *1500 tonnes* the corresponding figure was 29kg/hp).

The turbine machinery proved robust and reliable. However, the same cannot be said for the Sural-Penhoët boilers, which gave trouble throughout the ships' short service lives. Developed by Ingénieur Général du Génie Maritime M Norguet from the model installed in the *contre-torpilleurs* of the *Fantasque* class, the Sural boiler (which was also to be installed in the new fast battleships of the *Richelieu* class) had an operating pressure of 35kg/cm^2 (500psi), with a superheater temperature of 358 degrees, produced 60 tonnes of steam per hour (70 tonnes at trial speed), and employed both pressure firing and forced circulation. It represented yet another attempt to squeeze out further improvements in performance (the Yarrow-Loire small-tube boilers installed in *Le Fantasque* were rated at 27kg/cm^2, while those of the early postwar flotilla craft were rated at only 18kg/cm^2).

High steam pressures were very much the order of the day. The contemporary Type 34 destroyers built for the German Navy had boilers rated at 70kg/cm^2, and suffered constant breakdowns as a consequence. The Royal Navy, on the other hand, persisted with boilers operating at a relatively conservative 21kg/cm^2 (300psi), and achieved a high standard of reliability. Although the boilers installed in the *Le Hardi* class proved more successful than the German Wagner model, they were sensitive and unstable, and required highly trained personnel to operate them. The brickwork was defective and fragile, and following the Royal Navy attack on Dakar in the autumn of 1940 the captain of *Le Hardi* complained that they were unsuitable for making smoke (ironically, the captain of the battleship *Richelieu* complained that they produced far too much under normal operating conditions!) Moreover, the increase in speed was not as rapid as anticipated, and the ventilators were noisy.

Due to France's premature exit from the war and the difficult circumstances which followed the Armistice of June 1940, *Le Hardi* was the only unit of the class to complete trials, which began on 6 November 1939. She easily achieved her designed speed; at a displacement of 2429 tonnes she sustained an average 61,119shp over a period of eight hours and achieved speeds between 38.6 and 39.1kts. A cruise speed of 15kts was attained with only 2300shp. Her sister *Fleuret*, the only other ship for which records survive, achieved a maximum speed of 40.2kts on trials. The ability of these ships to operate at sustained high speed is illustrated by the transit of the

Table 4. *IMPROVED LE HARDI CHARACTERISTICS*

Displacement:	2215 tons standard (designed)
	2562 tonnes trials
	2929 tonnes full load
Length:	118.80m pp (389ft 9in)
Beam:	11.9m (39ft 0in)
Machinery:	Machinery as *Le Hardi* but 62,000shp for 35kts max
	and increased bunkerage. Same radius of action
Armament:	Six 130mm CA semi-automatic guns in three twin pseudo-
	turrets (1350 AP/HE shells, 60 starshell, plus 315
	practice rounds)
	Armament otherwise as *Le Hardi*

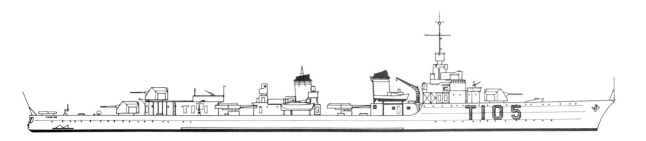

Mameluk as she appeared in April 1941 (see photograph of that date). The twin 13.2mm Hotchkiss AA gun mountings are located directly beneath the bridge, and single 13.2mm Browning heavy machine-guns have been fitted on the quarterdeck. The after rangefinder is in an enclosed housing, in contrast to earlier ships of the class. (Author)

latter from Casablanca to Toulon in late 1940, which was completed at an average speed of 36kts!

However, as with all French flotilla craft of the period, endurance was disappointing. The fuel capacity of 470 tonnes should theoretically have given *Le Hardi* a radius of 790nm at 36kts, 1100 at 30kts, 1770nm at 25kts, and 2760nm at 20kts. However, operations in wartime conditions following completion led to a significant reappraisal of these figures, and it was subsequently estimated that at 20kts 2000nm would be a more appropriate figure. The fault lay in part with the auxiliary machinery, which consumed large quantities of fuel even at relatively low speeds.

Series 1938 and 1938 bis

Even before the outbreak of the Second World War it was becoming clear that the anti-aircraft armament of existing flotilla craft was inadequate in the face of a growing aerial threat. Other navies, particularly the Pacific navies of Japan and the USA, had moved to dual-purpose main armaments for their own destroyers in order to enhance the protection they could provide for the battle fleets they were designed to accompany.

Moreover, a dual-purpose 130mm 45-calibre gun (the Model 1932) had been developed by the *Marine Nationale* as the secondary armament of the fast battleships *Dunkerque* and *Strasbourg*. This weapon was already in service aboard *Dunkerque*, and although initial experience had not been particularly favourable due to its vulnerability to electrical and mechanical breakdown, it was felt that these defects could be ironed out in time.

Notes submitted by the Naval General Staff between June and November 1938 therefore recommended modification of the last four ships of the series, authorized under the 1938 and 1938 *bis* programmes, to enable them to mount three twin 130mm dual-purpose mountings of new design in place of their original low-angle weapons.

It was acknowledged that this decision would have to be accompanied by an increase in hull size. Not only would the three 130mm dual-purpose mountings bring with them an additional 55 tonnes of topweight, but they would require larger magazines in order to accommodate both armour-piercing and fuzed HE rounds in sufficient numbers for both surface and aerial engagements. There would also have to be modifications to the fire control

system. The STCN responded by proposing an increase in length of some 7 metres (23ft) and an increase of 0.8m (2.6ft) in beam; standard displacement would rise to 2215 tons Washington, and full load displacement to just under 3000 tonnes (see table). There would be a slight increase in horsepower from 58,000shp to 62,000shp, but maximum speed would fall from 38kts to 35kts.

A number of other proposals were put forward, including the retention of the low-angle 130mm mountings with the addition of two twin 100mm (3.9in) Model 1931 AA mountings (the same model installed in the heavy cruiser *Algérie*), and a uniform main armament of eight 100mm AA guns in twin mountings. Further proposals, advanced in early 1939 in response to concerns regarding the machine-gunning of ships by aircraft when operating close to the shore, were for light protective plating to be added to the gunhouses and bridge. The study showed that this could be achieved at the cost of reducing the number of torpedo tubes from seven to six (in two triple mountings), and by replacing the original mixed AA armament, which included the heavy semi-automatic twin 37mm Model 1933, by a uniform armament comprising three or four twin 23mm mountings of new design.

In the end the General Staff returned to the original proposal of November 1938 for the four units authorized under the 1938 and 1938 *bis* programmes. However, the alternative proposals did influence the final design of *L'Opiniâtre*, the first of the four. The latter, although she had the larger hull of her sisters, was intended to be grouped tactically with the two ships of the 1937 Programme, *Le Corsaire* and *Le Flibustier*. In order to secure uniformity of artillery within the three-ship division, *L'Opiniâtre* was to have been armed with the three standard 130mm Model 1935 low-angle mountings together with two twin 100mm Model 1931 AA mountings. The number of torpedo tubes would have been reduced to six (in two triple banks), and she would have had a uniform light AA armament of four twin 13.2mm Hotchkiss mountings.

War Service

Although the first unit of the *Le Hardi* class had been authorized in 1932 no ships of the type had been completed by the outbreak of war. By June 1940, when the battle for France had been lost and the German armies

Mameluk *and* Casque *as they appeared in August 1942. The anti-aircraft armament is identical to that of* Le Hardi *as illustrated in the photo dating from December of the previous year.* Casque *has her after rangefinder in a housing of different design to that of* Mameluk. *Both ships have the twin depth charge 'tunnels' of the later units of the class.* (Marius Bar, 10 August 1942)

were sweeping down on Paris, only *Le Hardi* had run her full trials; *Fleuret* and *Epée* had completed hull and machinery trials and were fitting out at Toulon and Lorient respectively, and five other units had been launched and were in various stages of completion.

The *Marine Nationale* was particularly anxious that these modern ships should not fall into the hands of the Germans (who were themselves desperately short of

destroyers due to the heavy losses experienced during the Narvik campaign), and no fewer than seven managed to sail for North Africa, often in remarkable circumstances.

Le Hardi, flying the flag of Admiral Laborde (*Commandant des Forces Maritime Ouest*) for the evacuation of Brest (19 June 1940), escorted the incomplete battleship *Richelieu* first to Casablanca, and then to Dakar. At the same time *Epée* and *Mameluk*, which were fitting out and

Table 5. *FATES*

Le Hardi	Italian *FR 37*	towed to La Spezia 7.9.43, seized by Germans 9.43, scuttled 24.4.45.
Foudroyant (ex-*Fleuret*)	Italian *FR 36*	refloated 20.5.43 Toulon, seized by Germans 9.43, sunk as blockship 8.44.
L'Adroit (ex-*Epée*)	Italian *FR 33*	refloated 20.4.43 Toulon, seized by Germans 9.43, returned to MN and broken up.
Mameluk		refloated 1943 Toulon, bombed 8.44 and broken up.
Casque		refloated 1943 Toulon, bombed 27.4.44 and broken up.
Lansquenet	Italian *FR 34*	towed to Imperia 31.8.43, seized by Germans 9.43, scuttled at Genoa 24.4.45, refloated & towed to Toulon for repairs 19.3.46, but broken up.
Siroco (ex-*Le Corsaire*)	Italian *FR 32*	towed to Genoa 10.6.43, seized by Germans 9.43, sunk as blockship 28.10.43.
Bison (ex-*Le Flibustier*)	Italian *FR 35*	refloated 1943 Toulon, seized by Germans 9.43, used as smoke-pontoon, bombed spring 1944, sunk German submarine 25.6.44.

running trials respectively at Lorient, were escorting the half-completed *Jean Bart* to Casablanca. *Fleuret*, fitted out at Toulon, had been transferred to Casablanca some days earlier, arriving on 15 June. She sortied to escort the *Richelieu* into Dakar, then returned to Casablanca.

By far the most remarkable escape was that of *Lansquenet*, which on 17 June was in drydock at Bordeaux; the propulsion machinery had just been assembled, and the hull had received only its undercoat of red lead paint. The ship was hastily refloated and the three 130mm mountings were embarked that same afternoon. *Lansquenet* was then towed to Pauillac to take on fuel. Two boilers were theoretically operational but had not been tested. They were successfully lit, and in the early hours of 23 June *Lansquenet* left her moorings under her own steam, sortied from the mouth of the Gironde Estuary under fire from units of the German Army, and arrived at Casablanca on 27 June.

The other two units transferred to North African ports in June were *Casque* and *Le Corsaire*, which were fitting out at Toulon, and which arrived in Mers el-Kebir on 20 and 22 June respectively. They were at nearby Oran at the time of the British attacks of 3–7 July, and escaped damage. Neither was in a fit state to take part in any action against the British squadron; *Casque* had received her armament but the fire control systems were not yet operational, while *Le Corsaire* had sailed from France without any of her guns in place.

The move to North Africa proved a mixed blessing. It served to keep the ships out of the clutches of the Germans, while at the same time removing them from the naval infrastructure essential to speed their entry into service. The bases in North Africa had only rudimentary maintenance facilities in comparison with the metropolitan bases of Brest, Lorient and Toulon, and it would be many months before the new *torpilleurs d'escadre* would be fully operational.

In late September, following the abortive British assault on Dakar, *Epée* and *Fleuret* were dispatched together with the older *torpilleurs Fougueux* and *Frondeur* on a reprisal raid against Gibraltar. Neither ship had previously fired its guns in anger, nor had they had the opportunity to conduct gunnery practice on a firing range. During a brief and inconclusive engagement with a single British destroyer *Epée* managed to get off 14 rounds in six minutes before all her guns broke down; *Fleuret* experienced problems with her fire control director, which was unable to track the target, and in consequence did not succeed in firing a single shot.

The performance of *Le Hardi* at Dakar on the previous day provides an instructive contrast. This vessel had completed thirteen sessions on gunnery ranges before the June Armistice, firing more than 700 rounds in the process. When put to the test at Dakar *Le Hardi* fired 60 shells without experiencing any breakdown, bracketing the target with her first salvo.

Following the British attacks on the ill-protected North African bases, it was decided that the bulk of the French fleet would be withdrawn to Toulon. Five of the seven ships which had fled from metropolitan France in June (*Le Hardi, Epée, Mameluk, Fleuret* and *Lansquenet*) returned on 8 November 1940, escorting the old battleship *Provence*, which had been patched up following the attack on Mers el-Kebir. Three ships (T101 *Epée*, T102 *Le*

Hardi and T103 *Fleuret*) had been formed into the 10th Torpedo Boat Division during September, but as it would be some time before the sixth unit (*Casque*) would be fully operational the *Marine Nationale* added the fourth and fifth ships to the existing division, *Lansquenet* becoming T104 and *Mameluk* T105.

Photographic evidence suggests that the ships retained these hull numbers throughout 1941. On 1 April of that year two of the operational ships, together with two of the ships still fitting out, were renamed in honour of *torpilleurs* of the *1500 tonnes* type lost during 1940 (see table). *Lansquenet* was also to have been renamed, but this did not take place before the ship was scuttled in November 1942.

With the return to Toulon and the subsequent inactivity of the French fleet, the completion of the remaining ships of the class became a low priority. *Casque* finally replaced *Le Hardi* in the five-ship operational division on 1 May 1942, the latter ship being decommissioned with only a token crew aboard for maintenance and security. *Bison* (ex-*Le Flibustier*) was only 75 per cent complete on 27 November 1942, when all ships of the class were scuttled at Toulon. The four modified units of the 1938 and 1938 *bis* programmes were still on the stocks, and were only 13–20 per cent complete. Their hulls were taken over by the Germans, but subsequent construction was slow and hindered by sabotage.

Anti-Aircraft Armament

Wartime experience quickly showed up the inadequacy of the anti-aircraft armament of the French flotilla craft, and virtually all received additional AA weapons during 1941 and 1942. Unfortunately published sources cannot be relied upon, as they conflict with the evidence of the photographs in the author's possession.

The first five ships of the class were completed with the twin semi-automatic 37mm Model 33 mounting atop the after deckhouse, and two twin 13.2mm Hotchkiss guns forward of the bridge. In early 1941 two single 13.2mm Browning guns were fitted on the quarterdeck, just forward of the Type C sweep gear (see photos of *Mameluk* and *Epée*).

By late 1941 the new single 25mm Hotchkiss gun had become available, and photos of *Le Hardi* taken in December of that year show two single 25mm Hotchkiss forward of the bridge; the twin 13.2mm displaced from the latter position were relocated on the quarterdeck, and the single 13.2mm Browning guns relocated to platforms projecting from the base of 'X' mounting. This pattern can also be seen on photographs of *Casque* and *Mameluk* taken in August 1942, and can therefore be assumed to be standard for the class during this period.

Fates

Six of the eight *torpilleurs d'escadre* of the *Le Hardi* class scuttled at Toulon were salvaged by the Italians during mid-1943 with the intention of refitting them for active service. The remaining two ships, *Mameluk* and *Casque*, were refloated but were considered too badly damaged to recover, and remained at Toulon. Most were seized by the Germans when the Italians capitulated in September. All suffered ignominious fates (see accompanying table), being variously sunk by allied bombers or employed as blockships by the Germans.

Sources
Henri Le Masson, *Histoire du Torpilleur en France 1872–1940*, Académie de Marine (1963).
Robert Dumas, 'Les torpilleurs type *Le Hardi*', *Cols Bleus* 2114 (23 February 1991).
Official plans, Centre d'Archives de l'Armement.

SECOND WORLD WAR CRUISERS: WAS ARMOUR REALLY NECESSARY?

David K Brown analyses the action damage suffered by cruisers between 1939 and 1945 and questions whether the increasing dedication to armour in the late-1930s made design sense.

MOST of the naval powers which met to discuss arms limitation in Washington were already thinking of building large cruisers. The Royal Navy was actually building the *Hawkins* class of 9750 tons (legend) with seven 7.5in guns for trade protection and saw the need for many more such ships as the small cruisers built during the war lacked the endurance required.[1] Similarly, the US Navy wanted ships of that size for scouting in the Pacific. Agreement was soon reached that individual ships should not exceed 10,000 tons with guns no larger than 8in. No limit was set on the number of ships or on total tonnage.[2]

The size chosen (without liquids) was not excessive as many late nineteenth century cruisers were bigger. However, the limit did pose considerable problems to the designer in the light of contemporary operational thinking. A minimum of eight 8in guns was seen as essential to achieve reasonable salvo size and there was universal agreement that the new cruisers should be fast; 32–35kts was the target.

The existence of the British Hawkins *class was one factor in setting the Washington size limit at 10,000 tons for cruisers. This is* Effingham *entering Grand Harbour, Malta.* (All photos: CMP)

Weight and space were also needed for anti-aircraft armament and, perhaps, for carrying aircraft. All these requirements meant that there was little weight left over for protection. There was no question of protecting the vitals of the ship from hits by shells of the size carried on board. Since about 1912, British cruisers had a fairly standard scheme of protection with a belt about 3in thick and a light protective deck, about an inch thick, to keep splinters out of lower spaces. Such protection had been very effective in North Sea fighting keeping out all destroyer projectiles and the 4.1in shells of most German cruisers. It would also resist 6in high explosive (HE) shells.

PART I – WHAT WAS FITTED

First Generation

Britain was the only signatory to the Washington Treaty with direct experience in battle and for that reason the selection made by the Staff between different design proposals is of particular interest. Explosions in maga-

zines during the war seemed to demonstrate the need to provide them and perhaps the shell rooms with substantial protection and some of the early studies had no other protection. The Staff were not prepared to have the machinery spaces totally unprotected, vulnerable even to splinters and agreed to lighter machinery, with a 1½kt loss of speed, in order to provide weight for 1in side protection and a 1½in deck.[3] This level of protection weighed about 1000 tons, 10 per cent of the standard displacement.

There was a similar debate in the USA, leading to the *Salt Lake City* which had a short 2½in belt over the machinery and a 1in deck, together with 4in magazine sides leading to a recorded total weight of just over 500 tons.[4] The breakdown of weight between protection and hull structure was never very clear and certainly varied considerably from one country to another. The US Navy only counted vertical armour as protection with decks in the hull group while the British usually had an arbitrary thickness limit with thicker material counting as protection. There are indications that this breakdown in all countries may have changed from time to time. Comparisons of the percentage of armour weight, such as those in Fig 1, are probably valid within one navy but cannot be used to compare ships of different nationality.

Japan generally followed British wartime practice with a 3in belt and a splinter deck, usually less than an inch thick. The first French Washington cruisers had no plating over an inch thick with 480 tons described as

The first American treaty cruisers were the Salt Lake City *class, of which this is the name ship. The short belt over the machinery is just visible amidships.*

The first British treaty cruisers, of the Kent *class, had a small, narrow anti-torpedo bulge – very evident in this photo of* Cumberland *at light draught.*

protection whilst contemporary Italian ships had a 3in belt and a light deck.

Second Thoughts

The British and Americans paid great attention to weight saving during the detail design of the early ships with much increased use of aluminium, some welding (US) and the deliberate selection of lightweight fittings. In Britain the thickness tolerance allowed on the rolling of steel plates and sections was entirely 'under', giving a few per cent saving of weight. Forty tons were saved by using smaller rivet heads! In consequence, ships of these two navies completed well under 10,000 tons. The ships of other navies were over weight, some slightly, the Japanese by about 17 per cent.[5] This is not a trivial error; a naval architect can increase fighting capability very considerably given an extra 1700 tons.

When it became apparent that American and British ships had some weight to spare, there was renewed debate over the requirements for the next generation. The British were well satisfied with the *Kent*s and the two succeeding classes were generally very similar. Weight saving was used to obtain a little more speed. The *Surrey*s, cancelled in the depression, would have been radically different, sacrificing 2–3kts of speed to fit a belt up to 5¾in thick and a 2–3in deck weighing 1900 tons. One early variant had thick protection for the aft boiler room and splinter protection for the forward one. It is probably significant

that this move to heavier protection started while Chatfield was Controller as he was always an advocate of armour.

The US Navy made only slight changes to the protection of the *Northampton*s but the *Portland*s had a thicker belt, up to 5in. The US Navy was the first to use the concept of the 'immune zone', that bracket where the range is too great for the side armour to be defeated and too short for plunging fire to penetrate the deck. It will be noted that none of the first generation ships had any immune zone against 8in shells (except for some magazines). By 1929 the US Navy was demanding an immune zone of 12–24,000yds for the magazine and 15–24,000yds for the machinery against 8in shell. They also demanded protection for the gunhouses which in the earlier ships of all navies had only splinter protection and asked for an immune zone similar to that of the magazine. This aim was largely achieved in *New Orleans* with a 5in belt and 2¼in deck for a protection weight of 1500 tons and, with slight changes, such protection became standard for larger US cruisers.

The London Treaty of 1930 imposed an overall tonnage limit on cruiser fleets and, in order to get sufficient numbers, the Royal Navy concentrated on smaller ships. The style of protection adopted was a pragmatic interpretation of what weight was available rather than based on pure logic. In general they had a belt of 3½–4½in over the machinery with a similar thickness on magazine sides and a 1½–2in deck.

The graph (Fig 1) shows how the weight of protection as a percentage increased between the wars in both British and US cruisers. Whilst remembering that the definition of protection was different, it would seem that by the late 1930s both navies were devoting at least 15 per cent of standard displacement to armour.

It becomes even more difficult to produce similar data for Japanese ships as one can recognise at least three 'Standard' displacements; the very low, false published figure, the much higher figure at which the ships completed and the even greater one when strength and stability had been corrected.[6] It seems that about 15–20 per cent of the 'as completed' displacement went into protection which typically comprised a 4in belt (3in in earlier ships) which was carried far down in the hull, at reduced thickness as protection against diving shells, and a protective deck, usually just under an inch thick. Japanese cruisers all had a small anti-torpedo bulge (as did *Kent*) which was quite ineffective.

uss Augusta, *one of the* Northampton *class, which had minimal changes to the protection scheme of the* Salt Lake City, *but adopted a raised forecastle for improved seakeeping and a three triple turret main armament layout.*

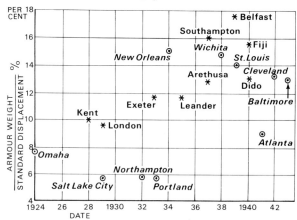

GROWTH IN PERCENTAGE OF DISPLACEMENT DEVOTED TO ARMOUR

∗ Royal Navy
⊙ United States Navy

The second generation of Italian treaty cruisers sacrificed the very high speed of the preceding Trento *class for additional protection, but even though the initial requirements could not be met, as completed the ships were still 1500 tons over limit. This is* Fiume *in 1933.*

PART II – HOW WELL DID IT WORK?

The Chance of Being Hit

It might be thought obvious that protection is only of value if the ship is hit but even this statement needs qualification. If the enemy knows that he is attacking an unprotected target he can use smaller weapons whose greater number and higher rate of fire increase the probability of hitting and also allow him to use the more damaging HE shell rather than SAP (semi armour piercing). In this sense, protection is always of some value though it is not possible to attach numbers to that value.

In the early, savage years the chance of being damaged in the course of a single year was very high indeed while even in the later years, damage was still likely.

The Causes of Loss or Damage

Armour was mainly intended to protect against gunfire and the tables above show that only about one-fifth of damage incidents involved gunfire. Of these, only about one in ten led to loss of the ship: shells were not very likely to hit a cruiser and very unlikely to sink it. The torpedo was the sinking weapon in both navies causing about half the Royal Navy's losses and almost all of the US Navy's. Bombs accounted for most damage to British cruisers and sank quite a number. This may be attributed to the greater time spent close to land-based air power, particularly off Norway and in the Mediterranean, and to the inferior British fire control. Some of the British losses were of very small First World War ships but omission of these from Table 2 does not affect these conclusions.

It is very much more difficult to comment on the value of armour in those ships which were hit by shells. Hits on the US ships can be identified fairly clearly in fifteen cases from sketches[7] as being high up, above any practical armour. In the seriously damaged ships, including those finished off by torpedo, such as *Astoria*, *Vincennes* and *Quincy*, fire seems to have been the major hazard. In one or two cases turrets were disabled. At Cape Esperance, on 12 October 1942, *Salt Lake City* was hit on her belt by a HE shell which caused no damage. The only other

Table 1. THE CHANCE OF BEING DAMAGED (BRITISH CRUISERS)

Year (Sept–Sept)	1939–40	1940–41	1941–42	1942–43	1943–44	1944–45
In commission	44	46	42	35	36	29
Damaged	20	53	45	14	22	9

Table 2. *THE CAUSES OF LOSS OR DAMAGE (BRITISH CRUISERS)*

	Shell	*Bomb*	*Mine*	*Torpedo*	*Total*
Sunk	3	10	1	13	27
Seriously damaged	9	42	8	24	83
Slightly damaged	22	45	2	—	69
Total	34	97	11	37	179

New Orleans *heralded a change in US cruiser protection policy, introducing a much heavier scheme of armouring, including a true turret in place of the earlier gunhouses. They were also the first to be designed for a specific immune zone of 12,000yds – 24,000yds at a target angle of 60 degrees against a 260lb 8in shell.* San Francisco, *shown here at Mare Island in 1944, survived the war, but three of her sisters did not.*

Table 3. *THE CAUSES OF LOSS OR DAMAGE TO US CRUISERS (CA & CL)*

	Shell	Bomb	Bomb & Torp	Torpedo	Gun & Torp	Kamikaze attack	Total
Sunk	1	—	—	5	4	—	10
Damaged	11	13	2	12	2	13	53
Total	12	13	2	17	6	13	63

Note: Reporting of damage may differ slightly between navies.

contribution which belts seem to have made was that on *Minneapolis* which kept out splinters from a near-miss bomb.

Lacroix's articles on Japanese 'A' class cruisers describe damage in some detail and again it is clear that most shells hit high in the ship; an 8in on *Chokai*'s belt being the only apparent exception. There were several cases in which turrets were put out of action and others in which the upper deck torpedo tubes or the reload stowages were hit causing very serious fires. The danger of large quantities of explosive on the upper deck, particularly in association with the liquid oxygen of Japanese torpedoes is apparent.

British losses from gunfire, such as *Sydney* and *Canberra*, were mainly due to hits above the armour causing uncontrollable fires. In the first cruiser gun action of the war, the River Plate, on 13 December 1939, *Exeter* was hit seven times by 11in shells from *Graf Spee*, all above the belt including two on turrets, while *Ajax* was

A midships close-up of the Japanese Chokai *revealing the armour belt.*

hit on 'X' barbette. It is doubtful if *Exeter*'s armour played any part in her final actions at and after the Java Sea in 1942.

There are four cases recorded in which belts were clearly of value. *Berwick*, whose belt was added during her refit in 1937–38, was hit by *Hipper*'s 8in four times on 25 December 1940. One hit 'X' turret and the other three were stopped by the belt (4in cemented) with little damage. *Liverpool, Ajax* and *Kenya* were all hit on their belts by small shells, mainly from destroyers. (Note that *Ajax* received six more hits above the belt.)

Details of some eleven other cases of damage from shells have been found, all involving damage above the armour. In none of these cases would any credible increase in protection have reduced the damage sustained.

It does not seem unfair to conclude that belt armour was almost useless. In considering the value of protective decks it is necessary to look at the effect of bombs, which is difficult. Those which penetrated deep enough in the ship to reach the protective deck were probably also capable of penetrating any likely thickness of armour.

The damaged Exeter *returning home in February 1940 after the River Plate action. A combination of temporary repairs and the attention of the censor makes serious damage difficult to identify, but there are numerous splinter holes in the funnel casing, bridge wing and hull forward.*

Most bombs were fuzed to burst high in the ship and the protective deck would only be hit by splinters. However, splinters come in all sizes and the biggest, such as the nose cone, may penetrate up to 3in of steel. On the other hand, the vast majority will be stopped by 1in plates, much reducing damage and casualties below.

A US Navy report,[8] written in 1944, has some interesting deductions on the effect of bombs. The 1000lb SAP bomb will penetrate a 2½in deck if dropped in level flight from above 5000ft or from 1600ft in dive bombing.

The GP bombs in Tables 4 and 5 will not penetrate such a deck but would penetrate a 1¼in deck. A single bomb is only likely to sink a modern cruiser if it hits and explodes a magazine. The report suggests that magazines occupy about one quarter of the exposed plan of the ship and that there is a 50 per cent chance of a hit causing an explosion. If the explosion is in the magazine, structural damage will cause flooding before an explosion takes place and the principal hazard is from explosions close enough for hot splinters to enter the charges without causing flooding.

Table 4. *EFFECTS OF BOMBS ON 6000–7000-TON CRUISERS*

Bomb	Charge wt (lbs)	Number of hits			
		1	2	3	4
			Probability of sinking (%)		
1000 SAP	250	12	24	75	99
1000 GP	500	12	70	95	99
2000 GP	1000	50	95	99	99

Table 5. *EFFECTS OF BOMBS ON CRUISERS OVER 10,000 TONS*

Bomb	Charge wt (lbs)	Number of hits			
		1	2	3	4
			Probability of sinking (%)		
1000 SAP	250	12	23	40	75
1000 GP	500	3	15	30	45
2000 GP	1000	15	45	80	98

This quarter view of the Glasgow *(taken in 1938 during exercises in honour of George VI) clearly shows the form and extent of the midships belt.*

From multiple hits the risk is loss by flooding and the report gives the following tables which the compiler says were produced from very little firm evidence.

The figures in Tables 4 and 5 seem reasonably consistent with British reports though serious fires led to the loss of some ships after what was initially rather minor damage.

The US report also looks at the effect of near-miss bombs. The 1000lb SAP would be relatively ineffective due to its small charge; the 1000lb GP would rupture the hull at 6ft and the 2000lb GP at 9ft.

Torpedoes

This article is primarily about the value of armour but some mention of torpedoes seems necessary since they were the main cause of sinking, particularly when account is taken of those ships disabled by another form of attack, which were sunk by torpedoes from their own forces. The US Navy report quoted earlier[8] also estimates the probability of sinking from torpedoes with a warhead equivalent to 660lbs TNT.

Table 6. TORPEDO HITS

Cruiser size	Number of hits			
	1	2	3	4
	Probability of sinking (%)			
6000–7000 tons	5	85	95	99
Over 10,000 tons	3	40	85	98

The unit machinery arrangement of the Amphion *class produced a radically different silhouette from the otherwise similar* Leanders, *with two upright funnels instead of the single trunked uptakes of the earlier ships.* Apollo *is shown here in October 1935.*

The figures in Table 6 were derived from US Navy experience but, with the reservations which follow, seem compatible with British and Japanese experience.

The survival of a cruiser hit by a torpedo depends on where it was hit. A single hit forward would not usually

be serious while a hit aft might disable the ship but would not sink it. If hit amidships much depends on the machinery arrangement. Virtually all US Navy ships and Royal Navy ones from *Amphion* onwards had machinery arranged on the unit system (boiler room – engine room – boiler room – engine room) and if the hit left either boiler room and either engine room intact, the ship could steam on two shafts. Of thirty-one US cruisers torpedoed, seven sank. Of these, eleven ships were hit in the machinery spaces of which only two were immobilized. The unit system was also of value in retaining mobility after bomb or shell attack.

British experience confirmed the value of the unit system but the way in which it was applied was seriously flawed. Small wing compartments were arranged either side of the after boiler room after it had been confirmed that flooding one of these spaces would only cause a small angle of heel. What had not been appreciated was that a torpedo in this part of the ship would flood three main spaces, much reducing stability, and the off centre moment of one wing space flooded would then cause a very large heel. Of seven ships with this arrangement, torpedoed in way of the after machinery, six capsized and *Cleopatra* was saved only by rapid and skilful damage control.

The Japanese made an even bigger mistake, fitting a centreline bulkhead in most machinery spaces. Of twelve ships torpedoed in this area, ten sank with seven capsizing. The moral is clear: longitudinal subdivision must be avoided unless part of a torpedo protection system which in the Second World War required a beam of over 100ft.

Conclusions

In examining past decisions, the historian should ask two questions: did the designer reach the best solution with the facts available to him at the time and, secondly, does this solution still seem right with additional, later information? In the case of Second World War cruisers it is suggested that the designer of *Kent* was correct in giving heavy protection to the magazines and a limited amount of splinter protection elsewhere. Indeed, this may well have been the best approach even had there been no limit on displacement. It is not clear if there were any magazine explosions in British cruisers during the war; there is an unconfirmed report that *Dorsetshire*'s 4in magazine exploded following a bomb hit just before she sank. There were at least six incidents in which one or two charges ignited without exploding the magazine which must, to some extent, have been due to the safer propellants introduced during the 1930s.[9] However, protection to a

mass of explosive such as that contained in a magazine seems a wise precaution.

Later British cruisers had a much greater weight of protection and if armoured in the style of *Kent* some 700 tons of weight could have been saved. Reduction in the weight carried would have led to a lighter hull structure and there would have been savings on the supporting frames to the armour and on the element of protection in the hull weight. Altogether about 1000 tons (10 per cent) could have been saved.

The ship could not have been made shorter as the length was determined by the upper deck layout of guns, aircraft arrangements and funnels. The weight saved, mainly in steel, would not equate to anything like a 10 per cent saving in cost so that, with a fixed budget, there was little scope for adding expensive guns or machinery. The British Naval Staff of the day seem to have seen speed as their secondary objective after armour and a 10 per cent weight reduction at constant length and power would, in itself, have given an extra ¾kt.

The later British cruisers, particularly the *Amphion*s and *Fiji*s were very cramped and a little of the weight saving could have been put into making them more spacious so improving the effectiveness of their unit system of machinery. It is likely that the lethal wing spaces in the boiler rooms were an attempt to squeeze too much in and they might not have appeared in a less cramped ship.

Overall, one may suggest that, even with hindsight, the designers of *Kent* were right and that any savings should have been put to increasing the number of ships within Treaty limits on displacement and government budgets.

Notes

[1] David K Brown, 'The Cruiser', in *The Eclipse of the Big Gun*, 'Conway's *History of the Ship*' series (London 1992).

[2] David K Brown, 'Naval rearmament, 1930–1941. The Royal Navy', *Revue Internationale d'histoire militaire* (Stuttgart 1991).

[3] Alan Raven and John Roberts, *British Cruisers of World War Two* (London 1980).

[4] Norman Friedman, *US Cruisers* (Annapolis 1984).

[5] E. Lacroix, 'The Development of the 'A Class' Cruisers in the Imperial Japanese Navy', *Warship International* 4/1977, 1/1979, 4/1979, 1/1981, 4/1981, 3/1983 and 3/1984 (Toledo, Ohio).

[6] *Ibid.*

[7] *Summary of War Damage*, BUSHIPS (Washington 1943–46).

[8] *Striking Power of Airborne Weapons* (Washington 1944).

[9] John Campbell, *Naval Weapons of World War Two* (London 1985).

Also consulted: DNC records of damage in the Second World War, now held in the Public Record Office, Kew.

ALLIED WARSHIPS IN GERMAN HANDS

This essentially pictorial article covers fifteen different types of Allied warships which were captured by the Germans between 1940 and 1942. Some saw German service while others did not, and the notes by Pierre Hervieux concentrate on their careers rather than technical details which are easily accessible in standard reference works like *Conway's All the World's Fighting Ships 1922–46.*

Ex-French Bombarde

The German torpedo boat *TA 9* was the former French *Bombarde*, captured at Bizerta on 8 December 1942 by the Germans and allocated to the Italian Navy on 28 December, in which she served as *FR 41*. She was transferred to the *Kriegsmarine* which recommissioned her on 5 April 1943 as *TA 9*, under the command of *Kapitänleutnant* Düvelius till July 1943 and from that

The TA 9 *(ex-French* Bombarde*) in German service. The 20mm 'Vierling' is clearly visible, aft of the 100mm gun.* (Drüppel)

month till 25 September 1943, when she was paid off, under the command of *Kapitänleutnant* Reinhardt. She had been built by the Ateliers et Chantiers de la Loire in Nantes, laid down in February 1935, launched on 23 March 1936 and completed in April 1937. *TA 9* belonged to the 4th Geleittorpedoboot-Flottille and from August 1943 to the 3rd Geleittorpedoboot-Flottille, being employed on escort duties.

During an American air raid over Toulon on 23 August 1944, *TA 9* was bombed and sunk. In German service the two torpedo tubes had been removed and the original light anti-aircraft armament replaced by two 37mm (2×1) and eight 20mm (1×4 and 4×1) guns. The complement was raised to 140 men. Incidentally, contrary to the claim of

The German escort vessel SG 15 *(ex-French* Rageot de la Touche*) equipped with a radar.* (WZ Bilddienst)

many sources, her sister-ship *TA 12* (ex-*Baliste*) was not sunk on 22 August 1943, and she never entered service with the *Kriegsmarine*. After she had been scuttled at Toulon on 27 November 1942, she was raised on 14 May 1943, with the intention of commissioning her into the German navy. However, Toulon was raided by a large force of B-17 Flying Fortresses of the USAAF on 24 November 1943 and *TA 12* was hit and sunk. *TA 9, TA 10* and *TA 11* were commissioned in the *Kriegsmarine* in April 1943; in addition to *TA 12*, there was *TA 13* (ex-*La Bayonnaise*) which was also not commissioned by the German navy.

Ex-French Rageot de la Touche

The German escort vessel *SG 15* was the former French minesweeping sloop *Rageot de la Touche*, built by the Ateliers et Chantiers de Provence in Port de Bouc. Launched on 2 September 1942, she was scuttled at Toulon on 27 November, salved and commissioned in the *Kriegsmarine* on 1 May 1943 as *SG 15* under the command of *Oberleutnant zur See* Obenhaupt, and belonged to the 3rd Geleitflottille. In February 1944 she was classified as submarine-chaser *UJ 2229* under the command of *Kapitänleutnant* Wachhausen and was scuttled in Genoa on 24 April 1945. In German service the armament comprised two 105mm (2×1) guns, two 37mm (2×1) AA guns and six 20mm (1×4, 2×1) AA guns, the complement reaching 103 men.

Ex-French Côte d'Argent

The German minelayer *Ostmark* was the former French cross-Channel passenger ship *Côte d'Argent* (3047 tons), built and launched by Les Forges de la Méditerranée in Le

Two views of the minelayer Ostmark *(ex-French* Côte D'Argent*) taken on 9 November 1941; her light AA guns comprised only one 37mm and two 2mm (2 × 1) at that time.* (ECPA)

Havre in 1932. After being captured in June 1940, from July she was used as an accommodation ship. After suitable refit she was commissioned as a minelayer on 5 October 1941. She could carry 240 mines and her armament comprised two 88mm (2×1) AA guns and fourteen 20mm (2×4, 6×1) AA guns. After a lucky career through the war years, *Ostmark* was bombed and sunk on

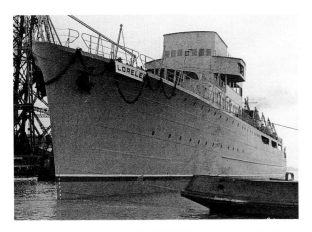

The M 551 *(ex-Dutch* Pieter Florisz*)*. (ECPA)

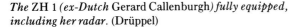

Two views of the Lorelei *(ex-Belgian* Artevelde *at launch on 28 August 1940*. (ECPA)

The ZH 1 *(ex-Dutch* Gerard Callenburgh*) fully equipped, including her radar*. (Drüppel)

21 April 1945 by British Mosquito aircraft, in the Kattegat, west of Anholt Island.

Ex-Belgian Artevelde

The German gunboat *Lorelei* (K 4) is shown just after being launched in Antwerp on 28 August 1940. She was laid down in 1939 as the Belgian *Artevelde* and captured by the Germans on the stocks of the Cockerill shipyard in May 1940. She was completed in August 1943 in the Dutch yard of Wilton-Fijenoord in Schiedam. Her armament comprised three 105mm (3×1) AA guns, four 37mm (1×2, 2×1) AA guns and ten 20mm (2×4, 2×1) AA guns. *Lorelei* could also carry 120 mines and had a complement of 180 men. She was particularly fast, with a maximum speed of 28½kts, compared with the 18kts of the ex-Dutch gunboats *K 1–K 3*. Returned to Belgium in 1945, her scrapping began in Brugge on 22 November 1954.

Ex-Dutch Pieter Florisz

The Dutch minesweeper *Pieter Florisz* is shown being salved by the Germans on 12 August 1940, after she was scuttled by the Dutch on 14 May 1940 in Enkhuisen. She had been built and launched on 11 May 1937 by P Smit in Rotterdam. Commissioned in the *Kriegsmarine* as *M 551*, the complement was raised to 59 and the armament comprised one 75mm AA gun and four 20mm (1×2, 2×1) AA guns. She was returned to the Dutch navy in 1945 and broken up in 1961.

Ex-Dutch Gerard Callenburgh

The German destroyer *ZH 1*, which was the former Dutch *Gerard Callenburgh*, laid down in 1938, launched on 12 October 1939 in the Rotterdam shipyard and scuttled incomplete by the Dutch on 14 May 1940. She was salved by the Germans and commissioned on 5 October 1942 under the command of *Korvettenkapitän* Barckow. In German service she retained the five original Dutch main guns of 120mm (2×2, 1×1). The anti-aircraft armament was augmented to four 37mm (2×2) guns and ten 20mm (2×4, 2×1) guns. The two 37mm mountings were mounted in the original 40mm Dutch positions: forward, behind the main turret and aft, between the two quadruple torpedo tubes. The two quadruple 20mm mountings were positioned each side of the after funnel and there was one single 20mm in each bridge wing. The German complement was raised to 230 men. *ZH 1* was sunk on 9 June 1944, at 0240, 20 miles north-west of the Ile de Batz, being scuttled by her crew with depth charges, after she had been torpedoed by the destroyer HMS *Ashanti* and damaged by gunfire from the same destroyer and her sister HMS *Tartar*. Thirty-three men were killed during the battle, including the commanding officer.

Two views of minesweepers of the RA 51 *to* RA 56 *series (ex-Dutch* Mv I *to* Mv VI*). (ECPA)*

One of the future Bulgarian or Romanian motor torpedo boats (ex-Dutch TM 51 *series) still flying the German flag. (Drüppel)*

Ex-Dutch Minesweepers

Two former Dutch minesweepers which served in the *Kriegsmarine* belonged to a series of six units, *Mv I* to *Mv VI*, which was captured incomplete in the Gusto shipyard in Schiedam in May 1940. They were commissioned in the *Kriegsmarine* the same year and became *RA 51* and *RA 56*. *RA 53* and *RA 55* were sunk in the Baltic, in August 1941, by Soviet mines in the western half of the Irben Strait. In the summer of 1942 the remaining four were sent to the Black Sea, via the Elbe up to Dresden, then on trailer-lorries along 450 kilometres of autobahns up to Ingolstadt and finally down the Danube. For about two years they survived unscathed, and were scuttled to avoid capture by Soviet forces in Constanţa on 24 August 1944 after the Romanian capitulation. In German service their anti-aircraft armament comprised one 37mm AA gun and three 20mm (3×1) AA guns.

The gunboat K 1 *(ex-Dutch 'A') in German service.* (WZ Bilddienst)

The gunboat K 2 *(ex-Dutch 'B') in German service.* (WZ Bilddienst)

Ex-Dutch MTBs

This photograph represents one of the seven motor torpedo boats completed by the Dutch shipyard Gusto Werf in Schiedam. The construction of another twelve boats did not materialize; eleven were destined to stay in home waters and the other eight to be sent to the East Indies. The prototype, *TM 51*, built by the British Power Boat Co, escaped to Britain in May 1940. *TM 52* and *TM 53* were captured incomplete by the Germans in May 1940 and became *S 201* and *S 202* in the *Kriegsmarine*. They were transferred to Bulgaria in 1942, being soon followed by a third unit, becoming *S 1, S 2, S 3*. Four more were completed for the Germans, who transferred them to the Romanian navy in 1942–43, becoming *Vantul, Vartejul, Vedenia, Vulcanul*. The picture shows one of the future Bulgarian or Romanian boats during her transfer.

Ex-Dutch Gunboats

These two photos depict *K 1* and *K 2*, former Dutch gunboats. *K 1* (ex-'A') was launched on 23 November 1940 by P Smit in Rotterdam. On 5 May 1945 she was bombed and sunk by Mosquito fighter-bombers at Aarhus (Kattegat), two days before the end of the fighting. *K 2* (ex-'B') was launched on 28 June 1941 by Gusto in Schiedam. On 9 October 1944 she was torpedoed and heavily damaged by a Beaufighter torpedo-bomber, west of Egersund (Norway) and foundered under tow at Delfzijl in 1945. On 26 July 1946 she was salvaged and scrapped in Vlaardingen between October 1947 and 1948.

K 3 (ex-'C') was launched on 22 March 1941 by P Smit in Rotterdam. She survived the war, was returned to the Dutch navy, renamed *Van Speyk* in 1946 and broken up in 1960.

The HM Submarine Shark, *unable to dive, with two German auxiliary minesweepers nearby, on 6 July 1940.* (Drüppel)

Laid down in 1938, they were all three captured by the Germans in May 1940 and commissioned by the *Kriegsmarine* in 1942. They were fitted with a German close range AA armament of four 37mm (2×2) and twelve 20mm (2×4, 4×1) guns, retaining the main Dutch armament of four 120mm (2×2) guns. By the end of the war they could also carry 200 mines. In the *Kriegsmarine*, *K 1*'s and *K 2*'s power was reduced from 3500 to 2770bhp, the speed dropping correspondingly from 18kts to 14½kts, *K 3* keeping the original power and speed. The German complement was raised to 161. The construction of another four units was cancelled.

Ex-British Submarine Shark

The photograph represents HMS *Shark* (Captain Buckley), surrounded by two German auxiliary minesweepers. On 5 July 1940, after having surfaced around 2200, about 30 miles from Skudesnes, *Shark* was attacked by a German seaplane some fifteen minutes later. She dived, but not quickly enough, and only 20ft down was considerably damaged by the explosions of four or five bombs which fell very close. Unable to dive, about midnight *Shark* was spotted and then attacked many times by more German aircraft with bombs, cannon and machine-gun fire, inflicting more damage and killing and

The RA 9 *(ex-ML 306) after being repaired by the Germans.* (WZ Bilddienst)

wounding many men. Lieutenant-Commander Peter Buckley had to surrender to a German seaplane and, being wounded, he was, with his Sub-Lieutenant Robert Barnes, flown off to Stavanger for medical treatment at about 0615 on 6 July. By this time, *Shark* was very low in the water, stern down and, overhead, at least ten German seaplanes, bombers and fighters were circling. At about 0830, the three German minesweepers, *M 1803*, *M 1806* and *M 1807* arrived and the wounded were then transferred to them, where they were looked after by a naval doctor sent out for that purpose. At 0900 two of the minesweepers attempted to take *Shark* in tow, but almost immediately she began to sink. The tow was hastily cut and *Shark* sank suddenly, stern first, in 700ft of water, 30 miles south-west of Stavanger.

Ex-British Motor Launch ML 306

This is the German motor boat *RA 9* which was the former British motor launch *ML 306* (1941, 75 tons) built by the Solent Shipyard at Sarisbury Green. During the St Nazaire raid, on 28 March 1942, at 0643, *ML 306* was sighted by the German torpedo boat *Jaguar* (*Korvettenleutnant* Paul) who opened fire with her light AA guns. The motor launch returned the fire very courageously but at 0651 *Jaguar* ceased firing, leaving the ML stopped and out of action. On board there were 16 crew members and 14 commandos, of which 9 were seriously injured and 7 killed during the action. *Jaguar* sent a boarding party to *ML 306* and the 23 survivors were taken prisoner, including the ML's captain who, unhappily, later died of his wounds. On *Jaguar*, 3 men were wounded, one of them seriously. After being captured, *ML 306* was repaired by the Germans and renumbered *RA 9*, being classified as a motor minesweeper. She was sunk on 14 June 1944 during an air raid on Le Havre. In the *Kriegsmarine* her armament comprised one 37mm AA gun and three 20mm (3×1) AA guns.

Two views of MTB 17, *probably in Ostend*. (ECPA)

MTB 666 *as captured*. (Drüppel)

The destroyer Hermes *(ex-Greek* Vasilevs Georgios*) showing a pattern of dark bars at various angles, and hence pictured between the end of 1942 and March 1943.* (WZ Bilddienst*)*

Ex-British MTB 17

This is *MTB 17*, a British Power Boat craft, which hit a mine off Ostend on 21 October 1940. *MTB 17* (18 tons standard, 22 tons full load) had been launched in 1938 and completed on 13 March 1939. She is seen here after she was beached and captured by the Germans, who scrapped her.

Two of the ex-Norwegian torpedo boats with a Focke Wulf FW 58 training plane flying over. The armament includes two 102mm, two 20mm AA guns and two torpedo tubes. It seems that the 40mm gun is not carried, but the emplacement is visible. (ECPA)

Ex-British MTB 666

This is the British *MTB 666* which was captured by the German patrol boats *V 1401* and *V 1418*, off Ijmuiden, on 5 July 1944 at about 0340, as she was lying stopped after having been hit, at about 0225, in the engine room by a 37mm shell from another German patrol boat, *V 1415*. The two patrol boats also rescued the MTB's crew and the Germans closed the sea-cocks, took *MTB 666* in tow and brought her to Ijmuiden. She is pictured shortly before she blew up at 0735! Note all the holes from German gunfire which were patched. *MTB 666* was a big Fairmile 'D' type of 102 tons, which had been built by Dorset Yacht Co in Hamworthy and completed on 10 June 1943.

Ex-Greek Vasilevs Georgios I

The destroyer *Hermes* was the ex-Greek *Vasilevs Georgios I* which was laid down in February 1937 by Yarrow and Co in Glasgow, together with a sister-ship, *Vasilissa Olga*. Launched on 3 March 1938, she was delivered to the Greek navy in February 1939. Damaged in a floating dock by German bombing in Salamis on 20 April 1941, *Vasilevs*

Ex-Norwegian torpedo boats on a training sortie, in company of the light cruisers Emden *and* Nürnberg. (ECPA)

Georgios I was salved by the Germans a month later, repaired and commissioned in the *Kriegsmarine* on 21 March 1942. The Germans retained the main armament of four 127mm (4×1) guns which were of German manufacture, as well as the four 37mm (4×1) AA guns. In

addition, five 20mm (5×1) AA guns were added: one on the forecastle, one each side of the bridge on a level with 'B' gun, and one each side of the main (or after) mast on a level with 'X' gun. This German destroyer had a very active career (on convoy duty and minelaying), sharing the destruction of the Greek submarine *Triton* on 16 November 1942, north of the Di Doro Channel in the Aegean with the submarine-chaser *UJ 2102*. Out of 56 men on board, 33 were rescued. On 21 April 1943, off Capri, *Hermes* depth-charged and sank the submarine HMS *Splendid*, 30 men being rescued out of 45. Off the Tunisian coast, on 30 April 1943, and at anchor on 1 and 2 May 1943, *Hermes* was attacked ten times by waves of fighter-bombers. Too damaged to put to sea, she was scuttled on 7 May 1943 at the entrance to Tunis harbour. She claimed no less than eight fighters and one bomber shot down by her light flak, 23 of her men being killed during the engagements.

Leopard (ex-Norwegian Balder*) which was the last of the four to be commissioned in the* Kriegsmarine. *She is carrying her full armament of two 102mm, one 40mm AA, . two 20mm AA guns and two torpedo tubes.* (WZ Bilddienst)

Ex-Norwegian Torpedo Boats

Six torpedo boats were laid down in Norway shortly before the Second World War. Three belonged to the *Sleipner* class, and were all built at the Horten Navy Yard. *Sleipner* was laid down in 1934, launched on 7 May 1936 and commissioned in 1937. *Aeger* was laid down in 1935, launched on 25 August 1936 and commissioned in 1938. *Gyller* was laid down in 1937, launched on 7 July 1938 and commissioned on 1 August 1939. They had a standard displacement of 606 tons. They were followed by the three slightly larger units of the *Odin* class, with a standard displacement of 642 tons. Two of these were also built at the Horten Navy Yard, *Odin* and *Balder*. The third, *Tor*, was built at the Fredrikstad Mekaniske Verksted. They were all laid down in 1938 and respectively launched on 17 January, 11 October and 9 September 1939. *Odin* and *Tor* were commissioned on 17 November 1939 and 9 April 1940, the beginning of the occupation of Norway by German forces. On that day, four units were ready for action, *Tor* being still on trials and *Balder* fitting out.

At the moment of the arrival of German troops, the *Sleipner* and the *Aeger* formed the First Division of destroyers, based originally at Bergen, whilst *Gyller* and *Odin* were stationed in Kristiansand South. The *Sleipner*, after participating in the Allied operations of April and having fired all her ammunition, sailed to Great Britain for repair and replenishment on 26 April 1940, arriving in Lerwick the next day. *Aeger*, which was operating in the defence of Stavanger, intercepted the German cargo ship *Roda* (1928, 6780 tons) near the mouth of the Boknafjord, on the morning of 9 April. She was loaded principally with AA guns and *Aeger* sank her with 25 rounds of 102mm fire. When the Norwegians boarded the German ship, the examining officer from the *Aeger* had been under orders to deactivate *Roda*'s wireless transmitter station. This he failed to do, and *Roda* probably called for assistance. Consequently, *Aeger* scarcely survived her victim, for she was shortly afterwards attacked by several German aircraft which had flown off from the Sola aerodrome, close to Stavanger, which, in the dawn, had been taken by German parachute troops. At 0830, *Aeger* was hit by a bomb amidships in the engine room and began to sink, the wreck drifting ashore on the north side

of Hundvag in the Amoyfjord and was scuttled. The ship lost 8 crew members.

Gyller offered no resistance to German forces, to whom she surrendered on 9 April in Kristiansand, at Tollbodbrygga. As for *Odin*, she was also based in Kristiansand, at Vigebukta and, like *Gyller*, she surrendered intact to the Germans on 9 April. On the same day, *Balder* was captured in Horten, at Karljohansvern, in the process of being completed. *Tor* was captured in Fredrikstad on 9 April, after having been slightly damaged by scuttling.

Being intact, *Gyller* and *Odin* were quickly commissioned by the Germans on 25 April 1940, under the names of *Löwe* (*Kapitänleutnant* Strelow) and *Panther* (*Kapitänleutnant* Neuss, who was also the Flotilla's leader). The other two, *Balder* and *Tor*, were renamed *Leopard* (*Kapitänleutnant* Jacobson) and *Tiger* (*Kapitänleutnant* Jüttner), and respectively commissioned on 26 July and 13 June 1940. The four boats formed the 7th Torpedo Boat Flotilla which, from June to August 1940, was employed on escort duty in the Skagerrak, Kattegat and in southern Norwegian waters. From July 1940 the torpedo boats also trained together, and with the light cruisers *Emden* and *Nürnberg*. In the *Kriegsmarine* they were first armed with two 102mm (2×1), two 20mm (2×1) AA guns and two 533mm (1×2) torpedo tubes. They could also carry 24 mines.

After the 7th Flotilla was disbanded in December 1940, the armament was reduced to one 102mm and two to four 20mm (2/4×1) AA guns and, until the end of the war, they were detailed to the training 27th U-Boat Flotilla in Gotenhafen (Baltic), for acting as torpedo recovery boats. Their useful but undistinguished career was quite uneventful, but they nevertheless were very lucky, surviving the numerous threats of the war, particularly air attacks and mines, which could have been dangerous for them, even in their long training role.

On 30 January 1945, the German passenger ship *Wilhelm Gustloff*, overloaded with more than 6000 refugees on board, was torpedoed and sunk by the Soviet submarine *S 13*, 28 miles north-north-east of Leba in the Baltic. *Löwe* succeeded in rescuing 252 survivors of the 904 who were saved. In May 1945 the four 'Norwegians' were handed back to the Norwegian navy, in which, after five years in the *Kriegsmarine*, they spent fourteen more years before being stricken.

ROMANIAN SUBMARINE OPERATIONS IN THE SECOND WORLD WAR

Following their description of Black Sea minelaying activities in last year's edition, Cristian Crăciunoiu and Mark Axworthy move on to chronicle the little-known operations of the small Romanian submarine flotilla. Much of the detail and most of the illustrations are new to English-language publications.

LIKE many smaller countries, Romania was soon attracted by the submarine's potential to challenge stronger surface fleets and first included a submarine in its 1912–15 naval programme. However, this vessel, an Italian *Medusa* class boat of 255 tons with a speed of 14kts and carrying two 450mm (17.7in) torpedo tubes, was taken over from the builders, Fiat in La Spezia, by the Italian government for its own navy when it entered the First World War in 1915. In 1920 plans for a small 350-ton submarine to be built by Schneider in France had to be abandoned for financial reasons after personnel had already been posted to Toulon for instruction.

Delfinul and Constanţa

When finance again became available in 1926 the curtailed 1912–15 naval programme was relaunched and another submarine, to be named *Delfinul* (Dolphin), was ordered from the Italian government. As Romania's main naval base at Constanţa then lacked the appropriate support facilities, a base ship, to be named *Constanţa* after the port, was also ordered. However, as part of its plan to develop the economy of the Adriatic ports it had gained in the First World War, the Italian government gave the order to the Quarnaro shipyard at Fiume (now Rijeka in Croatia) which had never previously built a submarine. Quarnaro's inexperience was to be the cause of problems that were to dog *Delfinul* throughout her career.

Both vessels were laid down in 1927 and a Romanian technical commission under Comandor Gheorghe Koslinski, who had been the first Romanian to undergo submarine training in France, supervised their construction. Progress on the base ship *Constanţa* was rapid, even though she failed in some respects to meet her original specifications, and she was soon launched in 1929. However, the construction of *Delfinul* lagged badly. She was launched on 6 June 1930 but a year later she had still not been fitted out and *Constanţa* had to leave for Romania without her. By early 1932 the shipyard was still unable to deliver the submarine so the Romanian government finally lost patience and withdrew its technical commission, cancelled the order and took Quarnaro to court in Romania for the repayment of the 135 million Lei already paid out of *Delfinul*'s cost price of 150 million Lei. Unfortunately, although the court case went in favour of the Romanian government, the Italians refused to recognise the Romanian court's jurisdiction in this matter.

There followed three years of deadlock before an accommodation was reached. In August 1935 the Romanian supervisory commission was at last able to return to the yard to commence performance and weapons trials. A stability problem was solved by fitting a small hump near the stern and the submarine responded well in the final diving trials on 16 November 1935, reaching 82m (270ft). However, later, when the Romanians had more experience, they were to realise that *Delfinul* had poor manoeuvrability when submerged and was slow to crash dive. Even now some machinery was still not performing up to specification and there followed yet another delay while the yard made final improvements. *Constanţa*, which had spent the intervening years as a school ship and survey

Delfinul *alongside* Constanţa.

Delfinul *had the Italian trademark of elegant lines and her gun was situated behind a streamlined bulwark. As built she retained two archaic signalling masts.*

Delfinul *under construction at Quarnaro in Fiume*.

General arrangement drawing of Delfinul.

vessel, returned to Quarnaro in February 1936 with *Delfinul*'s new crew aboard. *Delfinul* was finally handed over to Captain 'Niţa' Voinescu on 9 May 1936. Crew training began and in early June, in company with *Constanţa*, *Delfinul* sailed to Naples to load her torpedoes. However, it was found that when fully armed *Delfinul* lost stability; the situation could only be rectified by removing the reserve torpedoes. At last, on 27 June, they sailed for Romania where *Delfinul* was formally taken on strength on Navy Day, 15 August 1936.

Delfinul combined elements of German, Italian and French submarine experience from the First World War. She had a surface displacement of 650 tons, a submerged displacement of 900 tons, six 533mm (21in) torpedo tubes, a dual purpose surface and AA 102mm (4in) Bofors gun, two Zeiss periscopes, a surface speed of 14kts and a submerged speed of 9kts. She was powered by two Sulzer 1600bhp diesels on the surface and two Italian Monza electric motors when submerged. Her range was theoretically 10,000 miles but during the Second World War she reportedly had a practical range of as little as 2000 nautical miles. The crew of 40 consisted of 6 officers, 26 technical petty officers and 8 ordinary seamen.

The arrival of the submarine, which was the most technically advanced vessel in its armoury, was a source of particular pride to the Romanian navy. However, Quarnaro's inexperience meant that both her design and building standards were not all that they might have been. Her nine years under construction meant that her condition on delivery was that of a mature, rather than

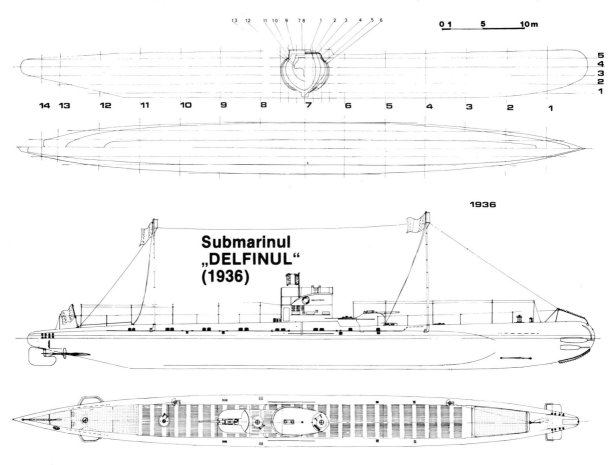

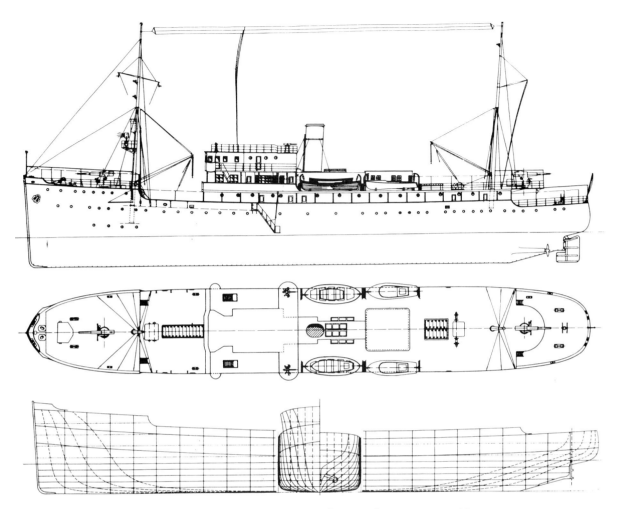

The depot ship Constanţa: *general arrangement.*

Operations, 1941–42

1. 22–27 June 1941

Delfinul was first deployed as a forward picket 30–60 miles ENE of Constanţa in correct anticipation of a Soviet surface raid on the port. However, although she spotted signal lights on several nights, including that of 25/26 June when the Soviet flotilla leaders *Moskva* and *Kharkov* shelled Constanţa, she was unable to identify their sources and was recalled on the 27th.

After the repulse of the Soviet surface raid on 26 June, the Soviet Black Sea Fleet was thrown increasingly onto the defensive by the need to support the Red Army retreating before the belated Romanian–German land attack which began on the night of 2/3 July. *Delfinul* now went over to a series of offensive operations directly tied to the developing land campaign. However, the German command in the Black Sea, to which the Royal Romanian Navy was subordinated, was worried that '*Delfinul* is not trained for operations in strongly defended areas and is probably not technically suitable'. As the only Axis submarine in the theatre she was far more valuable as a ship-in-being tying down large Soviet naval and air contingents in escort and anti-submarine duties across the whole Black Sea than for the amount of damage she was likely to cause the large Soviet naval and merchant forces in the theatre. Thus in 1941 her captains were instructed

new, vessel and she was to suffer technical problems throughout her career. Furthermore, due to the rapid advances made in submarine development since *Delfinul* had originally been designed, she was already obsolescent. During the ensuing war there were no older German U-boats or Soviet-built submarines in service and she would only have been suitable as a training vessel in more advanced navies.

In 1940 the first three torpedo boats which arrived from Britain were also attached to *Constanţa* to form a specialist unit, the *Grupul Submarin si Vedete Torpiloare*, comprising all the offensive torpedo bearing vessels of the Black Sea Division of the Romanian fleet. Under the enthusiastic leadership of Capitan Comandor Voinescu the submarine branch became arguably the most technically proficient arm of the *Forţa Navală Maritimă*, notwithstanding *Delfinul*'s mechanical deficiencies. In June 1940, when the Soviet Union forced Romania to relinquish the predominantly Romanian populated provinces of Basarabia and Northern Bucovina as part of its spoils agreed under the Molotov-Ribbentrop Pact, *Delfinul* was the only vessel immediately ready to put to sea. *Delfinul* was also immediately ready to sail on the outbreak of war with the Soviet Union on 22 June 1941.

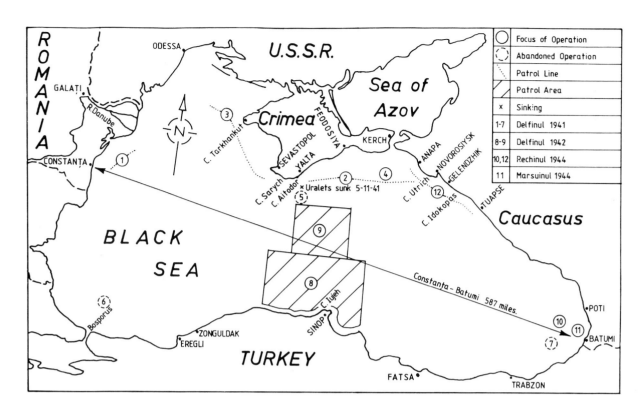

The Black Sea theatre of operations.

Delfinul *alongside an 'R' class destroyer on 15 August 1939.*

not to undertake any action likely to hazard the vessel and were prohibited from attacking escorted merchant vessels.

2. 10–20 July 1941

Delfinul's second mission was to attack Soviet convoys between the Caucasus and the front in the Cape Aitodor–Feodosiya–Novorosiysk region, with her centre of operations 40–50 miles south of Feodosiya. Throughout 1941 the most dangerous place for *Delfinul* was off Constanţa where she had to surface to make her way through the mine barrages and where several of the 44 Soviet submarines in the Black Sea maintained a blockade. Shortly after leaving port on the night of 10 July she received recognition signals from a Soviet submarine and had to crash dive. Throughout the patrol *Delfinul* had to evade numerous Soviet seaplanes and surface vessels without ever sighting a suitable target. On 19 July, as she returned to Constanţa, she met another Soviet submarine on the surface. Both manoeuvred for a surface action but the weather was too bad for either to man their guns and *Delfinul* was soon obliged to dive by a Soviet aircraft.

Constanţa's position in Constanţa harbour was extremely exposed to air attack and when *Delfinul*'s conning tower was perforated by shrapnel from a bomb on 3 August, the whole *Grupul Submarin si Vedete Torpiloare* had to be moved to a more secure mooring.

3. 12–20 August 1941

Delfinul's third mission was to attack Soviet transports between Cape Tarkhankut and Cape Sarych as they evacuated Odessa. In fact the Soviets were reinforcing Odessa but this was not immediately apparent. Her centre of operations was to be 15 miles NW of Cape Tarkhankut. She was specifically instructed not to go inshore or too close to Sevastopol as these areas were believed to be heavily mined.

Once again *Delfinul* was forced to crash dive several times a day throughout the patrol to avoid Soviet seaplanes and surface vessels and again got no shot at a target. At 1200 on 20 August, as she returned on the surface towards Constanţa, a Soviet submarine fired a torpedo which passed just astern of her. *Delfinul* returned machine-gun fire as the Soviet submarine's conning tower broke the surface but without noticeable result.

4. 3–19 September 1941

For her fourth mission *Delfinul* received a new captain, Comandor Corneliu Lungu. He was to attack Soviet communications in the Eastern Black Sea and on the last day to bombard the coast if a suitable target could be found in order to make sure the Soviets continued to tie down forces in coastal defence far behind the battle front.

On 9 September *Delfinul* lost an opportunity to attack the Soviet cruiser *Komintern* off Cape Ortschanok when she zig-zagged behind the cover of rocks off the cape. The distraction of the cruiser meant *Delfinul* also lost the opportunity to attack a large passenger ship under light escort. The following day a frustrated Voinescu apparently broke standing orders to attack two escorted merchant ships but one of their escorts bore straight down on *Delfinul* and in avoiding her the targets were lost. On 11 September another attack was frustrated by bad weather. Several times a day *Delfinul* had to avoid Soviet aircraft and anti-submarine patrol vessels. At this time Luftwaffe shipping reports began to be received, though they were often out of date by the time they could be acted upon. The coastal bombardment was not attempted as bad visibility meant that no target could be identified.

5. 2–7 November 1941

By early November German forces were breaking into the Crimea. *Delfinul*, now under her third captain, Constantin Costăchescu, was tasked with interdicting Soviet supply traffic between the Caucasus and Crimea and attacking Soviet vessels evacuating the Sea of Azov.

On her outward voyage on 3 November *Delfinul* met a Soviet submarine on the surface but quickly lost contact in bad visibility. At 0805 on 5 November she at last spotted an unescorted merchant ship off Yalta. *Delfinul* moved in to the coast at which point her target's zig-zag brought her into a perfect attacking position at about 800m (900yds). A torpedo fired from No 6 stern tube at 0845 hit squarely and was immediately followed by a large secondary explosion. The ship sunk was the 1975-ton *Uralets*, though at the time she was mistaken for a substantially larger vessel. At 0946 *Delfinul* detected approaching Soviet patrol vessels and between 1030 and 1840 was

Crew of Delfinul *on the after casing.*

Delfinul's conning tower and gun position.

repeatedly attacked. Costăchescu worked his way out to sea and away from the dangerous shallows inshore where his escape options were limited. Once in deeper water he dived below 80m and went silent. However, even at this designed depth the pressure popped some rivets. The Soviets made twenty-three depth charge passes overhead and between eighty and ninety explosions were counted. After eight hours *Delfinul* managed to move off south to the Turkish coast where she was able to surface and recharge her batteries the following night. *Delfinul* returned little damaged to Constanţa on 7 November. Although the sinking of the *Uralets* did not represent a major loss to the Soviets, it confirmed to them that defensive precautions were necessary along their entire coastline and was a great boost to Romanian morale.

6. 30 November–3 December 1941

Delfinul's sixth mission was to attack Soviet transports off the Caucasus coast and traffic to the Bosporus. The route out from Constanţa was to be via Cape Iujeh in Turkey to Batumi in the Caucasus. However the operation had to be aborted off the Bosporus due to a combination of bad weather and *Delfinul's* poor mechanical condition.

7. 6–13 December 1941.

The seventh operation was a repeat of the above but this also had to be aborted once Batumi had been reached for the same reasons. Two Soviet submarines had to be avoided as *Delfinul* returned to Constanţa. *Delfinul's*

previous three missions all had to be abandoned prematurely, so for five months over the winter she underwent major repairs to correct her mechanical deficiencies before returning to operations in May 1942.

8. 18–30 May 1942.

Delfinul's eighth mission was designed to coincide with the German–Romanian reconquest of the Kerch peninsula. She was to attack Soviet supply traffic to Sevastopol much of which was being directed from the Caucasus ports via Cape Sinop in Turkey. However, the patrol was completely uneventful apart from the usual aircraft scares, only one of which resulted in four bombs being dropped near *Delfinul* on the 27th.

9. 25 June–3 July 1942

Delfinul's ninth and last sortie was co-ordinated with the final German–Romanian assault on Sevastopol. She was to attack Soviet transports south of Yalta either evacuating or reinforcing Sevastopol. For this final sortie the operational restrictions placed on her in 1941 were lifted and she was at last permitted to attack escorted vessels. It was hoped that the winter repairs had rendered her mechanical condition more reliable and her crew were now deemed sufficiently experienced by the German command for more demanding missions. The Germans also probably now considered her more expendable as she was due to shortly be supplemented by six of their U-boats but, as she carried their only submarine cadre, the Romanian naval command was more cautious.

Within minutes of reaching her station on 27 June

Delfinul *in her 1941 camouflage scheme.*   Delfinul *from the bow.*

Delfinul was spotted from the air and subjected to bombing and depth-charging for eleven hours, 240 explosions being counted. The following day she was surprised on the surface by a Soviet aircraft which missed her with a bomb but succeeded in machine gunning the conning tower before she could crash dive. The damage was superficial. Early in the morning of 1 July *Delfinul* was spotted yet again from the air and over the following thirteen hours of daylight some 268 bombs and depth charges were dropped against her. Intensive Soviet air activity prevented *Delfinul* from identifying any worthwhile targets, which in any case were probably in short supply due to Luftwaffe activity, and once Sevastopol had finally fallen she was recalled to Constanţa on 2 July.

Delfinul's mechanical condition remained as unreliable as ever and she could not mount another mission before the first U-boats of the German 30th Flotilla entered the Black Sea via the Danube in October 1942. With the pressure thus taken off her she was sent for a total refit at the naval dockyard at Galaţi, which she reached on 24 November. However, it seems that the decision was taken not to expend scarce resources on a refit of *Delfinul* when they could be better used to fit out the new submarines *Rechinul* and *Marsuinul*. Furthermore, *Delfinul*'s experienced submariners were needed to form the backbone of the new boats' crews and she was therefore relegated to the role of training ship to the *Centrul de Instructie Submarine si Vedete* at Galaţi.

In 1944, with the Red Army by now inside Romania, *Delfinul* was towed up the Danube to the river yard at Islaz in order to avoid bombing. On 23 August 1944 Romania left the Axis, joining the Allies two days later, and the boat was surrendered to the Soviet Navy on 15 September 1944. She was handed back with some other unserviceable units to the Romanian Navy at Galaţi on 12 October 1945. *Delfinul* had by now long been overtaken by submarine developments elsewhere and was of little operational potential. She retained a technical crew aboard until 1954 when she was towed to Mangalia naval base for training purposes. She made a few local dives there but by now she had numerous leaks and was thereafter kept within the base. In 1959 she was decommissioned and sent to the breakers.

Following *Delfinul*'s withdrawal from operations in 1942 there was a twenty-two month suspension of Romanian submarine operations until *Rechinul* and *Marsuinul* became operational. In the meantime *Constanţa*, which supplied fuel, torpedoes and rations and charged the batteries for all Romanian submarines and MTB missions, also performed similar services for German S-boats and U-boats between 1942 and 1944.

Rechinul and Marsuinul

Romanian experience in the First World War had shown

Part of the original IvS 1:50 plans of Rechinul. *She appears to have undergone major modifications before entering service.*

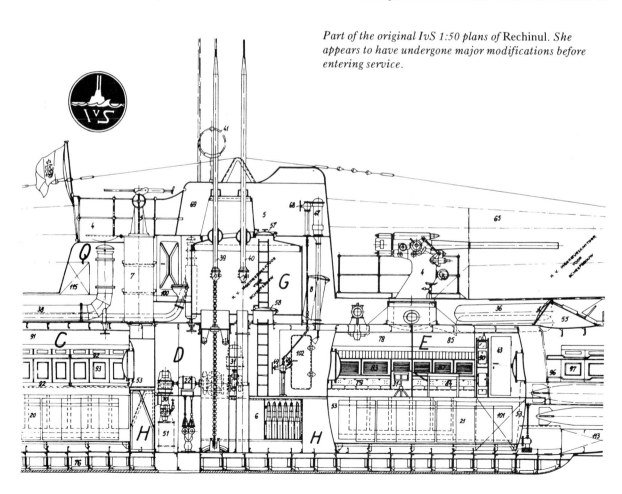

the danger of total dependence on foreign arms suppliers and the navy's bad experience with the *Delfinul* only confirmed the need for self-sufficiency. By the mid-1930s the Romanian engineers who had supervised the building of *Delfinul* had had nine years to closely study her construction and were convinced that they now had the expertise to build their own submarines. In the 1920s Romania had not had the industrial capacity to attempt such a project but the rapid expansion of the country's oil-based economy in the 1930s had encouraged the establishment of an iron and steel industry and the first naval dockyard at Galaţi. Thus when the *Subsecretariatul de Stat al Marinei* asked for tenders for the construction of two submarines in 1937 it was able to award the contract to the Reşiţa Iron and Steel works and the new

Santieri Navale at Galaţi.

The design contract was awarded to the Dutch I v S NV company which had been set up with German capital in order to evade the restrictions of the Versailles Treaty by keeping German engineers up to date with the latest naval developments. One of its products was the submarine *E 1* which had been built in Spain in 1929–30 and was subsequently sold to Turkey in 1934. There her superior characteristics to *Delfinul* had come to the attention of the Romanian admiralty after Turkey and Romania became allies in the Balkan Pact. The two new Romanian submarines were most closely related to *E 1*'s derivative, the German Type IA U-boat (*U 25-U 26*) built in 1935–36, although they were somewhat smaller. As Romania was still allied to France in 1938 the Germans did not initially allow I v S NV to incorporate their latest submarine developments in their designs and they had to undergo considerable upgrading which being fitted out in 1941–43 when Romania was in the Axis camp.

The launch of Rechinul *at Galaţi, 5 May 1941. She was initially known as construction No 929 at Galaţi and then as* S 1 *before her christening.*

Their construction, which began in 1938, was the responsibility of the Romanian engineers of the naval technical committee, many of whom had had experience on *Delfinul*. They were initially assisted by Dutch engineers of I v S and later by German engineers from the Herman Goering Werke. Building was delayed by the outbreak of the general European war and particularly the German occupation of the Netherlands. As a result alternative suppliers had to be found for a number of important components. On 5 and 25 May 1941 the two submarines, provisionally designated *S 1* and *S 2*, were launched. Shortly afterwards they were respectively named *Rechinul* (Shark) and *Marsuinul* (Porpoise). As both vessels were an original design their fitting out was to be a slow process lasting over two years.

In the spring of 1942 the *Centrul de Instructie Submarine si Vedete* was founded at Galaţi for the technical and tactical instruction of the crews for the second generation of Romanian submarines and MTBs. (Six ex-Dutch MTBs were also delivered by the Germans in 1942.) This allowed the Romanians to eventually phase out the very expensive German instructors during sea trials and alone of all Romanian vessels the submarines and MTBs sailed on operations without any German liaison staff aboard. The top naval graduates during the war showed a preference for the MTBs but the Romanian Admiralty reportedly directed them into the submarine arm, *Rechinul* having first choice.

Rechinul was handed over on 9 May 1943 to her first captain, Locotenent Comandor Corneliu Lungu, who had previously commanded *Delfinul*. She reached Constanţa

Marsuinul *on the stocks at Galati. She was launched on 25 May 1941. She was initially known as construction No 930 at Galati and then as S 2 until her christening. As a minelayer she had a broader beam than* Rechinul *but their relationship is obvious.*

on 24 May 1943 and began a long series of trials, initially focusing on ensuring a water-tight hull. Although only designed to dive to 80m *Rechinul* was successfully taken to 110m (360ft). Between November 1943 and February 1944 torpedo firing tests were carried out.

Rechinul displaced 585/680 tons, was armed with six 533mm (21in) torpedo tubes, a Krupp 88mm submarine gun and an Oerlikon 20mm light AA gun. The engines were MAN diesels and other precision devices aboard were also German, while the hull and many simpler internal components were Romanian-made.

The third Romanian submarine, *Marsuinul*, was inspired by contemporary Swedish minelayers and may have played a role in the development of the German Type XB minelayers. She was designed as a minelayer because the north-west basin of the Black Sea was relatively shallow and offered ample scope for mining and it was assumed that the massive Soviet Black Sea Fleet would make surface minelaying difficult. However, by mid-1942 the Soviets had lost all their naval bases in the western Black Sea and the Royal Romanian Air Force was the dominant air contingent over these waters, allowing Romanian surface vessels to mine the area with relative impunity (see *Warship 1991*). *Marsuinul* was therefore completed as a conventional torpedo-carrying submarine. She retained the potential to carry ten mines but ten other stowage compartments were converted to contain extra fuel tanks on her one operational sortie.

Marsuinul was built between 1938 and 1943. She was launched on 25 May 1941. Under Capitan Grigore Ciolac she reached Constanţa in August 1943. On 28 September 1943 *Marsuinul* had one sailor wounded during a Soviet air attack on Constanţa, the Romanian submarine arm's only combat casualty. She was formally handed over to the navy on 4 October 1943. The most difficult problem on trials proved to be suppressing the escape of gas when launching a torpedo which would give the submarine's

position away but this was eventually solved by a retired German engineer. Trials continued up to April 1944, when, after successful crash dive tests and deep dives to below 100m, *Marsuinul* was accepted into the navy shortly after *Rechinul*.

Marsuinul was a submarine of 508/630 tons and armed with six 533mm torpedo tubes, a dual purpose submarine 88mm gun and a 20mm Oerlikon AA gun. She had 45 crew – 5 officers, 25 technical petty officers and 15 sailors.

The new Romanian submarines were fitted with aerials which enabled them to pick up German long wave transmissions from Bernau while at a depth of 20m. The German XB Dienst had broken the Soviet naval codes and in 1944 was able to report overnight with extraordinary accuracy which Soviet aircraft or vessels had spotted or attacked the Romanian submarines the previous day and what follow-up action they were taking. This was particularly valuable because Soviet anti-submarine activity proved to be more capable in 1944 than it had been in 1941. It became operational practice to head temporarily for the Turkish coast when German reports indicated Soviet anti-submarine activity was reaching threatening levels. The Romanian submarines were also reportedly fitted with the German 'Enigma' decrypter for which they were given a special cylinder in a sealed envelope to be opened once on station.

Charts were German and had apparently been prepared by German merchantmen before the war. Food was also German, though characteristically the Romanians wondered why the Germans packed the best rations for the end of the voyage by which time it was quite possible for them to have already been sunk without the opportunity to enjoy them.

Marsuinul's two engines were named 'Lili' and 'Margo' after two well-known prostitutes from Galaţi who had a similarly high work rate.

Comandor Corneliu Lungu on the conning tower of Rechinul *in 1944.*

Vosper MTB Viscolul, Rechinul *and* Constanţa *moored in
Constanţa harbour in June 1943.* Rechinul *had recently
arrived and was just beginning trials.*

Operations in 1944

10. *Rechinul*: 20 April–15 May 1944

Rechinul's first mission, under Locotenent Comandor
Corneliu Lungu, was initially to complete her operational
training off the Turkish coast and then to proceed to
Batumi and interdict Soviet traffic trying to interfere with
the German–Romanian evacuation of the Crimea.

On 20 April *Rechinul* sailed to the Turkish coast and
began working up between Eregli and Fatsa. However,
on 26 April 1944 *Rechinul* received orders for a secret
mission not recorded in the operational files of the
Romanian GHQ. Turkey was under considerable Allied
pressure to take advantage of the imminent Axis loss of
the Crimea to declare war on Germany. *Rechinul* was
therefore to explore the Turkish coast between Sinop and
Zonguldak in order to find the ports where Axis submarines could cause the maximum losses to Turkey's
merchant fleet and to position herself for an attack at the
most vulnerable point. In Zonguldak harbour five or six
large ships were found loading coal and this port was
selected. Not knowing if Zonguldak was protected by
anti-submarine mines *Rechinul* waited until a Turkish tug
entered and followed in her wake to within two miles of
the ships; a distance far enough out to allow surfacing for
battery charging at night but an ideal platform from
which to launch a devastating attack on the unsuspecting
Turks. However, after two days poised in this position it
was learnt by radio that Turkey had opted to retain its

*The spiral thread around the periscopes was intended to
lessen the tell-tale wake behind them. A possibly
apocryphal Romanian story has it that the officers of the
Romanian river monitor fleet used to dangle champagne
bottles in the water over the side of their vessels to keep
them cool and noticed that a particular brand of
Romanian champagne, which came in a cane protective
cover with spiral ribbing, left almost no wake. The story
concludes that this principle was later applied by the
Romanians to* Rechinul *and* Marsuinul *and subsequently
taken up by the Germans in the Atlantic!*

neutrality and *Rechinul* was ordered to resume her patrol between Batumi and Novorosiysk and to attack any Soviet vessel above destroyer size capable of interfering with the German–Romanian supply or evacuation of Sevastopol.

Several times *Rechinul* was spotted and attacked by the Soviets. On these occasions German radio intercepts allowed her to avoid Soviet follow-up operations by sailing to the Turkish coast for 24 hours, returning when Soviet activity had subsided. On 9 May she received news that the final evacuation of Sevastopol was underway and was ordered to maintain her station until it was completed. Once the Sevastopol evacuation was concluded by 13 May *Rechinul* was recalled via the Turkish coast to Constanţa, entering on 15 May.

11. *Marsuinul*: 11 May–27 May 1944

Marsuinul's first and only mission was to conduct a final operational training cruise between Eregli and Trabzon on the Turkish coast and then to replace *Rechinul* off Batumi.

At 2200 on 11 May *Marsuinul* left the Constanţa barrages with a convoy for Sevastopol. At 0100 on 12 May

one of the convoy's German R-boat escorts fired on *Marsuinul* but desisted on seeing her recognition signal. At 0230 *Marsuinul* passed by a Soviet submarine but the two crews were so surprised that they simply sailed past each other without reacting. At 0630 an aircraft was spotted and *Marsuinul* crash dived. Neither gave the recognition signal with the result that the flying boat, which turned out to be a German BV, called in the German-commanded Croat KFK (*Kriegsfischkutter*, or MFV) flotilla of six vessels based in Bulgaria. This launched a series of attacks from 0830 onwards. Comandant Çiolac dived to 80–90m (260–300ft) and went silent, keeping under way at the minimum speed of 1–1.5kts. As was the unofficial practice established by *Delfinul*, all water-tight doors were kept open when under attack so that all crew shared the same fate. When an electrical compressor was shaken loose from its supports, causing a short circuit which could not be fixed for two days, it was decided to risk surfacing to launch a recognition signal. However, at 20m (65ft) the KFKs renewed their attack, forcing *Marsuinul* back down to maximum depth. At 2000 the KFKs broke off their attack having dropped some 420 depth charges. At 2145 *Mar-*

Loading a torpedo from the Constanţa. *'I have seen torpedoes loaded onto Italian, German and Romanian submarines. We, the Romanians, were just like the Italians; everyone simultaneously pushing and heaving and shouting advice and encouragement. On the other hand the Germans silently executed the operation under a single command. However, the loading times were the same.' Engineer Camil Cernat.*

suinul surfaced to signal that she had been attacked by 'U-Jäger aliat' (allied submarine chasers) but this was misunderstood ashore as being attacked by *Uliat*, an obscure vessel in the Soviet Arctic Fleet! During the following night divers checked for damage but apart from some missing wooden deck planking there was none.

She then sailed to the Turkish coast for final training before being sent to Batumi on 14 May. On arrival off the Caucasus coast she came to the surface to establish her exact position in order to avoid further cases of mistaken identity as a German submarine had been allocated a patrol station slightly further north off Poti. Within the hour she was depth-charged and was attacked several more times the same day while standing out to sea at periscope depth. During her escape manoeuvres she scraped a mine or buoy cable. She slipped back to the Turkish coast for 24 hours before returning to Batumi on the 17th.

No sooner was she back on station than she was again detected and depth-charged between 0400 and 1200 and as a result again had to head for the Turkish coast. However, the Soviets also shifted their operations to the Turkish coast and on the 19th she was again detected, receiving 43 depth charges. The following day she was apparently spotted by a Soviet submarine which missed her with a torpedo but called in surface vessels which dropped a further 31 anti-submarine grenades. On 21 May she was again detected and suffered another attack of 43 depth charges. At 2100 she was instructed that it was

clear to return to the zone of operations off Batumi. At 0455 on 23 May she may yet again have been detected but the depth-charging on this occasion was distant and inaccurate. However, from 0755 she was definitely detected and closely depth charged on and off throughout the rest of the day. At 2025 that evening *Marsuinul* was recalled to Constanţa. She returned via the Turkish coast.

On 26 May *Marsuinul* surfaced to meet an R-boat at the entrance to Constanţa mine barrage. However at 1100 she was surprised by a Soviet aircraft which dropped six bombs astern without effect. *Marsuinul* crash dived but missed her rendezvous and had to wait until the following day to enter Constanţa.

Marsuinul did not make any further patrols and was taken over by the Soviets on 5 September 1944. She alone of the Romanian submarines was not returned after the war, probably because her minelaying capacity was viewed by the Soviets as a continuing threat and a design inspiration. She was expended as a torpedo target in 1967.

12. *Rechinul*: 15 June–29 July 1944

Rechinul's final mission lasted 45 days and was the longest Romanian patrol of the war. She was to report on the movement of Soviet warships above destroyer size off the Caucasus coast between Anapa and Tuapse. It was from these North Caucasus ports that the Soviets were expected to launch any seaborne invasion of the Romanian coast. It would appear that her instructions may not have included orders to launch attacks. If true this would

Rechinul (foreground) and Marsuinul *under inspection. Their relationship is obvious from the similarities to be seen in the photograph. However,* Marsuinul's *hull was much broader than that of* Rechinul *in order to accommodate the mines for which she was initially designed but never carried.*

Rechinul *leaving Constanţa harbour.*

probably have been for political reasons.

Apart from once observing a major group of Soviet vessels exercising, *Rechinul* had only the usual attentions of Soviet anti-submarine vessels and aircraft to report. On 28 June she was depth-charged so closely that minor leaks were caused aboard. On 5, 19 and 24 July she was again depth-charged but without suffering further damage. She returned to Constanţa at 2215 on 29 July.

On 5 September 1944, shortly after Romania's defection to the Allies, she and the rest of the Romanian fleet were taken over by the Soviets. In August 1951 *Rechinul* was returned to the Romanian navy at Galaţi. However, the Peace Treaty of 1947 prohibited Romania from possessing operational submarines and she could not be recommissioned. She was in any case obsolescent and was broken up in 1959.

CB-1, CB-2, CB-3, CB-4 and CB-6

In late 1943 the Romanians had the windfall of five Italian pocket submarines, *CB-1, CB-2, CB-3, CB-4* and *CB-6*. As fellow Latins their Italian commanders had an extremely good rapport with the Romanians. When Italy surrendered to the Allies in September 1943 they initially declared continuing allegiance to the Axis but at the first available opportunity, 30 November 1943, they surrendered their vessels to the Romanians rather than continue operating with the Germans. The crews became prisoners of war and the Romanians formed the pocket submarines into their Second Submarine Flotilla despite German requests for both crews and vessels to be handed over. However, only two could be made serviceable and although they made practice dives in Constanţa harbour in 1944 neither became fully operational. Three of them were sunk at their moorings in the Soviets' only effective air raid on Constanţa on 20 August 1944. All were taken by the Soviets on 5 September.

Conclusion

The designs of *Delfinul, Rechinul* and *Marsuinul* were all based on foreign, mostly German, experience gained in largely oceanic waters. However, Romanian experience in the Second World War was to show that small submarines of 200–300 tons were more suited to the restricted threatre of operations in the Black Sea which was only 600 miles at its widest and where most traffic was in the shallows off the coast. The Soviet Black Sea Fleet, which unlike the Romanians had had submarine experience in these waters in the First World War, had adopted the Molodki 'M' class Series VI (161/202 tons) and Series XII (205/256 tons) coastal submarines with some success and when the Germans brought submarines down the Danube in 1942 they had the benefit of *Delfinul's* experience and opted to deploy six 279-ton Type IIB U-boats.

The direct impact of *Delfinul's* operations was very limited, only a single merchant ship being sunk. The reasons for this were a mixture of her poor and extended construction which resulted in endless mechanical problems, an obsolescent design by Second World War standards, and her initially inexperienced crew. When these were combined with her importance to the Axis as a ship-in-being they led to crippling restrictions being placed on her operations in 1941. Unfortunately, she met no suitable targets after these restrictions were lifted in June 1942. Nevertheless, her mere existence tied down infinitely larger Soviet resources in 1941–42 and she passed on an experienced cadre of submariners to *Rechinul* and *Marsuinul.*

Rechinul and *Marsuinul* had time to conduct only three patrols between them, two of which included operational training exercises and the third was apparently restricted to observation. Thus, though they were new vessels of comparatively modern design and *Rechinul's* long final cruise indicated that Romania's submarine arm had reached operational maturity, they were destined to have little impact in the few months before Romania left the Axis on 23 August 1944.

Three of the Italian midget submarines of the CB-1 *type in Constanţa harbour in June 1942.*

The six German U-boats in the Black Sea claimed twelve Soviet freighters averaging 2440 tons each in two years of operations (only five of which appear to have been confirmed by name from Soviet sources). Thus *Delfinul*'s confirmed sinking of one freighter of 1975 tons in her one year of operations is similar to German results. Furthermore, the U-boats claimed no Soviet merchantmen in 1944 during the period when *Rechinul* and

Rechinul in Constanţa harbour, 1944. The camouflaged vessel moored astern of her is the naval auxiliary Romania *which was then acting as base ship for German S-boats.*

Marsuinul had their equally barren operational service. By contrast the 55 Soviet submarines used in the Black Sea in the Second World War sank about 20 Axis merchantmen for the loss of 28 of their own number. Thus, on the thin statistical evidence available, the limited results achieved by the Romanian submarines were consistent with those of the Germans in the Black Sea, while their loss rate was vastly better than that of the Soviets.

Note: The following specifications for *Delfinul, Rechinul, Marsuinul* and the submarine depot ship *Constanţa* are taken from Romanian naval records and refer to their actual operational capacities during the Second World War, rather than their theoretical or designed specifications. In particular it can be seen how severely limited *Delfinul* was.

Delfinul *TECHNICAL SPECIFICATION*

Builder:	Quarnaro; Fiume, Italy (now Rijeka, Croatia)
Design:	Quarnaro
Laid down:	August 1927
Launched:	22 June 1930
Commissioned:	15 June 1936
Broken up:	1959
Displacement:	650/900 tons
Dimensions:	68m × 5.9m × 3.6m
Machinery:	Two Sulzer 1600bhp diesels; two shafts; 14kts surfaced. Two Monza electric motors; 9kts submerged
Range:	2000 nautical miles; approx 15 days (Designed range 10,000 miles.)
Armament:	1–102mm (4in) Bofors gun; 58 rounds 6–533mm (21in) TT (4 bow, 2 stern); 6 Whitehead torpedoes; no reserve 2 British machine-guns; 5 rifles; 5 pistols
Crew:	40 (6 Officers, 26 technical petty officers, 8 ordinary seamen.)

Rechinul (S 1) *TECHNICAL SPECIFICATION*

Builder:	Santieri Navale, Galaţi, Romania
Design:	NV Ingenieurskantoor voor Scheepsbouw, Den Haag, The Netherlands
Laid down:	1938
Launched:	5 May 1941
Commissioned:	9 May 1943
Broken up:	1959
Displacement:	585/680 tons (?)
Dimensions:	58m × 5.6m × 3.6m
Machinery:	Two MAN 1840bhp diesels; two shafts; 17kts surfaced Two electric motors; 9kts submerged.
Range:	7000 nautical miles; approx 45 days.
Armament:	1–88mm Krupp submarine gun; 60 rounds 6–533mm (21in) TT (4 bow, 2 stern); 10 G7E German torpedoes 1–20mm Oerlikon AA gun; 3200 rounds 1–8mm MG; 2 SMGs; 5 rifles; 5 pistols
Crew:	45 (5 Officers, 25 technical petty officers, 15 ordinary seamen.)

Marsuinul (S 2) *TECHNICAL SPECIFICATION*

Builder:	Santieri Navale, Galaţi, Romania
Design:	NV Ingenieurskantoor voor Scheepsbouw, Den Haag, The Netherlands
Laid down:	1938
Launched:	25 May 1941
Commissioned:	4 October 1943
Broken up:	Unknown
Displacement:	508/630 tons (?)
Dimensions:	68.7m × 6.5m × 3.6m
Machinery:	Two MAN 1840bhp; two shafts; 16kts surfaced Two electric motors; 9kts submerged
Range:	8000 nautical miles; approx 45 days
Armament:	1–88mm Krupp submarine gun; 60 rounds 4–533mm (21in) TT (2 bow, 2 stern); 6 G7E German torpedoes 1–20mm Oerlikon AA gun; 3200 rounds 1–8mm MG; 2 SMGs; 5 rifles; 5 pistols
Crew:	45 (5 Officers, 25 technical petty officers, 15 ordinary seamen.)
Note:	*Marsuinul* had originally been designed to carry 20 mines, ten on either side. However, she was completed with only five mine storage bays per side, the remainder being converted to carry extra fuel

Constanţa *(SUBMARINE DEPOT SHIP)* *TECHNICAL SPECIFICATION*

Builder:	Quarnaro; Fiume, Italy (now Rijeka, Croatia)
Laid down:	15 August 1927
Launched:	8 November 1928
Commissioned:	1931
Displacement:	2300 tons
Dimensions:	77.32m × 11.28m × 4.1m
Machinery:	Two 1000bhp diesels; two shafts; 13kts
Radius:	12,000 miles
Armament:	2–3in (76mm) Armstrong guns 2–20mm Oerlikon AA guns 2–13.2mm Hotchkiss AA guns
Facilities:	Engineering shop; Torpedo shop and loading room; bakery; salvage gear; diving apparatus; submarine signalling equipment
Crew:	136
Note:	*Constanţa* was originally equipped with two Bofors 102mm (4in) dual purpose guns but these were transferred to the minelayer *Amiral Murgescu* before the war and replaced by two 76mm (3in) guns which had been removed from Romania's 'M' class destroyers in the mid-1920s

KORMORAN VERSUS SYDNEY

This battle was the only clash between an auxiliary cruiser and a conventional cruiser during two world wars in which the latter was sunk. Because there were no survivors from *Sydney*, and no other Australian or allied eyewitnesses whatsoever, historical accounts depend exclusively on descriptions provided by survivors of the *Kormoran*. In the following analysis of the battle Kim Kirsner describes the event, outlines the way it has been dealt with historically, identifies issues of continuing controversy, reconstructs the aftermath of the engagement including the movement patterns of lifeboats, lifebelts, liferafts, oil and other flotsam and jetsam, and, finally, advances a simple reconstruction of these movements. The reconstruction successfully explains most of the variance in the data, but it leaves some questions about the destruction of *Sydney* unanswered. The search planned by the Western Australian Maritime Museum may yet yield answers to the most challenging mystery in twentieth century naval history.

AT first glance the waters off the coast of Western Australia and what used to be called the Dutch East Indies appear to be far from the naval conflicts of the twentieth century, yet these conflicts left their mark. As early as 1864 a Confederate States raider cruised briefly off the coast of Western Australia, and left a string of songs and legends in Fremantle. In 1914 the SMS *Emden*, a German light cruiser caught in the Far East by the outbreak of the Great War, was tracked down off the Cocos Islands south-west of Batavia (now Djakarta) and sunk by the first HMAS *Sydney*, a light cruiser of the then fledgling Royal Australian Navy. In 1940 the HSK *Atlantis* and the HSK *Pinguin*, auxiliary cruisers in the *Kriegsmarine*, passed this way too, leaving mines, sinking ships, and trade disruption in their wake. In 1941 the HSK *Kormoran* approached the coast of Western Australia after nearly twelve months at sea, during which time she had captured or sunk eleven allied vessels. This article deals with the end of the *Kormoran*'s voyage, and the events surrounding the more or less simultaneous loss of both that ship and another HMAS *Sydney*, the second light cruiser of the RAN to bear that name.

The Official Account

According to the captain of the *Kormoran* (Detmers, 1959), his vessel was proceeding north at 11kts when *Sydney* was detected to the north-north-east. The *Kormoran* then steered west, ignored signals from *Sydney* or replied by flag, broadcast a 'suspicious ship' signal, and then, when *Sydney* closed to a distance of about 1000yds, lowered the Dutch (or Norwegian) flag then flying, raised the German flag, and opened fire with both main and short range weapons. The engagement lasted about 30 minutes. The *Kormoran* was only hit by two or three 6in rounds, but these critically damaged her, and the crew abandoned ship at about 2300, using scuttling charges to ensure the vessel's final destruction. The *Sydney* was last observed on fire and steaming or drifting to the south-west until about 2100–2300. She had been hit by between 50 and 150 150mm (5.9in) rounds and one or two torpedoes. There were some reports that she eventually blew up. Over the ensuing 209 hours, 318 *Kormoran* survivors reached the West Australian coast north of Carnarvon (about 600 miles north of Perth/Fremantle), or were rescued from lifeboats or liferafts at sea. Although the first survivors from the *Kormoran* were discovered and rescued by chance by a passing passenger vessel, the *Aquitania*, some 84 hours after the battle, the Australian naval authorities were not aware of critical details until many hours later, and Search and Rescue (SAR) aircraft were not over the area of the battle until about 135 hours had elapsed. One vessel, an Australian tug, *Uco*, recorded but did not immediately report an unclear QQQQ signal (*ie* 'disguised merchant raider') at 1803 on 19 November

1941, and one shore station (Geraldton) recorded a garbled message at the same time. According to Detmers (1959) the battle commenced in position 111°E 26°34′S (26°00′ in an initial report) at 1555 on 19 November 1941, and the *Sydney* was last seen drifting or steaming south-south-east at approximately 6kts, giving a further correction in that direction of about 20km, depending on assumptions about her subsequent speed and time of destruction.

HMAS Sydney *was a light cruiser of the three-ship* Amphion *class (launched in 1933) which were originally built for the Royal Navy and transferred to the Australian before the outbreak of war. This photo was taken early in 1941.* (By courtesy of D K Brown)

A poor photo but one of the few known views of the raider Kormoran – *with the armament concealed, a typical cargo ship of the period, although of characteristically German build to the knowledgeable eye.* (Australian War Memorial, Canberra)

Captain Detmars of Kormoran. (Australian War Memorial)

Alternative Accounts

The account outlined above is a summary of the official version as first described by John Curtin, the Prime Minister of Australia, on 3 December 1941, and as re-stated by the official historian of the RAN, Hermion Gill (1957). The critical feature which distinguishes the official account from a range of alternatives is that it involved a one-stage battle, whereas most of the alternatives describe a two-stage battle. Remarkably perhaps, a two-stage battle was described by Bernard Hall in London's *Daily Express* barely six days after the first survivors came ashore north of Perth (*ie* on 1 December 1941). According to Hall,

> It was a torpedo which sank the cruiser *Sydney*. In one of the strangest actions of the sea, it was fired at the moment of the Australian warship's triumph.
>
> By gunfire she [*ie Sydney*] had shattered a powerful armed raider, and she was closing the range to sink her and pick up survivors when she was hit, and victor and vanquished went to the bottom.

One reason why Bernard Hall's account is remarkable is that it actually antedates publication of the official story. Another is that it antedates all even remotely comparable reports in the *West Australian*, the local newspaper (one account with similar elements appeared on 4 December 1941). A third is that there appear to be no other references to a two-stage battle in the London newspapers of the time; this account 'sank' without trace. And finally, Bernard Hall, though still alive in 1991, cannot recall writing the article. The two-stage account gains additional support from the presence of independent descriptions of other aspects of the event. One of these is from a survivor who is recorded as stating that he was in a lifeboat between the vessels when *Sydney* (presumably bent on rescue) was hit by a torpedo (discussed by Montgomery, 1981 and Winter, 1984). The second is from a discussion in which one of the survivors was identified as the torpedoman who remained on board *Kormoran* after she had been damaged specifically in order to sink *Sydney* (copy in possession of WA Maritime Museum). And finally, there is eyewitness testimony that *Kormoran* survivors appear to have left the ship in two stages, before twilight and in disarray (Gosseln, 1953), and in an orderly manner some four to five hours later (Detmers, 1959).

In yet another account, Montgomery (1981, 1983) suggested that a Japanese submarine, then in contact with *Komoran*, was responsible for sinking *Sydney*. Montgomery goes on to review evidence that communications involving Roosevelt were subsequently censored to conceal the fact that both British and US authorities were aware of Japanese involvement in this action, just 18 days before the attack on Pearl Harbor.

Questions and Issues

Design and Tactics. The most remarkable aspect of *Sydney*'s tactics concerns the way in which her captain apparently brought her to about 1000yds from *Kormoran* – then claiming to be '*Straat Malakka*' – without having first tested and confirmed the identity of the ship with shore authorities. Such a procedure was already well in place, and used effectively by HMS *Devonshire* against HSK *Atlantis* in the South Atlantic just three days after the *Sydney–Kormoran* battle. At this range, as her captain would have known, *Sydney* was far inside the inner edge of her immunity zone for 150mm shells, and, as *Kriegsmarine* raiders were known to be armed with these weapons, she was courting disaster from an unidentified ship.

A related issue concerns the protection provided *Sydney*'s fire control system. Winter (1984) claimed that *Sydney*'s fire control system should have been protected against battle damage under the conditions actually encountered during the engagement with *Kormoran*, and that the major responsibility therefore lay with her designers. Against this, however, it may be noted that Royal Navy designers had tried and failed to develop a protected fire control system just before *Sydney* was designed (Raven & Roberts, 1980, p133). However, even if this system had been installed it would not have protected *Sydney*'s fire control system from 155mm rounds at the range of the battle with *Kormoran*, and it is unlikely that even the far larger US cruisers built toward the end of the Second World War had fire control systems which would have survived medium artillery at this range. The fire control systems of the day were high in the ship, and the weight and stability penalties associated with stronger structures, power, and armour plate at this height were too great.

Communications. There is no direct evidence that *Sydney* received advance information about the presence or location of *Kormoran* prior to visual contact at 1600 on 19 November. The role of advance information in the account depends critically on the position of the initial contact between the vessels. If contact occurred on or near the direct route between Sunda Straight and Fremantle, advance information is probably irrelevant; and it may be assumed that the ships met by chance. But if initial contact took place at or to the west of 111°E – substantially to the west of the direct route from Sunda Straight to Fremantle and Cape Leeuwin – the case for a signals intelligence contribution to the meeting may be stronger. That signals intelligence could have played a role is clear from evidence that both the submarine and raider codes were being read during November 1941. That the German submarine codes were being read and used is suggested by the exceptionally low merchant ship losses and the relatively high submarine losses for the month (Showell, 1987, p21–22), although the coincidental movements of U-boats to the Mediterranean may have been another factor reducing their performance and survival rate at this time. Evidence that the raider code was penetrated is less clear, although Van Der Vat (1990, p316) claims that HSK *Atlantis*'s position was revealed by

Sydney's *Captain Burnett*. (Australian War Memorial)

Junior officers of the Sydney *posing in front of a carley float of the type found by* Heros. (West Australian Maritime Museum)

penetration of the raider code rather than the submarine code.[1] Finally, if a Japanese submarine was involved – as argued by Montgomery (1981, 1983) – the relevant communications through Berlin or Tokyo may have been penetrated and read at that time.

Controversy surrounds the existence of a signal or signals from *Sydney* in the hours immediately after contact. According to the official account, there were no transmissions from *Sydney* prior to or during the engagement. However, a signal transcription together with depositions regarding its authenticity have been widely circulated in Australia in recent years (1988–91), and the official response from the Australian Department of Defence – indicating that the signal emanated from a depot in the *city* of Sydney – does not receive convincing support from scrutiny of the transcription. Why, for example, would a depot in the city of Sydney have sent a signal about a vessel with a name like '*Straat Malakka*' (phonetic analysis suggests that the signal is a corruption of Straat Malakka) on 19 November 1941?

Survival. Much of the emotion surrounding the engagement between *Sydney* and *Kormoran* stems from the absence of survivors from *Sydney*. Was this surprising? Unfortunately the answer to even this simple question is not clear, and hinges critically on the form of the engagement between the vessels. If the description given by *Kormoran* survivors was substantially correct, and *Sydney* caught fire after being hit by 50 or more 155mm rounds, the absence of survivors may not be surprising. According to this version of events, battle and fire damage may have precluded the use of lifeboats and even liferafts,[2] and, although the water temperature off Carnarvon in November would not have proved fatal (69–73 degrees), dehydration would have left few if any survivors when the first SAR aircraft reached the relevant area 135 hours after the engagement. However, if *Sydney* was sunk by a torpedo or torpedoes, it may have been possible to launch liferafts or even lifeboats, and survivors might then have been expected.

The loss of the USS *Indianapolis* en route from Guam to Leyte in July 1945 provides an interesting yardstick (Newcomb, 1958). The *Indianapolis* was hit by four torpedoes, and sank in 12 minutes. No effective signal was transmitted after the initial damage, and no lifeboats were launched. Of her crew of 1200, some 800–900 survived the sinking and awaited rescue on liferafts or in the water. The survivors were discovered by chance by a passing aircraft 84 hours after the disaster, and between the 84th and 108th hours, 301 sailors were rescued by aircraft and ships which converged on the area. If anything, the conditions were more benign than those which applied off Carnarvon, and it is clear that there would have been very few survivors from *Sydney* when the first SAR aircraft reached the general area 135 hours after the engagement. Furthermore, if the most appropriate drift location was only identified after 190–200 hours by *Wyrallah* and *Heros*, the absence of survivors from *Sydney* is not surprising. It is not obvious, however, why no bodies from *Sydney* were discovered; several ships spent four or more days finding and sinking bodies and other debris from the *Indianapolis*.

Leadership and Loyalty. The history of the engagement between *Sydney* and *Kormoran* has generally been written as if the *Kormoran* survivors were bound to tell 'the truth, the whole truth, and nothing but the truth' by some ancient code of the sea. This focus on largely unstated moral issues has tended to polarize the historical accounts, as evidenced in the books by Montgomery (1981, 1983) and Winter (1984). Yet, in practice, it may have been wiser to assume that the primary duty of the *Kormoran* survivors *as they saw it* was to withhold information from an enemy, where this could have included information about the *Kormoran*, the battle, the location of the battle, and much more. Put simply, instead of adopting the account or accounts supplied by *Kormoran* survivors as 'eyewitness testimony', it might have been safer to treat them as a 'prisoner-of-war' yarns from the outset, and therefore vulnerable to both omission and confabulation.

The conflict inherent in the position of *Kormoran* survivors is clearly illustrated in Detmers' (1959) own account of the battle. Where survivors are concerned, Detmers' *attitudes* and *behaviour* are in stark conflict. For example, with reference to his *attitude* when he was rescued, he writes that

> On their account [*ie Sydney* survivors], I decided that as soon as possible I would give the position at which our engagement with the Australian cruiser had taken place so that the search could be properly sited and there would be the best possible chance of picking up survivors (Detmers, 1959, p198).

and

> He then asked me where the engagement had taken place, and I told him immediately, as I had made up my mind to do: 111°E by 26°34′S. He immediately made a note of the position, and I knew that the search would now take place where it would be the most effective, and perhaps save the lives of more of my men. (Detmers, 1959, p200)

But contrast this with his comments about the sighting of *Aquitania*,

> Then that morning we sighted a white steamer with no less than four funnels. The men wanted to fire rocket signals, but I forbade it. I immediately recognized the vessel as an auxiliary cruiser. As I discovered later, it was the *Aquitania*, as she continued her course at a distance of about five miles without her look-out having spotted us. . . . At first the men had been very disgruntled when I refused to allow them to do anything to attract the attention of the ship, but when I explained to them why,[3] they realized that I was right and their mood improved. (Detmers, 1959, p200)[4]

The significant feature embedded in these quotations is not that the alternative decision – to signal the *Aquitania* and inform her crew that there were survivors in the

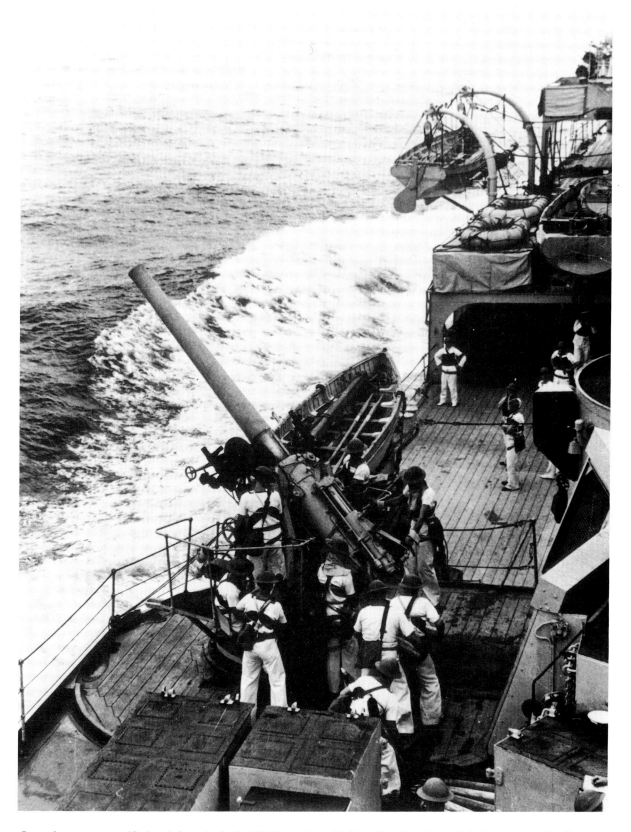

Crew close up to one of Sydney's *four single 4in Mk V mounts amidships. The disposition of the boats and carley floats gives an indication of their vulnerability and, apart from the seaboat under the davits, the difficulty of getting them into the water quickly.* (West Australian Maritime Museum)

Survivors from Kormoran *being rescued.* (The J S Battye Library of West Australian History)

water nearby – might have spared the lives of *Sydney*'s survivors. The significant feature is that at that precise moment the alternative decision might have been the only way to save surviving crew from either *Sydney* or *Kormoran*. On 23 November 1941, Detmers was not in a position to have known that nearly all of the *Kormoran* crew who survived the sinking would eventually reach the coast or be rescued at sea. Nor did he, presumably (he makes no mention of it), witness the *Aquitania* picking up survivors. Put in other words, Detmers' *actions* were not those of a person committed to preserving life – irrespective of nationality.

Reconstruction

The destruction of *Sydney* and *Komoran* left many clues floating in and on the water for the forensic historian. Most of this information is summarized in Table 1.

Figure 1 depicts the movement of objects which were

Table 1. *SUMMARY OF OBJECTS*

Summary of objects showing Elapsed Time (from 1800 on 19 November 1941), Latitude, Longitude, Origin (*Sydney* or *Kormoran*, where known), Source of report, and Type of object (with reason for omission from drift calculations, where appropriate). Drift reconstruction was used for items 1, 5, 6, 7, 8, 9, 10 and 11. Point of origin calculations used these items and reconstruction of *B/Meyer*'s voyage from a diary written by Malapert. (e = estimate, t = to arrival on coast).

Item	ET	Latitude	Longitude	Origin	Source	Type of object (reason for omission)
1	84	24°35′S	110°57′E	*Kormoran*	*Aquitania*	raft
2	109	24°06′S	111°40′E	*Kormoran*	*Trocas*	raft (under sail)
3	120t	24°06′S	113°25′E	*Kormoran*	*B/Kohn*	lifeboat (no data)
4	134t	24°2′S	113°25′E	*Kormoran*	*Malapert* in *B/Meyer*	lifeboat
5	188	24°6′S	110°49′E	*Sydney*	*Evagoras*	belt
6	192	24°22′S	110°49′E	*Sydney*	*Wyrallah*	belt
7	206	24°10′S	110°54′E	*Kormoran*	*Wyrallah*	belt
8	207	24°10′S	110°54′E	*Kormoran*	*Wyrallah*	float
9	208	24°10′S	110°54′E	*Kormoran*	*Wyrallah*	kennel
10	209	24°7′S	110°58′E	*Sydney*	*Heros*	raft
11	209e	24°7′S	110°58′E	???	*Heros*	linseed oil
12	209e	23°49′S	110°10′E	???	Catalina	oil (too far from set)
13	1890e			*Sydney*	Christmas Island	raft (length of delay)

entirely or primarily subject to the influence of wind and current, and the final positions of the two lifeboats which reached the coast. The current values (0.33kts/3°) were based on three sources widely used by the Australian Maritime Safety Authority for Search and Rescue (SAR) operations (The Meteorological Office [UK] Routeing Chart Indian Ocean, The Australian Pilot, and The US Hydrographic Office Charts). The wind values were based on reconstructions by two experts from the West Australian Bureau of Meteorology using the synoptic

charts and other data from 1941, and averaged by the total drift vector method. Leeway was assumed to be 2 per cent of wind for items 5, 6, 7, 8, 9, 10 and 11. A figure of 4 per cent was used for item 1.

Figure 2 is a reconstruction of the tracks of the four lifeboats for which information is available. The track for *B/Meyer* (Meyer was in command of the lifeboat) is based on a detailed diary kept by Malapert, a survivor on that boat. The diary records changes in the bearing and velocity of the lifeboat, changes in the direction and

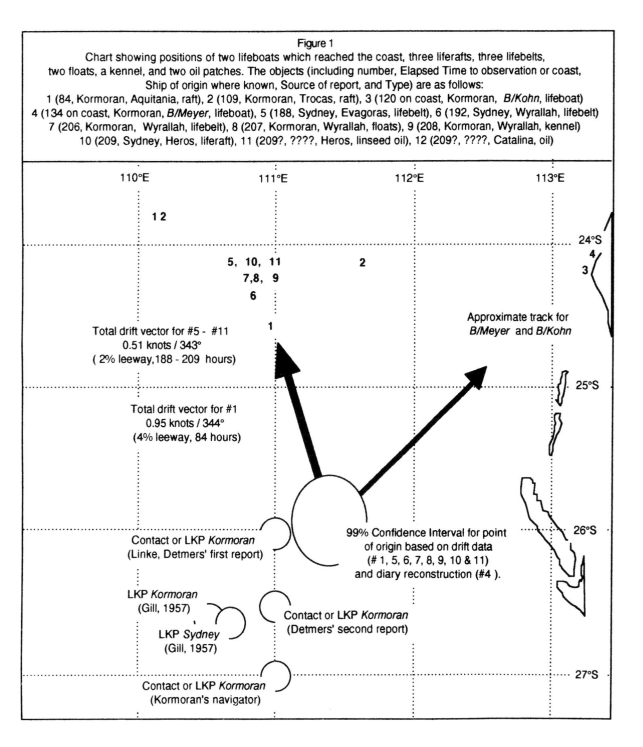

Figure 1
Chart showing positions of two lifeboats which reached the coast, three liferafts, three lifebelts, two floats, a kennel, and two oil patches. The objects (including number, Elapsed Time to observation or coast, Ship of origin where known, Source of report, and Type) are as follows:
1 (84, Kormoran, Aquitania, raft), 2 (109, Kormoran, Trocas, raft), 3 (120 on coast, Kormoran, *B/Kohn*, lifeboat)
4 (134 on coast, Kormoran, *B/Meyer*, lifeboat), 5 (188, Sydney, Evagoras, lifebelt), 6 (192, Sydney, Wyrallah, lifebelt)
7 (206, Kormoran, Wyrallah, lifebelt), 8 (207, Kormoran, Wyrallah, floats), 9 (208, Kormoran, Wyrallah, kennel)
10 (209, Sydney, Heros, liferaft), 11 (209?, ????, Heros, linseed oil), 12 (209?, ????, Catalina, oil)

velocity of the wind, and distance covered each day, and the reconstruction assumes that these variables were stable between entries.

The tracks of *B/Detmers* and *B/Gosseln* involve two distinct stages and, therefore, two forces. The second of these stages depicts the lifeboats sailing more or less due east at 1.25–1.75kts (see Figure 2) after ET133. These tracks are based on three observations for each lifeboat. The first of these was at 133 hours when *B/Gosseln* was

observed by a SAR aircraft and Detmers observed a SAR aircraft circling a lifeboat, presumably *B/Gosseln*. The second point for each boat involves a SAR aircraft observation. The third observation for each lifeboat is its position when a SAR vessel reached it. The easterly tracks are based on the method of least squares applied to the sets of latitude and longitude values separately for each lifeboat. If these tracks are extrapolated to ETO (*ie* to 1800 on 19 November 1941), they yield estimated points of

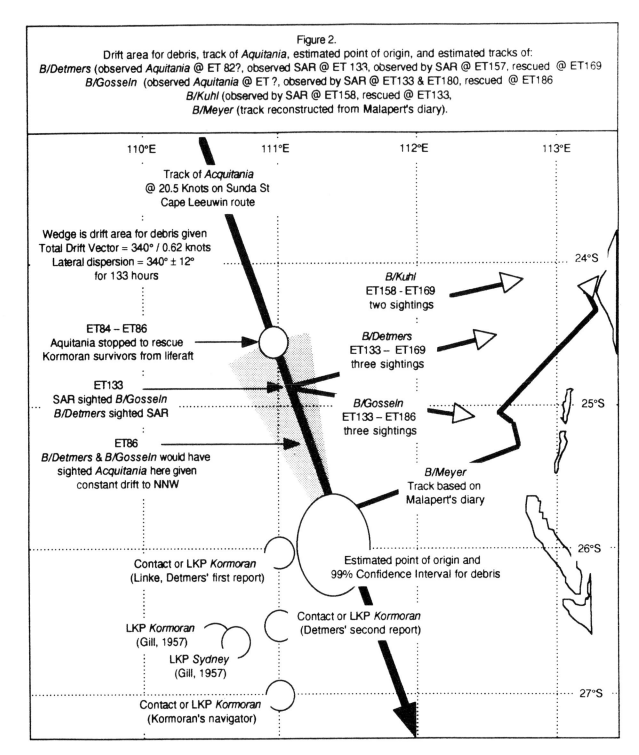

Figure 2.
Drift area for debris, track of *Aquitania*, estimated point of origin, and estimated tracks of:
B/Detmers (observed *Aquitania* @ ET 82?, observed SAR @ ET 133, observed by SAR @ ET157, rescued @ ET169
B/Gosseln (observed *Aquitania* @ ET ?, observed by SAR @ ET133 & ET180, rescued @ ET186
B/Kuhl (observed by SAR @ ET158, rescued @ ET133,
B/Meyer (track reconstructed from Malapert's diary).

origin to the west of 110°E or even 109°E. Analysis of *B/Kuhl*'s progress from the SAR detection and rescue positions yields an estimated point of origin which is even further to the west, near 106°E.

The above observations cannot be reconciled with the point of origin based on the drifting objects and *B/Meyer unless* it is assumed that *B/Detmers*, *B/Gosseln*, and probably *B/Kuhl* drifted with the wind and current for the first four or five days, hence their NNW tracks, before they sailed east. Further evidence that this is what they did comes from *their* reports that they observed *Aquitania* between 82 and 88 hours, on a course which can be reconciled with the full set of data if it is assumed that they drifted with the current and wind until *B/Gosseln* was sighted by a SAR aircraft at 133 hours. Thus, the first and second stages for these lifeboats reflect the influence of drift and sailing forces, respectively.

Conclusion

The present analysis explains the position of most of the objects observed in or recovered from the sea off Carnarvon after the engagement between *Sydney* and *Kormoran*. The estimated point of origin is about 25 nautical miles from the position initially given by Detmers (111°E 26°S), although the discrepancy is much greater (55–60 nautical miles) if it is assumed that Detmers supplied the initial contact position and a correct description of the action, which involved a further movement to the SW. If, however, it is assumed that Detmers actually gave the position at which *Kormoran* sank (his book is not clear on this point), then the present analysis brings the initial point of contact between *Sydney* and *Kormoran* to less than 25 nautical miles from the direct route from Sunda Straight to Fremantle, an outcome which is close enough to the optimal route to resolve uncertainty about the circumstances of their meeting.

The two-stage tracks attributed to *B/Detmers* and *B/Gosseln* do not resolve uncertainty about their actions after the battle. One rumour which permeated both early and recent accounts of the action claimed that *Kormoran* survivors killed *Sydney* survivors in the water (for evaluation, see Montgomery, 1981, p153–163 and Winter, 1984, p229), and the northerly drift observed for two or possibly three lifeboats is consistent with this account. A second possibility is that they were searching for some forty *Kormoran* crew who fell into the water when a liferaft capsized shortly after *Kormoran* was abandoned.

A third possibility is that they decided to remain in a group with one or more of the liferafts for as long as possible. Regardless of the last sad hours of *Kormoran* and *Sydney* survivors in the water, the planned search for the two wrecks should answer questions about the last hours of HMAS *Sydney* and HSK *Kormoran*.

Notes

[1] HSK *Atlantis* was sunk on 22 November 1941 by HMS *Dorsetshire*.

[2] One liferaft and two lifebelts from *Sydney* were recovered in the area after the engagement, and a second raft was found by Christmas Island near Java several months later. None of these items appear to have been damaged by fire.

[3] That is, 'because I was hoping to fall in with a neutral steamer' (p194), an explanation which the crew would have known to be plausible or implausible, and one which Winter dismissed. (1984, p166)

[4] Winter (p166) claims that Detmers (while on the lifeboat) 'drew his pistol and vowed to shoot dead any man who touched the Chinese. Seeing his grim, set face, they had to believe it; their Captain was not a man who said one thing and meant another'.

References

T Detmers, *The Raider Kormoran*, William Kimber (London 1959).

G H Gill, *Royal Australian Navy 1939–42*, Collins & Australian War Memorial. (Sydney 1957, 1985).

J von Gosseln (1953), 'The sinking of the *Sydney*', *Proceedings of the US Naval Institute* (March 1953), pp251–55.

Meterological Office: Monthly Meterological Charts of the Indian Ocean, HMSO (London 1949).

M Montgomery, *Who sank the Sydney?*, Cassell (Sydney 1981, 1983).

R F Newcomb, *Abandon Ship: Death of the USS Indianapolis*, Henry Holt (New York 1958).

A Raven and J Roberts, *British Cruisers of World War Two*, Arms and Armour Press (London 1980).

J P M Showell, *U-Boats under the Swastika*, Ian Allan (London 1987).

Surface Currents and Temperatures (November). In *Atlas of Surface Currents: Indian Ocean* (1970). US Hydrographic Office. Washington DC.

D Van Der Vat, *The Atlantic Campaign: The Great Struggle at Sea 1939–1945*, Grafton Books (London 1990).

B Winter, *HMAS Sydney: Fact, Fantasy and Fraud*, Boolarong Publications (Brisbane 1984).

JAPANESE SPECIAL ATTACK WEAPONS

In what is planned to be the first of a series of articles, Dr Jiro Itani and Tomoko Rehm-Takahara with the help of Hans Lengerer offer a Japanese perspective on the ethos, evolution and technology of suicide weapons, concluding with an outline of the preparations made to defend homeland Japan from the expected invasion of 1945.

SPECIAL attack weapons were adopted by the Imperial Japanese Navy (IJN) as well as the Imperial Japanese Army (IJA) during the final phase of the Pacific War. These weapons comprised not only aircraft, surface and submersible craft (explosive boats, manned torpedoes, midget submarines etc) but also demolition charges, mines and so forth for ground troops and navy personnel which were employed by special attack units (*Tokubetsu Kogekitai* = *Tokkotai*), when undertaking special missions (*Tokko*). Special attack unit was the official designation given to any group consisting of men willing in principle[1] to sacrifice their lives in pursuit of the certain destruction of the target.

Wars always have given birth to unusual tactics, especially by the inferior side. Desperate situations sometimes give rise to desperate weapons and tactics, particularly if the defeated side has no will to surrender and wishes to resist the enemy to the last. At the final stage of the Pacific War, there were many Japanese soldiers who eagerly volunteered for suicide weapons which could be more certain to kill the enemy rather than to adopt less effective conventional tactics which against overwhelming odds might lead to equally certain death. However, it was the traditional policy of IJN not to take such suicide measures, and ideas of this nature were always rejected. The midget submarines which took part in the Pearl Harbor operation were only allowed to participate after some form of rescue had been organized, even if the chances were very slim.[2]

Nobody wants to die in vain. The weapons which would have more opportunities of success attracted young eager patriots who were glad to die for their country. They were all volunteers at first: to the last the IJN never coerced (at least officially) those who did not want to board these deadly weapons but preferred to fight in an orthodox way. Vice-Admiral Ōnishi, the formal initiator of the idea, later sorrowfully admitted that special attack was a wrong direction in the war which would never be understood nor counternanced by the rest of the world. He faced his responsibility after the war by choosing the most painful way of suicide. Some admirals achieved the same end by attacking overwhelming enemy forces. At Pearl Harbor, no boat came back to the rescue submarines and before launching the crews had seemed to rule out survival after the attack. It is known that they assumed an attitude of indifference to their fate rather than calm, and if they chose to sacrifice their lives it was not as a result of an order from higher authority.

The midget submarine naturally grew into a larger sized boat as other weapons did all the time, and as it developed into a smaller version of a conventional submarine it lost its simplicity and ease of production. The *Kaiten* human torpedo was born almost inevitably to fill the gap. This idea was initially rejected by the High Command, but the rapid worsening of the war situation forced them to adopt this sure-death arms. Many soldiers of course responded willingly.

In conclusion, the true concept of the special attack tactic came into being as a result of successive reverses suffered by Japanese forces in the Solomons and in New Guinea between 1942 and 1944 and the IJN's inability to halt the enemy's offensive across the Central Pacific. The special attack weapons were inspired by the absolute necessity to devise some counter to the overwhelming enemy superiority in all aspects of military power. The employment of special attack units reflected the strong determination of the Japanese GHQ, subordinate commands and fighting forces to overcome at any cost this growing military material disparity. The resort to special attack weapons and tactics depended on the deeply inculcated spirit of patriotic self-sacrifice which not only was the characteristic feature of the military forces but also reflected the psychology of the whole Japanese nation. This spirit was the product of centuries of religious and moral training.[3] It led Japanese troops, often starving and cut off from all hope of relief, to fight on rather than surrender and brought about volunteers in ample number for every special attack unit and mission. It also spurred the nation to still greater efforts despite the successive defeats and the heroic example of the first Kamikaze units[4] gave an impetus to the still wider adoption of special attack methods.

By the end of the war in the Pacific, the production of Special Attack Weapons was on a prodigious scale. Taken in October 1945 this photo shows some of the Kōryū *type left uncompleted in a dry-dock at Kure Navy Yard. Among the eighty-four boats visible, there are four variants, the two in the right foreground being training craft.* (All uncredited photos: US National Archives)

Japan's Military Situation at the Beginning of 1944

From a high-water mark of conquest, the decline in the military and political situation from the middle of 1942 (failure of operations against Port Moresby and Midway, retreat from Guadalcanal and other Solomon Islands, withdrawing actions in New Guinea) forced the Imperial General Headquarters (GHQ) to fundamentally revise the still officially offensive operational policy.[5] In the IJA-IJN Central Agreement of 30 September 1943 an 'absolute national defence sphere' was defined which brought about the withdrawal of the main defence line to the west,[6] the establishment of strategic bases along this line by the spring of 1944, and the decision to defend key points in the South-east Area (extending from Eastern New Guinea to the Solomon Islands) by local forces only. The main reason for this change was the condition of the front along the line East New Guinea – Northern Solomon Islands – Marshall Islands which was on the verge of collapse. This change of operational policy marked the official change to the strategic defence.

Japan had no time to establish a strong defence line. Before the end of 1943 allied forces had penetrated the outer defence sphere by the occupation of the Gilbert Islands and continued their advance at the beginning of 1944 with the invasion of the Marshalls. The Gilbert/Marshall campaign was accompanied by raids of the fast carrier task forces which forced IJN surface forces to retreat to the outer Western Pacific and began the destruction of Japan's air forces. Truk and the East Carolines were neutralized and eliminated as effective parts of the inner defence system; the striking power of the air forces east of the Marianas was broken.

Raids against key points within the inner defence sphere proved that Japan could not oppose the fast task forces and made plain how much the homeland was threatened. In New Guinea the advance of the allies along the coastline was also speeded up at the beginning of 1944. In conjunction with the fall of the Admiralties, this precipitated the complete collapse of the outer defence ring in the South-east Area.

A Kaiten *Type 2 human torpedo.* (Jiro Kimoto)

From March 1944 on the allied advance aimed at the conquest of the Marianas in the centre of the national defence sphere. The IJN had lost important advanced bases. The naval forces had been able to avoid a battle, but not the deterioration of their situation. While attempting a decisive sea battle in the Philippines area under the cover of strong air forces, the latter were nearly annihilated by US naval aircraft. The loss of transports prevented the erection of the planned impregnable positions along the inner defence sphere and the permanent pressure of the allied forces prevented the assembly of forces for offensive operations. The sea and air forces faced the allied offensives nearly helplessly. Supremacy at sea could no longer be achieved without the possession of air superiority.

Judged by the number of heavy surface forces, the IJN was still strong at the beginning of 1944 but the fleet was poorly balanced. The extreme shortage of escort vessels limited the operations of the heavily reduced merchant ship tonnage. The fuel problem was already obvious as a result of the many tanker losses. The shortage of destroyers reduced the value of the big ships and since Midway no operation had been possible under the umbrella of carrier based aircraft. But carriers and naval air forces were the key to success. The operations of the First Air Fleet during the first four months of the war already had proven this very clearly and it was now the turn of the allied task forces to do the same. The four carrier battles of 1942 had been costly in ships and experienced pilots and the next generation of aircrew had

been sacrificed together with their aircraft in the quite useless *I Go* and *Ro Go* operations. The replacement of carriers and well-trained pilots could not be expected and the IJN's situation was nearly hopeless in this respect. But air power capable of winning at least local air superiority was imperative for the successful prosecution of the war and in recognition of this the production of 55,000 aircraft to build up the forces of the Army and Navy had been required under the "Future Strategy' policy, dealt with in the Liaison Conference of 25 September 1943. GHQ judged present national power and national resources not only insufficient to build warships in excess of the goal fixed in the current ship-building programmes but even lowered the targets because of the concentration of production efforts on aircraft – the increase in naval strength had to be concentrated principally on the expansion of air power and secondly on the production of *special attack craft* and anti-submarine vessels and equipment. The building of all other types of craft had to be postponed.

The Navy General Staff's Requirements for Special Attack Weapons

The inevitable loss of the South-east Area had already become apparent by the middle of 1943. At that time the concept of special attack tactics was already under discussion by all levels of frontline forces including high-ranking officers of the Army and Navy and proposals were submitted. But the central organizations of both military forces still hesitated to adopt such desperate tactics and it was not until special attack methods had been indirectly sanctioned by the Liaison Conference of the General Staff and the Navy General Staff that the building of such weapons was ordered.

In April 1944 the chief of the Navy General Staff (*Gunreibusōchō*) submitted a memorandum on special attack weapons to the Navy Minister (*Kaigun Daijin*). It contained nine proposals for the building of attack craft (*Kōgekitei*) and weapons (*Heiki*) which were chosen as the most realistic of around 300 schemes for special attacks that could reverse the military situation. According to the Navy General Staff these weapons could '. . . make good the defeats and lead to the victory over the allied forces . . .' and '. . . if these special attack weapons are not employed we shall undoubtedly lose the war . . .'. The Navy General Staff requested that the construction of these devices be given the temporary designation '*Maru Ichi* to *Maru Kyū*' (the ciphers 1 to 9 inside a circle) and the addition '*Kanamono*' ('hardware').

The Navy Ministry immediately responded to this urgent demand for the production of weapons suitable for special attack tactics and ordered the Navy Technical Department chief to decide the bureau or bureaus responsible for research, design, test production and development until mass production stage. The naval authorities were fairly optimistic about the success of the project at that time as the IJN had been studying weapons of this type for some time (see below for the origin of each weapon). The greatest difficulty was that the urgent need for such weapons allowed little time for research, trial manufacture, tests, improvements, and further development.

The designation *Maru Ichi* hid the design of a one-man

A captured Shinyō *explosive boat, now displayed aboard the preserved* USS Massachusetts *at Battleship Cove, Fall River, Massachusetts. (By courtesy of Al Ross)*

submarine for attacking enemy submarines. It was to be carried by merchant ships and was to be released during a submarine attack. The armament consisted of an explosive charge with time fuse fitted in a detachable extension of the bow. This small submarine was to ram the enemy boat, attaching the explosive charge to its hull, while the time fuse would allow the attacker to make off. The basic design of this hunter-killer submarine was assigned to the 2nd and 4th main bureaus but by the end of the war no operable boat had been built, mainly due to the failure to develop reliable locator equipment.

Maru Ni was the temporary name of the 'Funryu' rocket, designed to counter the B-29 (Superfortress) bomber. Development was nearly finished at the end of the war; the test area was the Chichibu mountains.

Maru San was the collective name for several types of midget submarines, like the SS kanamono (*Kairyū*) and its predecessor the S kanamono. The 4th main bureau also worked on a solely battery-driven type. Besides these craft a very original idea was tried: at each side of a small hull which formed the control room a torpedo was to be mounted. Basically this was the design of a very simplified *Kairyū*. Furthermore the 2nd main bureau tried the development of a submersible motor torpedo boat (*Kasen Gyoraitei*). None of these projects came to fruition except the *Kairyū*.

In contrast to this the design and construction of the *Shinyo* explosive boat was much more successful. Several types were developed to mass production stage under the designation *Maru Yon*. The 1st main bureau worked on the design of a self-propelled depth charge (*Jiro Bakurai*) which was called *Maru Go*, but the war ended before the completion of this highly original weapon.

Maru Roku was the code name for several types of human torpedoes (*Ningen Gyorai*) which later were designated *Kaiten*. Type 1 was actually used in operations, and types 2, 4 and 10 were test-produced.

The marks *Maru Shichi* and *Maru Hachi* hid radar and ECM devices whose design and construction were unsuccessfully developed by the 3rd main bureau.

This series of special attack weapons ended with *Maru Kyu*, which was another midget submarine, of which nine boats were produced. Building ceased because of the shortage of carrier submarines and the continuous defects of the locator equipment.

Thus, only the projects *Maru San* (limited to *Kairyū*), *Maru Yon* (*Shinyō*), and *Maru Roku* (*Kaiten*) were developed to mass production stages and brought into action by the end of the war. *Maru Kyu* (*Shinkai*) was virtually finished but was not operational; the other projects all remained incomplete.

In addition to these officially sponsored weapons, numerous other freelance plans and designs were adopted or developed and even trial manufactured in some cases. These sometimes very curious devices will be described later under 'Other Weapons'.

Characteristics of Underwater and Surface Special Attack Weapons

The underwater special attack weapons (*Suichu Tokko Heiki*) to which this article mostly refers can be divided into three kinds by their construction, handling and planned tactical utilization.

Class One: *Kōhyōteki* type D (*Kōryū*)

The *Kōryū* was a true, conventional type midget submarine with a relatively high surface and submerged performance, armed with two 45.7cm (18in) torpedoes in outboard-loading tubes at the bow. Further characteristic features were good streamlined shape, main ballast tanks arranged outside the pressure (inner) hull, comparatively easy handling, high endurance, and effective ventilation plant. The displacement varied between 59 and 63 tons. There were boats with diesel-electric propulsion (which was the standard system) and direct drive (*Kōryū* modification 1). Two contra-rotating propellers were used in the prototype but this was reduced to one propeller in the boats built in series in order to reduce the building time, building costs and to save materials. In this case torque-correcting planes were added to the horizontal tail-fins.

Surface endurance was 1000 miles at 8kts; submerged 125 miles at 2.5kts could be achieved (or 16kts for 40 minutes). The battery was recharged by one 150hp/100kW motor generator within 8 hours. They had wooden engine bearers but fitted in non-shock proof mountings. With a crew of five men the operational endurance was five days.

A detail of the cockpit of a Shinyō *suicide boat, showing the simple steering, unprotected fuel tank and a makeshift armament of two 5in rockets.* (Author's collection)

The *Kōryū* and its modified version were the end products of a steadily developed series of midget submarines collectively called *Kōhyōteki* that went back to 1933. After building two trial boats the Imperial Japanese Navy built the Type A whose sole purpose was to participate in the decisive battle between the main fleets of Japan and the USA. These boats were to be transported to the operation area by depot ships, released at a favourable moment and after launching of their torpedoes, to wait until picked up again by the depot ship. In the early period of the war the IJN wanted to use *Kōhyōteki* Type As for the defence of local bases but this operational concept could not be adopted because of their short endurance and inability to recharge the battery. Therefore Types B (one trial boat only) and C (standardized mass production type) were designed and built. The diameter of the hull was increased, a 40hp/25kW motor generator was added and several other modifications were made. By these, surface radius of action increased to 300–350 miles at 5kts, while in submerged condition 120 miles at 4kts became possible. But the recharging of the battery took 18 hours. Despite the improvements, radius of action was still criticised as too short and seaworthiness and habitability remained as insufficient as they had been before. These disadvantages finally resulted in the design and construction of the *Kōryū*. After building three types with gradually increased diameter, length, displacement, various propulsion systems, different tank arrangement,

the *Kōryū* achieved the status of a true miniature submarine; mass production, standardized on this design, commenced at the beginning of 1945. Taking into consideration the mode of operation and the construction features, these types cannot be classified as pure special attack weapons, but in reality they must be treated with these weapons because they had practically no chance to escape from the very strong escort forces of the US fleet before or after firing their torpedoes.

Class Two: *Kairyū*

Compared to the *Kōhyōteki*, the *Kairyū* was a much smaller submarine with less speed, shorter endurance, and lower performance in general. The construction idea was inspired by aircraft: *ie* the idea of the conventional submarine was given up in favour of an underwater craft in whose design fast submerging and surfacing were the dominant factors. The most conspicuous feature was a horizontal stabilizer on each side of the hull which looked like the wings of an aircraft.

This type was also built on a conveyor belt system like the *Kōryū* using several parts produced for other weapons or civil demands, such as aircraft and trucks. Therefore the design and construction were comparatively easy, the

A Kōryū type midget submarine lying incomplete at Yokosuka Navy Yard in September 1945. The stern section is missing.

The US netlayers Catclaw *(AN–60) and* Baretta *(AN–40) raising a* Kōryū *sunk during the Okinawa campaign.*

small displacement of only about 20 tons being roughly one-third of that of the *Kōryū*. Mass production was begun in April 1945 with the intention to make up the insufficient numbers of midget submarines due to difficulties with the production of the *Kōryū* and to improve the preparations for the defence of Japan proper. Therefore the tactical concept was nearly identical to that for the *Kōryū*, but because of the lower surface and submerged speeds (7.5kts and 10kts respectively) and surface and submerged radius of action (450 miles at 5kts and 36 miles at 3kts) their operational area was necessarily limited to local points.

The armament was to consist of two 45.7cm torpedoes slung in two external recesses (in the underside of the hull). But neither the production of the launchers nor that of the torpedoes kept pace with that of the *Kairyū* itself and thus the idea of torpedo attack had to be abandoned. Therefore the boats were usually fitted with a large warhead to make a suicide attack. In this configuration the *Kairyū* was a pure special attack weapon but the speed was too low to attack any ship underway.

Class Three: *Kaiten*

Kaiten were human torpedoes, *ie* piloted, mobile explosive charges. Four types were designed and constructed but only one type reached the stage of mass production

and was operationally used. Common features of Types 1, 2 and 4 were high speed (30–40kts) but only short endurance (23–83kms, 14–51 miles). They were armed with a very large warhead and were pure special attack weapons despite the fact that the first produced *Kaiten* were equipped with a lower hatch by which the pilot was to disembark after fixing the steering gear (the late production *Kaiten* had no such hatch).

Kaiten were transported by submarines (the transport by surface vessels was also planned) to their operational area and released at an opportune moment. For this purpose the carrier submarine had a tube, the *Kaiten* a corresponding hatch so that the pilot could man his torpedo and start it by the remote release equipment without the mother submarine having to surface.

Type 1 used the air chamber (oxygen vessel), engine and tail section of the Type 93 oxygen torpedo. Types 2 and 4 were substantially enlarged models of this type with a hydrogen peroxide, hydrazin hydrate, fuel and water (Type 2) or kerosene and oxygen (Type 4) propulsion system. Type 10 of which only a few trial units were produced before the end of the war, was essentially the Type 92 battery torpedo with the fewest possible modifications. This model differed greatly from the Type 1 in its smaller size (roughly one-third), lighter explosive charge (300kg compared to 1550kg), lower speed and endurance (3.5kts/7kts to 23kts/30kts). It also had no lower hatch to allow entry from the submerged carrier submarine. The crew was one pilot in the case of Types 1 and 10, and two (a pilot and technician) for the Types 2 and 4.

The Imperial Japanese Army also designed and test-produced underwater special attack weapons. Besides a true miniature submarine for local defence, a submersible attack boat was designed, for the same role as the midget.

Two views of a Kairyū *with the hull cut away for display purposes at Etajima*. (Kunio Kitamura)

Its curious construction warrants attention and it will be described in a future article. Other weapons will be included, too, mainly because of particular unique features.

With regard to the surface special attack weapons no classification is necessary since only one type was actually utilized. The *Shinyō* was the only surface special weapon (*Suijo Tokko Heiki*) of the IJN adopted, mass produced on a large scale, and actually sent into action. *Shinyō* was

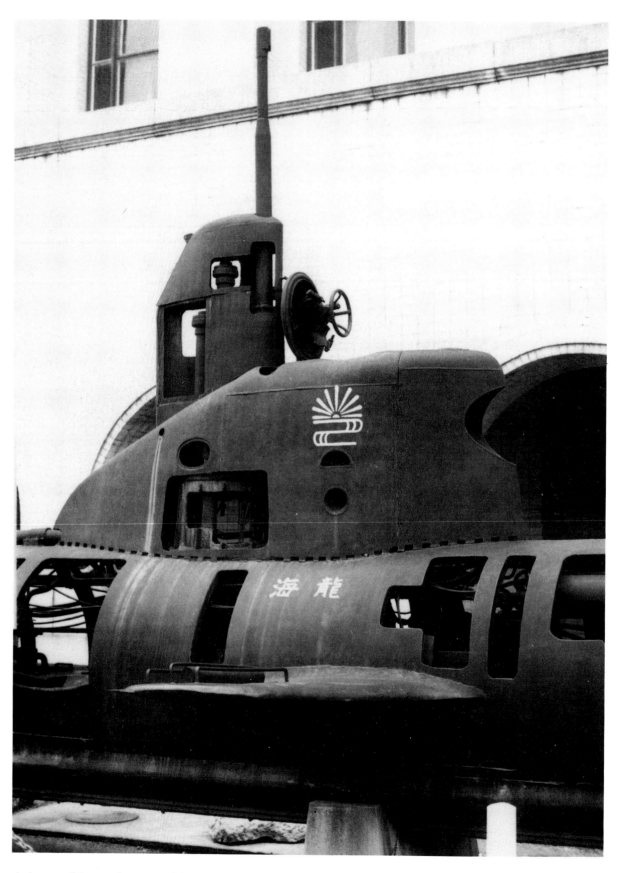

A close up of the conning tower of the preserved Kairyū *at* Etajima. (Hoyashi Yoshikaru)

A Kaiten Type 1 on its launching cradle at Dublon, Truk Atoll in November 1945.

the collective designation of small, wooden, medium-fast boats, propelled by truck engines and armed with a comparatively heavy explosive charge (about 250kg) in the bow to be piloted by a crew of one or two men alongside an enemy ship for surprise attack or employed in large numbers for coast defence: *ie* attack on enemy landing forces. Like the *Kaiten* Type 1 the pilot of the *Shinyō* Type 1 or the pilot and the rifleman of the *Shinyō* Type 5 were to abandon the boat after fixing the steering gear and wait in the water until they could be picked up by a friendly ship. In fact it was expected that the pilot would stay with the boat until it rammed the enemy to obtain a sure hit, so the *Shinyō* can be classified as a pure special attack weapon.

The Type 1 was the real attack boat, Type 5 a division leader boat, and the Type 8, constructed immediately before the end of the war, a squadron leader boat. This latter type was a pure control boat and was not designed as an attack boat. Even though it was also armed with two 12cm rockets in simple launching rails as the Types 1 and 5 it had no bow explosive charge and the machine-gun, a feature of the Type 5, was also omitted. The Types

5 and 8 were virtually straightforward enlargements of the Type 1.

The building of trial boats with rocket propulsion and jet propulsion was completed but these boats became unstable at high speeds (about 60kts) and development had to be abandoned.

The 'Type 4 Suicide Attack Boat' (*Yon Shiki Niku-Haku Kogekitei*) or 'Communication Boat' (*Renrakutei*) of the Army was very similar to the *Shinyō*, but was not to be operated as a pure special attack weapon. The boat had no bow charge, but instead the armament consisted of two combined depth charges which were to be released alongside the hull of an enemy ship. A time fuse (6 seconds) was to allow the pilot to turn the boat away and escape. *Renrakutei* were employed together with the IJN's *Shinyō* from the end of 1944. Incidentally, the IJA also worked on the design of rocket propelled and remote controlled boats like the IJN. All these projects will be dealt with in a future article about surface special attack weapons.

The Resort to Special Attack Tactics

The Army and the Navy had proceeded with the

179

formation of special attack units and the production of special attack weapons but the Imperial GHQ had not yet issued general orders to man such units on a compulsory basis. The highest command level still considered special attacks a method of coping with local situations but not an overall policy. Even though it counted upon special attacks to a large degree in the Philippines campaign no orders were issued to impress personnel into special attack units because numerous volunteers were available.

Even in this situation the special attack tactic was still beset with problems which were not solved by voluntary reporting to the special attack units and it was regarded as a great tragedy that Japanese field commanders were forced to resort to such desperate tactics because of the rapidly deteriorating situation. But the importance of special weapons and tactics increased inexorably as the allied forces advanced. When the enemy attacks on the homeland defence perimeter began with the invasion of Iwo Jima, keystone of the Ogasawara Islands sector of this perimeter, military forces were still too weak to seek a decisive battle in that area but during the defence of Okinawa special attack weapons and tactics already played a major role; in the Imperial GHQ's planning for the decisive battle for Japan proper by which the invasion forces had to be thrown back, they were to form the backbone.

The planning for the final battle for the Japanese homeland had already begun and by mid-January 1945 the need for a new and far-reaching strategic plan to replace the now defunct *Sho-Go* scheme (defence of the Philippines) became pressing. On 20 January a general policy directive headed 'Outline of Army and Navy Operation' was issued after Imperial sanction and this became the basis for all future homeland defence

planning.[7] Essential items were:

– The armed forces will prepare for this battle by immediately establishing a strong strategic position in depth within the confines of a national defence sphere delineated by the Bonin Islands, Formosa, the coastal sector of east China, and southern Korea.
– These preparations will be completed in Japan proper by the early autumn of 1945.
– During this time the enemy's approach to the homeland defence perimeter will be delayed by resistance in the Philippines and key strong-points within the defence perimeter zone including Iwo Jima, Okinawa[7] . . .
– In general, Japanese air strength will be conserved until the enemy landing is actually underway on or within the defence sphere. The Allied invasion fleet will then be destroyed on the water, principally by *sea* and *air special attack units*.

The importance of special attack was also explicit in the orders given to the major subordinate commands: 'efforts will be made to annihilate the Allied forces on the sea through the vigorous application of special attack tactics . . .'.

The efforts to formulate a sound and workable air policy culminated in the draft of a 'Joint Army–Navy Air Agreement' for the first half of 1945 on 6 February. According to this draft, 'primary emphasis will be laid on the speedy activation, training and mass employment of air special attack units' and in accordance with the different skill level 'the main target of IJA aircraft will be enemy transports and of IJN aircraft carrier task forces'.[8]

In the execution of this agreement the Navy General Staff issued its overall policy directive No 513 on 20 March which clearly set forth the basic concept of the Navy's participation in the homeland defence campaign. The 'Imperial Navy Outline Plan of Immediate Operations' designated the Ryukyu Island as the focal point of the decisive battle, and placed special emphasis on the destruction of enemy ships by the prompt and vigorous

Kairyū in tunnelled shelters. The midget submarines were transported to their launching positions on a railway cradle. (Author's collection)

A captured Type A Kōryū *(No 51) displayed at a US base on Guam in May 1945.*

use of *sea* and *air special attack forces*. On the same day, the General Staff transmitted the preliminary draft of a voluminous operational plan for the defence of the homeland, the so-called *Ketsu-Go* Operation.[9] As the IJN's general policy had already been announced in the aforesaid 'Outline Plan . . .' no operational detail was issued at that time but the draft was studied of course and was agreed later with some alterations.[10]

Concurrently with the dissemination of the *Ketsu Go* plan on 8 April the Imperial GHQ also issued the text of an Army–Navy Joint Agreement regarding ground operations. In its execution IJN established a General Navy Command on 25 April to exercise supreme operational control of all surface and air forces.[11]

The *Ketsu Go* plan required the total mobilization of all national resources and in order to achieve this the Imperial GHQ gave the nation a warning that the homeland, inviolate for centuries, now stood in imminent danger of invasion. This was successful in evoking a readiness in both the armed forces and the civilian population to take the most extraordinary measures to repel the enemy. This national attitude became the basis of tactical policy. The general concept for the defence of the homeland was divided into four phases each with sub-phases. Phase I dealt with the time prior to the sailing of the enemy convoy (invasion fleet) and involved the use of submarines, submarine-borne aircraft, and long-distance surprise air raids. Phases II and III will be dealt with in more detail as the growing importance of special attack units and weapons is outlined.

In phase II (*ie* after the sailing of the enemy invasion convoy) all available special attack weapons were to be activated:

1. When the advance elements of the invasion force enters the outer Japanese air defence perimeter, long range Navy bombers will attack them vigorously, and short range submarines[12] will launch torpedo attacks.
2. When the main invasion convoy reaches a point 180–200 miles off Japan, the massed strength of all IJA and IJN air *tokko* (suicide) forces will begin to be committed. *Kōryū* midget submarines will also join the attack.
3. As soon as the place and time of landing have been determined, air raids will be carried out against forward enemy air bases supporting the invasion. The purpose of these attacks will be to disrupt enemy air activity and thus facilitate Japanese *special attack* operations.

Phase III was to consist of operations to be carried out after the arrival of the enemy convoy off the coast with the purpose of preventing the landing.

1. When the convoy is in the process of anchoring, *Kōryū* will attack in force.
2. *Kaiten* (human torpedoes) will strike in force at gunfire support ships and transports.
3. The anchorage will be kept under constant interdiction, particularly at night, by means of attacks by *Shinyo* and *Renraku-tei* (the former are IJN, the latter IJA explosive boats).
4. Long range artillery will shell the anchorage.
5. The air *tokko* (suicide) offensive will continue.
6. While the enemy is engaged in ship-to-shore movement, transports and landing craft will be swept with fire by all available artillery strength.

Phase IV was to consist of a series of activities after enemy troops had landed. Since these attacks have no relation to special attack tactics the details have been omitted, but before the ground forces were committed air and sea special attack forces were to continue their attacks.

This outline of the general scheme of the defence makes it clear that the chief burden of blunting the allied invasion spearhead fell upon the special attack forces acting in the air and at sea. It is worth noting also that the special attack principle was extended for the first time to ground combat, mainly for anti-tank defence, for which Japanese forces were ill-equipped.

Concentration of Production on Special Attack Weapons

The growing tactical importance of special attack was inevitably reflected in logistics and production. In view of the steadily worsening military situation, it became increasingly clear that the allied forces were about to launch large scale air raids against the Japanese homeland and from March 1945 Japan proper became the target of day and night air raids which occurred almost continuously. The IJN was forced to disperse its production facilities (for building and repair) and to shift them partly underground. Despite all efforts these air raids resulted in heavy damage to personnel and equipment. The materials for building aircraft, surface ships and submarines as well as special attack craft were already in short supply, while aircraft fuel and heavy oil were also very scarce commod-

A view of some of the uncompleted Kōryū *at Kure.*

ities. In this situation close cooperation between the Army and the Navy was a matter of absolute necessity in order to obtain the maximum production rate.

Talks about cooperation as well as joint production and employment of weapons suitable for both services had been carried on since summer 1944 and the IJN's war preparations had been executed in close cooperation with the IJA since the beginning of 1945. Driven by the very critical situation at that time the negotiations finally ended successfully and on 1 April 1945 the 'Agreement Between the Army and the Navy Concerning War Preparations for the First Half of Fiscal Year 1945' was concluded between the vice-chiefs of the General Staff and the Navy General Staff. This gave priority to the equipment of the air forces and the special attack weapons, and further prioritized air, surface and underwater special attack weapons.

War preparations for the first half of fiscal year 1945 (April to September 1945) were decided in a conference held between the Navy General Staff and the Navy Ministry. The minutes of the 'Conference on War Preparations in the First Half of Fiscal Year 1945' (Navy General Staff Secret Document No 31) were distributed to every chief of the Navy Aeronautical Department, Navy Technical Department, and Navy Civil Engineering Department and in an annex to this the top priority of the special attack weapons was again expressed very clearly.

The Navy Ministry completed all research work and obtained full agreement with the War Ministry. After the adjustment of some slight differences in estimates, the Navy Ministry mapped out a plan of execution which was generally in line with the Navy General Staff's demand

and endeavoured to achieve its targets. But in the meantime allied forces began the invasion of Okinawa in early April and intensified their air activity over Japan proper. The incendiary bomb campaign against large urban complexes and then medium-sized and small cities nearly paralysed production, transportation and communication facilities. In conjunction with the mine blockade and submarine disruption of the logistic lines to mainland China and Korea, the entire social and economic structure of the nation was threatening to disintegrate. The blockade, ever rising merchant ship losses, and the destruction of industrial installations resulted in a sharp decline in national production of war materials. Even though top priority had been granted to the special attack weapons the production of special type aircraft lagged considerably behind the target and for underwater and surface special attack weapons only approximately half of the planned total was realized.

Table 1 lists the production requirements and the totals to be achieved. This table was compiled from data published in the official Japanese War History Series (*Senshi sosho*), contained in copies of some Japanese documents, supplied by Messrs Endo Akira, Tamura Toshio, Dr Morino Tetsuo etc or published in books like

Showa Zosenshi (History of Shipbuilding in Showa Era), *Kaigun Zosen Gijutsu Gaiyo* (Outline of the History of Shipbuilding Technology), *Shusenji ni okeru Nihon Kantei* (Japanese Naval Vessels at the End of the War) etc. Because of the destruction by fire of most of the documents in the Navy Ministry and local commands at the end of the war by the order of the Navy Minister there are inevitably some blanks. Furthermore, the accuracy of reports and statistics made immediately before the end of the war is questionable and therefore the figures for real production could not be assessed with any worthwhile degree of accuracy, so have been omitted.

Notes

[1] 'In principle' because there was a theoretical possibility of abandoning most weapons shortly before impact. In fact, a suicide attack was assumed by all.

[2] Japanese warfare, and the IJN's short history afforded examples of desperate attacks against heavy odds.

[3] This mainly refers to the Japanese fighting spirit (*Yamato damashii*) as a product of the Japanese version of their divine origin, the warrior caste (*Samurai*) and their Bushido code

Table 1. *JOINT NAVY/ARMY AGREEMENT ON PRODUCTION OF SPECIAL ATTACK WEAPONS FOR THE FIRST HALF OF FISCAL YEAR 1945, DATED APRIL 1945*

Weapons	Apr	May	Jun	Jul	Aug	Sept	Total	Responsibility for Procurement (*chief responsibility)	Remarks
K1-115 Special Attack Plane	50	150	300	400	500	600	2000	Army	
Special Type Plane				2000				Navy	
Oka	300	300	300	300	300	300	1800	Navy	
Kōryū Midget Submarine	35	35	50	100	150	180	540	Navy	
Kairyū Midget Submarine	100	120	130	150	200	200	900	Navy	Maximum efforts will be made to increase production
Kaiten Human Torpedo	100	100	100	110	120	120	650	Navy	
Small Submarine		1	5	8	13	13	40	Navy	
Shusui Plane	100	150	200	200	250	300	1200	{ * Army Navy	To be allocated equally to the Army and the Navy
Shinyō Navy Crash Boat	600	600	600	600	600	600	3600	{ Army * Navy	
Maruhachi Army Crash Boat		500	500	1000	1000		3000	Army	
Fu Go Bomb carrying Balloon				1000	1000	1000	3000	Army	

Notes:

1. In addition to the weapons mentioned in this table, 10,000 'Ke' rocket bombs, 1000 'I Go' bombs and 300 'Kikka' suicide attack planes are scheduled to be procured during the first half of the current fiscal year. But the decision relative to their procurement will depend upon the results of research and examination.

2. Procurement of other weapons now under consideration will be determined and added to this table after the research results are made available.

Table 2. *SPECIAL ATTACK CRAFT PRODUCTION AS PLANNED BY NAVAL GENERAL STAFF
CONFERENCE, 6 APRIL 1945*

Weapons	First Quarter Apr–June	Second Quarter Jul–Sept	Third Quarter Oct–Mar 1946	Remarks
Special type aircraft	2000		To be determined by a later conference	To be replenished with *Suisei*, *Tenzan*, K1–115 and others. The details will be determined by a special conference.
Oka Plane	900	900	As above	A special conference will be held to discuss improvement of performance.
Kikka Plane		300	As above	
Shusui Plane	450	750	As above	To be constructed through cooperation between the Army and Navy. Approximately one-third of this number will be constructed by the Navy.
Karyu Plane		5	As above	
Kaiten Human Torpedo	300	360	300	
Kairyū Midget Submarines	350	550	1000	To be constructed by advancing the deadline as much as possible.
Kōryū Midget Submarines	110	430	1000	Improvement in the performance of the *Kairyū* will be considered in the last half of the fiscal year.
Small Submarines		40	120	Of the submarines scheduled for the first half, 40 will be readied by August. They will be equipped to recharge while cruising underwater as soon as possible.
Shinyō				
No of Vessels	1680	1800	1200	
Engines	2250	2250	1300	

Notes:

The number scheduled for the Third Quarter and thereafter is an approximate figure. The details shall be determined by a later conference.

including the practice of ritual suicide (*Seppuku*), the establishment of State Shinto at the time of Meiji Restoration, the growing of ultra nationalism, especially military factions promoting the concepts of 'Greater Japan' and then the 'Greater East Asia Co-Prosperity Sphere' and to defend and preserve the national policy (*Kokutai*).

[4] The term *Kamikaze* (Divine Wind) was originally limited to naval air units using special attack methods but later came to be applied by the allied forces to all special attack air units.

[5] The GHQ decided the new policy of directing operations of the IJA and IJN on 15 September 1943 and this was embodied in the 'General Outline of the Future War Direction Policy' adopted at the Imperial Conference on 30 September.

[6] A line extending from the Banda Sea through the Eastern and Western Carolines and through the Marianas.

[7] To support the operational plans the Supreme War Direction Council promulgated the basic national logistics plan on 25 January. The order of priority was (1) aircraft, (2) special attack weapons, (3) AA guns, (4) petroleum products, (5) food, and (6) ships.

[8] The Navy General Staff delayed ratification until 1 March in order to have time to study the actual trends of production and training.

[9] The *Ketsu Go* operation in the homeland and adjacent areas was divided into Ketsu Nos 1 to 7 and the component operations were as follows:

Ketsu No 1: Hokkaido, Karafuto (Saghalin), and the Kurile Islands
2: Northern Honshu
3: Kanto District
4: Nagoya-Shizuoka area
5: Western Honshu and Shikoku
6: Kyushu
7: Korea

[10] The Navy General Staff was intensely preoccupied with the *Ten-Go* operation (air defence battle over the East China Sea) and had delegated detailed planning for *Ketsu Go* to the Combined Fleet.

[11] Admiral Toyoda Soemu, C-in-C of Combined Fleet, was designated C-in-C General Navy Command, holding both positions simultaneously.

[12] This was the *Ha 201* class.

COUNTERING THE MAGNETIC MINE: 1939–45 AND TO THE PRESENT

Thomas G Lynch describes the development of degaussing and other methods of dealing with a ship's magnetic signature from the time the influence mine became a threat in 1939 to some of the latest innovations.

THE disturbance of the earth's magnetic field caused by a ferrous metal object was recognized very clearly by the turn of the century and had been practically utilized in the magnetic mine as early as 1918. However, it was first scientifically researched in the mid-nineteenth century when it was discovered that if a ferrous material was placed in a uniform magnetic field, it would acquire an induced magnetism over time and hence, would deform or distort the original magnetic field. Recognizing this fact, scientists working on mine countermeasures set out to discover ways to minimize this effect, with two practical methods eventually coming to the forefront.

The first method was eliminating 'permanent' magnetism by reducing it to zero. This process was found to counter permanent magnetism by locking in opposite polarity permanent magnetism and was thereafter referred to as 'deperming'. This theory and subsequent applications eventually led to the magnetic treatment of induced magnetism in ships (deperming), while a second technique, 'wiping', was developed to treat both permanent and induced magnetism. 'Wiping' was achieved by opposing the magnetism with an electric solenoid. It was found that by running a specified current of electricity through a solenoid, wrapped around a simple cylindrical metal object, the magnetism could be dramatically reduced. This simple principle and subsequent technique would eventually evolve into the process known as 'degaussing'.

Of course a ship is not a simple cylinder and induced magnetism is introduced by an external field, the earth itself, and in a number of ways. As the steel is milled and rolled at the steel plant, it acquires a degree of permanent magnetism. Fortunately, as the ship is fabricated, these plates are used randomly, without magnetic orientation and the total effect on the ship's final magnetic influence is small. However, the greatest influence in creating the ship's permanent magnetic field is the very working and welding of the steel that makes up the ship's structure. The degree of magnetism also depends upon the shipyard's location and orientation within the earth's magnetic field. For example, a ship built in a yard lying north-south will have a greater permanent magnetic field in the fore and aft plane than one built lying east-west (a ship built in an east-west orientation would have a greater athwartship magnetism than one built north-south). Additionally, ships built in northern latitudes would have less horizontal, but more vertical magnetism than one built in southern yards.

To further complicate the problem, it was discovered that there are three types of permanent, and three types of induced magnetism within a steel-hulled ship. Although not strictly fundamental truths of a scientific nature, the descriptions of permanent and induced magnetism were simply notions that permitted a conceptual simplification, allowing workers in the area to more readily come to grips with practical problems. Thus induced and permanent magnetism are nothing but somewhat vague distinctions between the rate of time or, more properly, the amount of applied energy required to alter the orientation of the magnetic domains within a material. Vague they may be, but for practical purposes these are:
1. Permanent longitudinal magnetism or PLM;
2. Permanent vertical magnetism or PVM;
3. Permanent athwartships magnetism or PAM;
4. Induced longitudinal magnetism or ILM;
5. Induced vertical magnetism or IVM;
6. Induced athwartships magnetism or IAM.
However, because of the absolute beam dimension of most warships, the athwartships magnetism is the least of these worries. For example, some Second World War

HMCS Onondaga *(SSK-73), 18 April 1991. The submarine, newly returned from a major refit, is seen in Bedford Basin, Halifax, NS, with the deperming barge alongside and with the deperming solenoid rigged. The C$30 million, 18 month-long refit saw the replacement of the old Type 187C attack sonar with the Type 2051/CSU3-41, which is contained in the bulbous bow dome.* (Duckworth/LYNCAN)

American battleships had A-coils (see below). This may have been motivated by the knowledge that these battleships would be operating in the high horizontal field areas of the equatorial Pacific, unlike British ships which chiefly roamed the North Atlantic.

The total vertical magnetism is composed of both the permanent and induced factors, but with the induced a variable factor, since it is a direct response to the earth's local magnetic field and varies as the ship sails about the world, and even reversing as the ship crosses the equator. Indeed, the permanent factor is *not* permanent, but rather the mean figure that the ship's structure reaches if operated in one locality over a period of time. Hence, if the ship should be moved elsewhere in the world, this value would gradually change as the vessel progressed to its new station and thereafter would reach a new equilibrium sometime after entering service in the new locale. Further, it was found that all three types of permanent magnetism were altered by the application of mechanical energy – the battering experienced in high seas, near-miss bombs, explosions, hydrostatic pressure on a diving submarine, etc.

However, in the case of both types of longitudinal magnetism in a ship, the change occurs at a far more rapid rate than for its vertical component. This is because the induced magnetism of a ship varies with its heading and reverses with a 180-degree change in heading, which can happen in a few moments. One of the prime examples is the PLM alteration that takes place when a ship makes a long voyage in storms while on a north–south heading. As

in the case of PVM, the permanent longitudinal magnetism is not stable over long periods. Hence it can be seen that there are six components to a ship's magnetic signature, all of which vary at different rates in different directions for different reasons. All of these were not realized at once and hence were dealt with on a whole basis, often with the corrective step aggravating another factor. It was only when all aspects of the interlocking of the components making up a ship's magnetic field or signature were grasped in the mid-1940s and treated individually that the problems of controlling the magnetic signature of a ship were minimized.

The Threat: The Second World War

The first indications that Germany had perfected a workable magnetic mine came right after the declaration of war in September 1939. Both merchant ships and warships were mysteriously sunk, with fast-moving destroyers seemingly particularly vulnerable. In November, HMS *Adventure*, one of Britain's first purpose-built minelayers was damaged by a magnetic mine and nearly sank. On 13 November, the destroyer *Blanche* was sunk by an underwater explosion while in the Thames Estuary.

Magnetic mines were nothing new to the Admiralty: the Royal Navy had had a crude one called the 'M-sinker', a one-ton ground mine housed in a dome-like concrete casing and deployed during the First World War. However, it proved unreliable and was dropped from inventory after the war. Meanwhile, the idea had been taken up by the Germans and, quite independently of British efforts, they perfected a sophisticated ground magnetic mine that could be dropped by air, by fast surface, or submarine minelayer.

The first German mines were dip-needle triggered, with later models utilizing an induction coil sensor. The thought that fast-moving destroyers were particularly vulnerable to the earlier type proved erroneous. The simple fact was that they were relatively more sensitive to underwater explosion. However, with the later induction coil types, increased speed did contribute to effective mine sensitivity, making non-armoured hull ships like destroyers more vulnerable.

Aircraft proved to be the best delivery system for the Germans and ultimately the undoing of the secret of the magnetic mine. Meanwhile, countermining with depth charges by the Royal Navy was proving to be futile. Recovery of a mine at sea proved to be highly dangerous, with the drifter *Ray of Hope* being sunk on 10 December 1939 by a mine she was trying to recover. However, an intact mine was recovered from the tidal flats near Southend on 22 November when revealed by the receding tide. A brave disarming party from the Navy's mining school, HMS *Vernon* at Portsmouth, dismantled the mine, and with the polarity and sensitivity of the mine's firing mechanism known, it was relatively simple to devise appropriate countermeasures.

With the problem identified, a number of solutions were worked out fairly quickly. The first of these was 'coiling' or 'degaussing' and was an established practice by 1940. The other methods were 'wiping', and 'deperming', which are discussed below.

Wiping

Wiping was primarily developed for vessels of less than 2000 tons that had insufficient electrical generating plant capacity to support degaussing. Wiping was, and still is, carried out by encircling a ship's hull with a single (or multiple, if sufficient current cannot be carried by a single wire) horizontal cable so arranged that it can be lowered to a position below the ship's waterline and then hauled back up so that it is in close contact with the hull. When satisfactorily positioned, a large DC current, which may be between 1000 and 6000 amperes, is passed through the coil(s) and the cable raised vertically, perhaps accounting for the term 'wiping'. Wiping seeks to impart magnetism opposing the sum of the permanent and induced vertical components (VM = PVM + IVM) produced by the earth's magnetic field in the area where the ship will operate. The treatment was good for about three months maximum as practised by the Royal Navy if done with a process referred to as 'over-wiping'. 'Over-wiping' consisted of a reduced amperage, reverse (flash-back) current being passed through the cable after the initial or 'over-wipe', with the 'flash-back' sometimes repeated several times to achieve the desired value (typically about −40 mGauss amidships at beam depth). During this three-month period, the ship slowly aged back towards its resident

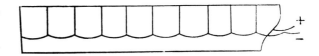

A simplified diagram of the rig used in wiping.

value and then had to be wiped again. However, in actual practice, with small ships operating in suspect waters, wiping was done about every six weeks, where possible.

Subsequently, it was found that for a given zone of operation and barring mechanical misadventure, the wiping interval is a function of the magnitude of overwipe and subsequent ageback. The higher the intensity of the treatment, the more stable the signature. Canadian practice, developed during the Second World War, used a more vigorous treatment than practised in the UK, with signature longevities of up to two years. Further, in the Canadian experience, ageback was accomplished by cycling a longitudinal solenoid wrap, rather than the reverse current method developed by the British. By 1944 the solenoid method was widely accepted, and is still in use worldwide, commonly in place at the same time as wiping to deperm the ship longitudinally, thus the procedure does not entail additional labour.

Drawbacks of the early wiping process were the unevenness of the vessel's vertical magnetic signature after being done, caused by difficult stern contours, rubbing strakes, and built-up areas, which necessitated additional wiping of sections of the vessel. This is referred to as sectional wiping and is time-consuming. Additionally, the effects of early wiping techniques were very transitory in duration, since only a very limited number of 'tight' molecules within the hull were close enough to the wiping cable to be affected, and vibration and opposing fields generated by machinery accelerated the decay process. Higher amperage/magnetic fields resulted in greater stability in most cases, but the process at best is about equal to the results obtained in operating a simple degaussing M coil.

Deperming

Deperming was developed to reduce or eliminate the permanent longitudinal and (to some degree) the athwartship magnetization of a ship. It works on the principle that the smaller the PLM, the smaller the current required in the ship's degaussing coils when the ship is operational. To this end, most ships were depermed on a regular basis.

To deperm a ship, under a process known as 'Deperm C' in the UK, it was wrapped with cables, with the placement of the coils so that they lie in a vertical athwartships plan, otherwise the process could cause unwanted magnetic effects. Even this configuration caused some unwanted effects, but was the best compromise possible, with minimal unwanted characteristics. Again in Canada, the process evolved during the war and a technique known as 'Deperm SR' was developed which

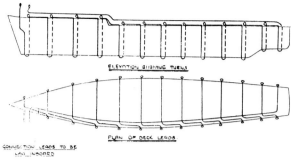

ELEVATION SHOWING TURNS

PLAN OF DECK LEADS

CONNECTION LEADS TO BE
LAID INBOARD

SOLENOID RIG FOR DEPERMING

A diagram of the solenoid rig used for deperming.

proved more stable than the British 'Deperm C', but using the same wrap. 'Deperm SR' is still in common use in Canada to this day.

For a ship of a destroyer size, the solenoid turns are spaced about 15ft apart. To deperm the ship, a DC current of up to 3000 amperes is passed through the coils for 20–30 seconds to stabilize the magnetic field. The value and direction of flow are calculated to reduce the PLM to as close as zero as possible. However, it was found by mid-war that a process known as 'flashing' would impart greater stability to the PLM. The ship's original PLM was first reversed to roughly 2.5 times the original PLM value and then 'flashed' back to as near zero as possible. The process is further enhanced (especially in ships that will serve in distant waters) by repeating the process twice more, with the equivalent of the ship being turned 360 degrees at the Equator the result, with the process known as 'cycling'. The resultant PLM value for the ship is sufficient to over correct for the ship's original PLM, so that the new permanent magnetism ages back to

Diagram showing the location of 'M', 'F', 'Q', and 'A' coils in a typical warship.

a stable low value.

Flash 'D' was a special method of 'flashing' developed in the US, and used primarily for some classes of submarines and various types of landing craft. The ship was placed in a strong vertical field opposite in polarity to the earth's vertical field. This was accomplished by locating the ship at the centre of a rectangular loop laid either at water level or on the sea bed. This rectangular loop was known as a 'Z' loop.

While the 'Z' loop was activated, the ship was 'shaken' longitudinally, using heavy current flashes of alternating polarity, and in decreasing amplitude in a solenoid rigged round the ship. The 'Z' loop was then shut off and the ship again subjected to current flashes, but this time in increasing amplitude until the magnetization obtained in the earth's vertical field approached the final desired value. Finally, a normal deperm by reversals was carried out to remove the PLM remaining after the second phase of the operation. Flash 'D' required permanent berthing facilities and required a greater powerplant than the British overwiping system. However, it was widely utilized in the US and Pacific, and to a limited extent, by the British in European waters.

Degaussing

At the front of countermeasures suggestions were those of a Canadian from Winnipeg, Manitoba. Joining the Royal Navy in 1939 while attending college in the UK, Charles Goodeve had been experimenting with magnetic properties for months without a great deal of official encouragement. Fortunately, for the Allies, a memo from the Admiralty debunking his findings was not received until just after Goodeve and two associates had proved that their findings were workable!

What Goodeve had found was that if electrical cables were wrapped about a ship and controlled currents of electricity were sent through the cables, the magnetic 'signature' of the ship's metal hull could be dramatically reduced. He called this procedure 'Degaussing' after the

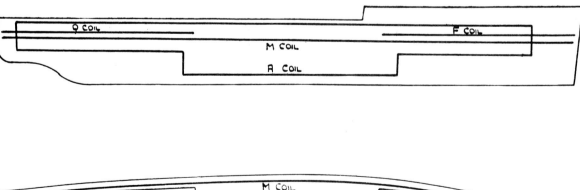

Q COIL   F COIL

M COIL

A COIL

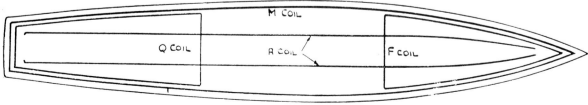

M COIL

Q COIL   A COIL   F COIL

German mathematician Karl F Gauss who had done so much theoretical work in the field of magnetism in the early to mid-1700s.

By June 1940, more than 2000 ships had been degaussed. Of 218 ships lost in the evacuation of Dunkirk, only two fell victim to magnetic mines. In turn, to counter the degaussing procedure and the first crude minesweeping devices, the Germans made the bar magnet in the influence triggering device more sensitive at first, then added a 'counter' which simply delayed the arming of the mine until a certain number of ships had passed over the mine's location. To counter this, the British, with the aid of Goodeve's work, devised the 'LL' sweep, which was an array of buoyant electrical cables that trailed aft of a minesweeper or other suitably equipped ship. When energized, these cables set up enormous magnetic fields that detonated magnetic mines within a 4-acre area (20,000sq yds) around the sweeps. 'Counters' were defeated by repeated sweeps with the 'LL' arrangement, and as the Germans developed new 'wrinkles', the 'LL' was modified to match it; the system, used individually or in tandem with acoustic or pressure-wave systems, became the standard for the rest of the war.

Although the 'LL' countermeasures have been well documented, the distinctions of the degaussing systems developed and used throughout the war have not. This narrative will concentrate on the shipboard installations, commonly referred to as 'DG' systems.

'Coiling' or degaussing consisted of permanent coils, aligned to the major planes of a ship. In later installations, these coils were fitted into the ship during construction, but in 1940–41, these had to be fitted by laboriously drawing cable throughout the ship's structure, after the necessary glands had been installed through all watertight bulkheads and decks. Degaussing evolved into quite a science in the course of the war, requiring combinations of different coils to minimize the ship's magnetic signature. These different coils are discussed below.

'M' (or Main) coils. These were some of the first fitted to British ships. Later, these were split into several indi-

vidual coils positioned along the length of the ship and these countered the vertical magnetism. Some countries also refer to this arrangement as the 'Z' coil.

'A' coils. The athwartships magnetic field is neutralized by the means of 'A' coils. These are large loops, arranged in a vertical-longitudinal plane, somewhat inside the hull, usually about 70 per cent of the keel-to-beam distance away from the keel on either side of the ship. Where the hull narrows toward the bow and stern, frequently only a single coil on the midships line is used.

In some early applications, the 'A' coils in effect carried two currents: one which was set up and not changed during the voyage countering the effects of permanent athwartships magnetism, while the other, which was variable, countered the induced athwartships magnetism. However, in most ships, the PAM is small and 'A' coil capacity and currents compensating for just IAM was judged sufficient.

'L' coils. To counter the PLM and ILM in a ship, two methods are used. One is the use of 'L' coils which are mounted in the vertical athwartships plane of the ship. As in the case of the 'A' coils, the 'L' coils carry two currents: one fixed to counter the PLM and one variable to counter the ILM.

'F' & 'Q' coils. Quite simply, 'F' stands for forecastle and 'Q' stands for quarterdeck, denoting where these coils were installed. If the current in these two coils were properly set, the effect of the ship's longitudinal magnetic field could be minimized at a specific depth. However, with this system of the coils the full effect is not effective at all depths, as it is with the 'L' coils. However, when used in conjunction with an 'M' coil, the ship's signature was dramatically reduced.

Diagram showing the location of 'M', FI', 'QI', 'FP', and 'QP' coils in a typical warship.

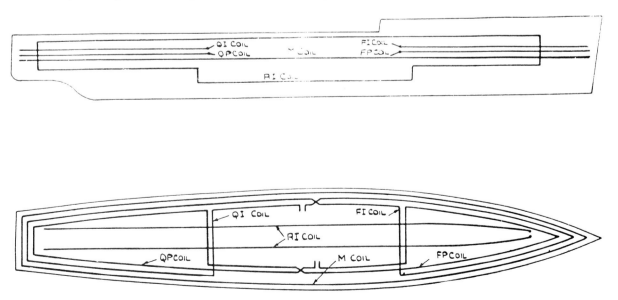

Compass Correction. Because the DG coils create a magnetic field aboard the ship, they adversely affect the ship's magnetic compasses. To solve this problem, the compass is equipped with compass correction coils. Current within these coils is proportional to the currents induced into the DG system. The magnetic field produced by these correction coils can be tailored to exactly cancel the magnetic field effects of the DG coils upon the compass.

System Types: The Low Voltage Coil System

The first of the systems devised were referred to as low-voltage degaussing systems, and normally consisted of only an 'M' coil. Using a low-voltage motor-generator set, a copper band was affixed to the outside of the ship's hull and isolated electrically from the hull by the use of rubber mountings. The band assembly was only treated with varnish, making it a maintenance nightmare, with salt readily making unwanted electrical 'bridges' to the hull and shorting the system out. Generator settings or ratings were usually about 10 volts, with kilowatt ratings of about 24kW for older aircraft carriers, down to about 4kW for *Halcyon* class minesweepers. Maximum amperages were from 2400 to 400 amps, respectively.

With the shortcomings of the first system readily apparent by early 1940, experiments with coils either run on deck or inside the hull plates were successful and in mid-1940 DG policy was changed so that the fitting of permanent internal DG coils to HM ships was standardized. A number of low voltage motor-generator sets were still being delivered and these were coupled with internal coils as an interim measure. In ships over 7000 tons displacement, 'M', 'F', 'Q' and 'A' coils were installed. Fleet minesweepers such as the *Halcyon*s had 'A' coils added too, in view of their specialized tasks.

However, these motor-generator sets were found not to be stable while working at low voltages. If the perimeter of the DG coils was small, its resistance was very low and large currents would flow for a very low applied voltage. Further, compass corrector coils were designed for 4- or 5-volt operation and consequently, the DG coils had to operate at comparable voltage. It was therefore necessary to increase the circuit resistance so that the voltage required to produce a given number of ampere-turns was high enough to ensure the above conditions. To this end, two or three series-turns of cable were frequently wound in coils of short perimeter, such as 'F' and 'Q' coils, so that machinery would operate under stable conditions.

In large ships, the size of cable required to carry the total current in single-turn 'M' coils was very large and it was common for the coil to be made up of two, three, or more parallel cables. This method was adopted purely to give the required cross-sectional area of copper cables which could be easily handled, since a single-core cable of adequate cross-section would prove unwieldy during reeving.

This low-power DG type installation was fitted in battleships, light and heavy cruisers, fleet carriers, monitors, depot/repair ships, AMCs, destroyers up to and including the 'P' class, but excluding the 'Town' and 'Hunt' classes, and the *Halcyon* class minesweepers in 1940.

With specialized tasks such as minesweeping, closer attention to the various types of magnetic components making up the ship's signature had to be addressed. Hence, *Halcyon* class minesweepers were converted to a modified form of the low-voltage 'split' system in 1942, in which the existing 'F' and 'Q' coils were split into two components each, these being the 'FI', 'QI', and 'FP', 'QP' coils as in the split system below. One low-voltage motor-generator was used to supply the 'FI' and 'QI' circuit, and a reversing switch located on the bridge was connected in the field circuit of the generator. The switch controlled the polarity of the 'FI' and 'QI' coils as required, while the strength of the ampere turns in these coils was preset on the field regulator which was pinned so that it could operate in only one direction.

'FP' and 'QP' coils were fed from the second motor-generator set, and were used to compensate PLM and were not variable with changes of a ship's heading. The field circuit of the 'A' coil motor-generator set was also supplied via a change-over switch located on the bridge and the 'A' coil was used for the compensation of IAM only.

High Voltage Coils – The Controller System

With the introduction of internal coils and the elimination of attendant problems of exposure to the elements, it was no longer necessary for a low voltage to be used and so a more economical high-voltage, multi-core system was adopted. In this system the cores were conducted in series through a suitable regulating resistance to the ship's mains, thus avoiding the need for motor-generator sets. Resistance controllers such as these, fed from the ship's mains supply, were feasible because ships of the era used 240v DC. Modern ships, however, use AC mains power and such controllers were rendered unusable by the end of the 1950s.

The type of resistance regulator originally employed on the high-voltage system was known as the controller. These started to appear in early 1942, as ships previously outfitted with low-voltage sets were updated during refits. The operation of the controller gave seven equal steps of current in the coil in either a forward (+) or reverse (−) direction. The fifteenth position, mid-point between the forward and reverse positions, was the 'Off' position. The actual resistance elements were mounted separately from the controller in a well-ventilated compartment, the connection between the resistance bank and the contacts of the controller being made through a suitable multi-core cable.

This type of installation was made in the following:
Destroyers – 'Town' class, first 30; 'Hunt' class, first 40.
Corvettes – 'Flower' class, 1939–40 Programme.
Minesweepers – *Bangor* class, first 28.
Corvettes – subsequent classes, unless used for minesweeping.
LCT and minor requisitioned vessels under 35ft in beam.

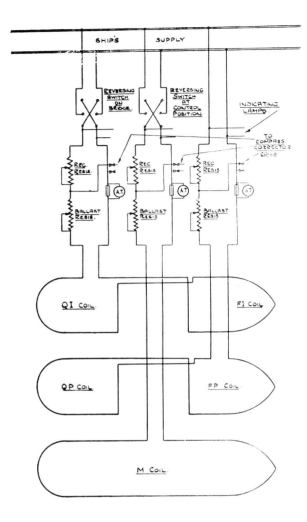

Schematic diagram of the Split System.

The Split System

One of the major problems that was found with the original degaussing system was that the use of controllers was unsuitable for carrying out switching operations required during course corrections, as the steps between the ampere turn values were rather too large, and the operation for change of course was unsatisfactory, particularly in darkness. A system was therefore devised in which the 'F' and 'Q' coils were each split into two separate components to compensate for the permanent longitudinal and induced longitudinal magnetism, the latter being altered as the ship changed course. This arrangement became known as the 'Split System' and was made up of:

1. to neutralize PLM, part of the turns of the 'F' coil were connected to part of the turns of the 'Q' coil reversed. These coils were designated as 'FP' and 'QP';
2. to neutralize ILM, the remaining turns of the 'F' coil were connected to the remaining turns of the 'Q' coil reversed, and these coils were designated as the 'FI' and 'QI' coils.

One resistance regulator was connected in series with the

'FP' and 'QP' coils, and the other resistance regulator in series with 'FI' and 'QI'. The supply to the 'FI' and 'QI' coils was taken through a reversing switch which was located on the bridge, so that as the ILM changed when the ship's heading changed, the switch could be operated to supply the current in either a forward or reverse direction, with the 'off' position for easterly or westerly courses.

To assist in the operation of course corrections, a switch position indicator was fitted beside the changeover switch to show the required position of the switch for all ship's headings. Sample settings were:

When the ship's head lies: within 70 degrees of magnetic north – switch 'up'.

within 20 degrees of E or W – switch position 'off'.

within 70 degrees of magnetic south – switch 'down'.

When the switch was 'up', the current flowed in a forward (+) direction in the 'FI' coil, and a reverse (−) direction in the 'QI' coil. When the switch was 'down', the current flowed in the reverse direction in the 'FI' coil, and forward in the 'QI' coil.

Early *Bangor* class minesweepers and 'Flower' class corvettes fitted for minesweeping were also converted from high-voltage controller regulation to the high-voltage split system. The turns in the 'F' coil were split into sections 'FI' and 'FP', and the turns in the 'Q' coil split into sections 'QI' and 'QP' as described for the *Halcyon* class above. 'FI' and 'QI' were connected in series and supplied through a changeover switch on the bridge for the operation of course correction, and the 'FP' and 'QP' coils were connected in series and used to compensate the ship's PLM.

In 1944 arrangements were made for ships larger than destroyers fitted with high-voltage 'F' and 'Q' coils to be converted to the split system. The 'F' and 'Q' coils were each split into two parts: 'FI' and 'FP', and 'QI' and 'QP'. The 'FI' and 'QI' coils were connected in series and of opposite polarity, and controlled by one resistance regulator and a reversing switch at the central control position. The 'FP' and 'QP' coils were also connected in series and controlled by a second resistance regulator.

With the fitting of 'LL' minesweeping equipment in vessels larger than trawlers, these were also fitted with an 'AI' coil which was supplied through a regulating resistance and a reversing switch in the same manner as the 'FI' and 'QI' sections of the split system. A further switch position indicator was fitted beside the reversing switch in the bridge to show the required position of the switch for all headings. With the switch 'up', the current flowed in a forward direction in the coil and vice-versa when the switch was down. This compensated for athwartships magnetism, and further reduced the ship's magnetic signature.

Minesweepers equipped with the 'LL' system also had an arrangement whereby the 'LL' batteries could act as a back-up power supply to the degaussing system in case of primary supply failure. Further, a resistance in the emergency supply leads to the DG coil helped minimize voltage drops during actual minesweeping operations.

The resistance regulator superseded the controller in the

split system in 1942, giving further refinement in control of current. The regulator was a face plate type, with twelve studs, the resistance values being so arranged that the following percentages of the maximum available ampere turns could be obtained: 100, 95, 85, 80, 75, 70, 65, 60, 50, 40 and 30 per cent. When these resistances were used to supply 'M' coils, an additional stud gave 17 per cent of the maximum ampere turns value. The supply to the coil regulating resistance was made in this case through a reversing switch so that polarity of the coil could be reversed without altering the regulator.

This split system was fitted in the following classes:
Later *Bangors*, after the 29th;
'Flower' class corvettes using 'LL' minesweeping gear;
Algerine, Aberdare, and *Bathurst* class minesweepers;
minesweeping frigates;
ocean-going rescue ships;
survey vessels;
wreck dispersal vessels;
cablelaying ships.

The following classes of ships were fitted with a resistance regulator and an 'M' coil only, and in the case of the 'Hunt' and 'Q', 'R', 'S' and 'T' class destroyers, a re-entrant loop was installed in series with the 'M' coil to improve the compensation in the forward part of the vessel where there was a raised forecastle:
Destroyers – 'Hunt' and later; 'Q', 'R', 'S', 'T' classes, plus 'Town' and later;
Sloops – All Emergency classes.

On all high-voltage installations, a ballast resistance was permanently connected in series with the DG coils. The resistance was to provide a method of adjusting the final ohmic value of the DG coil, plus ballast, to a predetermined value. When DG coils were installed, it was sometimes necessary to make small deviations in the coil runs, which caused differences in the total length of cable installed in ships of the same class or type. With the ballast in series with the coils, the total resistance could be 'trimmed' until the ampere turns corresponded to the maximum values specified for that class of ship. Ten 'steps' in the ballast resistance allowed 'fine tuning' regulation, but it was not intended for regulating the DG current when making adjustments after ranging. Indeed movement of the ballast resistance link would necessitate re-adjustment of the compass corrector coils.

Further Refinements

Small minesweepers. Early in the war and to maximize protection of small minesweepers from magnetic mines, subsidiary coils and windings were devised to compensate for local 'peaks' in the ship signature. These included windings in the following places:
1. rudder post windings or coils of cable around the rudder post;
2. rudder post loops around the stern of the vessel, connected in series with the 'M' coil;
3. SA (acoustic hammer) frame magnets, used to neutralize the field in the forward part of the ship where SA gear was fitted.
The latter measure as used in wooden minesweepers with

SA gear was discontinued in 1943, when the 'flashing' deperming of the frame at manufacture fully compensated for this. In 126 MMS wooden motor minesweepers however, where the SA frame forward compensated for the vertical magnetism of the ship, the practice of placing frame magnets continued. The SA frame magnet and adjusting resistance were permanently connected in parallel with the 'M' coil, and controlled by the coil switch and resistance regulator. All special coils were only adjusted by DG officers during survey and once set, they were not to be altered by the ship's crew.

Rudder post windings were not fitted after late 1943, but several systems were still in use in 1945. Rudder post loops were fitted as part of the coiling system in 105ft and 126ft wooden motor minesweepers right through until after the war's end.

Trawlers and similar auxiliary vessels were only fitted with an 'M' coil as a general rule in home waters, but if required to sweep overseas or to act as fuel carriers, were fitted with 'FI' and 'QI' coils, controlled by a reversing switch on the bridge for course correction as in the split system. No 'FP' or 'QP' coils were fitted, as deperming was relied upon to neutralize PLM. The reversing switch was subsequently supplemented by a resistance regulator that was capable of reducing the 'M' coil current to a minimum value of 50 ampere-turns in 1944.

Larger Ships. Starting in 1943, research showed it was desirable to have the 'M' coil at different heights above the keel, in different parts of the ship, and also that it was sometimes necessary to have different values of ampere turns to compensate for the vertical magnetism of the ship in the centre portion of the ship, compared with the forward and aft portions. For this reason the original 'M' coil was divided into three parts:
1. the 'MF' coil around the forward portion of the ship;
2. the 'MM' coil in the midships section;
3. the 'MQ' section around the stern portion of the ship.
These coils were usually located at different heights, and each was separately adjustable, being connected through a series resistance regulator of a similar type as used in the split coil system. This regulator had either twelve or twenty stops, the latter being more precise and flexible.

By late 1944, a common regulator for both warships and merchant ships was under design. It had twenty equal current stops for regulating 'M', 'MF', 'MM', 'MQ', 'FP' or 'QP' coils. The advantage of this controller was that in changing stops, the current to the coils was uninterrupted. In the case of 'FI', 'QI' and 'AI' coils, a twenty-stop controller was used, but the resistance bank was arranged so that current regulation was from 100 to 25 per cent. With these coils, it was unnecessary to change current values below this minimum.

Also by 1944, the appearance of automatic controls for the DG course correction were making their appearance. An M-type repeater motor, controlled from the master gyro-compass panel, was coupled through suitable gearing to a series of cams. These cams, in turn, closed micro-switches, which in turn, energized the operating coils of 'contractors', thus making or breaking the power supply to the DG coils. By suitable arrangements of these cams, current could be supplied to the DG coil in either

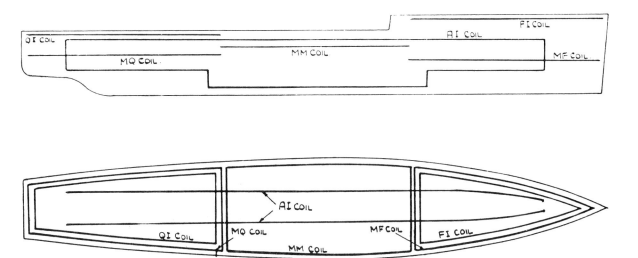

(+) or (−) direction, or the coil could be switched off or on in order to meet the requirements of course changes.

Because of their light weight, micro-switches were less liable to suffer from shock over mechanical switches, but were unsuitable for opening or closing circuits carrying currents in the order of one ampere at 220 volts DC. For this reason, the additional staging by use of a set of 'contractors' was necessary to relieve the micro-switches of any load.

Although complicated, this arrangement vastly simplified the job of adjusting the DG coils fitted within a ship, leaving little room for human error.

US and Lend-Lease Warships

American efforts in the field generally paralleled systems developed by the UK, with certain warships built for the

Diagram showing the location of 'MF', 'MM', 'FI' and 'AI' coils in a typical warship.

Royal Navy using American pattern equipment. This was very similar to the British type high and low voltage split systems, the former using special motor-generators and control via field control of the motor-generator set. Both systems used a unique system whereby control of the settings from the bridge, or central DG control or local control, was done by pushing one or two buttons. These, in turn, drove a small motor, which moved the resistance arm from stud to stud, allowing very fine adjustments in the coil turn amperage. Of course, the largest drawback to the system was that if either button was pushed too long, it was possible to produce corrections far in excess of that needed, and if the maximum was applied, the residual magnetism in the ship could be altered. This could only

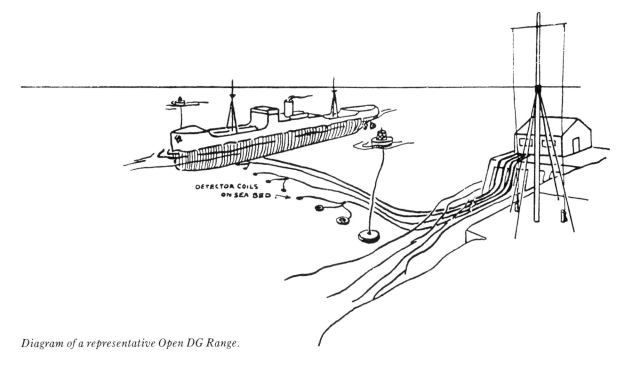

Diagram of a representative Open DG Range.

then be corrected if alternating, decreasing flows of current were passed through the DG coils until the residual magnetism returned to normal values.

American pattern installations also featured re-entrant loops connected in series, and it was customary to give coil settings in amperes, instead of ampere-turns as in the British systems.

A number of wooden fleet tenders built in the US were fitted with a reversing turn 'M' coil. This consisted of nineteen turns of cable, connected through a special controller in such a way that individual turns could be reversed in polarity. The current was constant in the coil and set by adjustment of the ballast resistance during the initial trials of the ships. Subsequent alteration of the coil strength was by means of the controller.

In the 'full' position, all turns were connected to flow in the same direction, but as the controller was turned, a turn would be reversed in polarity. A reversing switch allowed for complete reversal. This system proved as effective as its British counterpart, but remained a logistical headache in British use, with attendant shortages of spare parts. However, it was widely used by the US Navy and with excellent results.

Another American arrangement was the 'Malmaux system', which was fitted in American-built MMS or BYMS. In this system, an 'M' auxiliary coil encircled the whole ship in the same way as a normal 'M' coil, but in addition, each large mass of magnetic material in the ship was separately degaussed by means of an 'M', 'A' or 'L' coil. All the 'M' coils were connected in series and controlled by a single regulator. Similarly, the several 'A' and 'L' coils were respectively connected in series and controlled by their own regulators. The system offered further refinement in the control of 'spikes' in the ship's magnetic signature. The single controller which dominated all US designs was a smart move when compared to British offerings of the day, since it reduced the number of control parameters which the ship's crew had to set, thereby reducing the chances for error. Indeed, the single controller concept survives in the US Navy to this day.

DG Ranging

By 1945, there was a comprehensive number of DG ranges throughout the Commonwealth. These became necessary as DG systems became more prevalent, worldwide, in the latter stages of the war, since a degaussing range was necessary to set up a degaussing system.

A degaussing range of the era was normally laid out in a north-south orientation for major warships. However, modern trends are to update ranges to accommodate north-south and east-west sailing, as ships of all sizes are being fitted with 'A' coils. The general pattern of DG ranges for MSOs was to lay them down in pairs, so that the ship can traverse them on an east-west heading or on a north-south heading. For MSOs, a pair of north-south runs determined the values of the PLM and ILM, while a pair of east-west runs determined the athwartships factors. However, the separation of the PVM and IVM is difficult and requires the use of a seabed-mounted 'Z' coil to locally change the value of the vertical magnetic field.

Most Second World War UK, USA and Canadian ranges (the latter to date) required the ship to steam over the range. These are referred to as 'open' ranges and consisted of bottom-mounted induction coils and required the ship's motion to read the results. However, postwar this changed, spearheaded by the US, who moved from induction coils to bottom-mounted magnetometers. The UK is slowly changing over, but Canadian ranges continue to use the coil technique, although with modern amplifiers and data processing equipments.

With the 'open' type range, the ship passes through it with the DG system off, and the signature is recorded. Then the ship repeatedly passes through the range with only one coil in operation at a time, until all the coils have been activated. This is known as coil calibration. Once the coil signatures have been established, it is then a matter of calculation to determine the number of turns per coil and required current to compensate for the ship's original signature. Depending upon the coil suite and

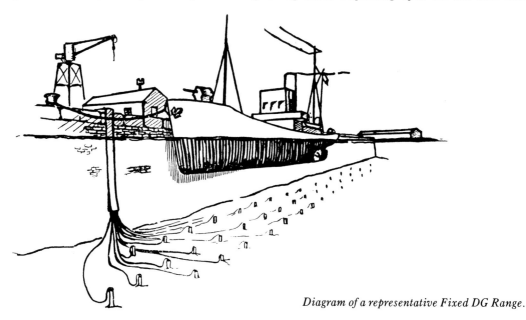

Diagram of a representative Fixed DG Range.

complexity, the stability of the PM factors and the accuracy of the control system, the ship can be rendered nearly magnetically neutral.

'Fixed' ranges came about with the switch-over to magnetometers. With this type range, the ship to be calibrated is moored in a stationary position over the range during the process of magnetic measurement. Measurements are taken at a series of equidistant points below the keel, and the magnetic field due to the ship is calculated at each point by noting the change in field experienced when the ship is present, compared to when the range is empty. In this manner, a series of point readings are obtained and if these are plotted in the form of a graph, the ship's signature is obtained. In Commonwealth experience, these were normally found on the seabed, usually alongside a wharf or quay, but could also be 'free-standing' ranges, utilizing mooring buoys and lines to position the ship. A modern US degaussing range, therefore, consists of a number of seabed-mounted magnetometers over which the ship positions itself and the magnetic signature read.

The last significant type of range to be widely used were the 'loop' type. This consisted of a long, narrow, rectangular loop laid across a shipping channel or fairway, in water depths between 5 and 10 fathoms. Such loops varied in laid width between 7ft and 18ft and in length, between 400ft and 1600ft, depending upon water depth and width of the channel. The sides of the loop are kept at a uniform width by the use of copper or steel spreaders, and a cast-iron, oval-shaped 'dolly' was attached to the end of each spreader, to which the cable is lashed. These spacers were weighted with lead or concrete to ensure the loop maintained its position on the seabed.

Ships undergoing testing normally passed over the centre of the loop at right angles to the length of the loop. However, the record obtained from a loop-type range differed significantly from that of an open or fixed range. The loop recording integrated the total flux along its length at any instant, and were normally used to ensure that a ship's magnetic state was satisfactory, rather than pinpointing the specific value of the vertical component of a ship's magnetic field at a definite point below the ship, as in the case of open or fixed ranges. Consequently, loop ranges act more as a screening measure, and thus have declined in naval importance since Korea.

Table 1. *NUMBER OF DG RANGES, WORLD-WIDE, OCTOBER 1944*

DG open ranges:	UK	39
	Overseas, excluding US	49
	US-controlled	36
DG fixed ranges:	UK	25
	Overseas, excluding US	3
	US-controlled	0
DG loop ranges:	UK	36
	Overseas, excluding US	18
	US-controlled	27

Postwar Developments

Degaussing methods remained largely the same postwar, with greater refinements of the control systems as technology allowed. In the 1950s, advances were most felt in the minesweeping field, when electronics were introduced to degaussing controllers, allowing mine countermeasures vessels to compensate for the magnetic changes required in the 'M' and 'L' coil currents due to the rolling of the ship in a seaway. Roll, quite apart from the obvious induced component variation, imparts a secondary effect: eddy currents caused by a moving conductor (the ship's metallic parts) in a magnetic field (the earth's magnetic field). These eddy currents in turn generate an AC magnetic field of a frequency equivalent to the roll characteristics of the ship. These new controllers sensed this period and fed currents to the degaussing coils to negate the generated magnetic fields. However, such systems were not fitted in modern warship construction of the time, since the effect was too far below the residual ferromagnetic fields to be of concern.

In the 1960s, warship degaussing controllers were fitted with masthead magnetometers to sense directly the strength and ship-relative orientation of the local geomagnetic field. This was the first real advance for steel-hulled warships since the end of the war. This information is used to derive optimum coil current settings to compensate for the induced components (M,L,A) of magnetism, with the technique obviating the need for manual settings of the ships' degaussing systems.

In the latter portion of the 1960s, Canada fielded the first completely solid state manual and automatic degaussing power supply controllers. These have equipped Canadian warships ever since.

DG systems as described in the 1944–45 period were still found in warship construction to date, albeit with more sophisticated controls. However, by the 1980s, the advent of variable permanent magnets which can be set electrically to have a given value within a prescribed range, made it possible to produce a simple degaussing system that only requires small amounts of power from a ship. The positions, attitudes and settings of these permanent magnets are chosen so that the fields they produce cancel those of the ship.

These variable moment magnets are a Crown-patented invention of Mr A B Cotton, OBE, formerly of the Admiralty Research Establishment, Portland in the UK. The technique is being marketed by Marconi Naval Systems for degaussing and other applications, but with a marked lack of success in the former. The system is markedly more expensive than conventional designs and in its present state of development, offers little advantage over the well designed coil system.

Additionally, with the advances in computers and magnetic modelling algorithms made in the last twenty years, it is now possible for a ship to deploy a simple two sensor degaussing range on the seabed in coastal waters, and once deployed, the ship can range itself. After the necessary runs, the ship can then carry out the necessary adjustments to its own DG system to yield the lowest minimum signature for that area of operation. This allows

Diagram of a representative Loop DG Range.

the ship to compensate for the ageing of its LPM and VPM at any time, in any locality, without resorting to a DG range, the nearest of which may be thousands of miles distant.

The system, developed by Dr Alan Theobald of ARE, Portland and extended by various companies contracting to the UK MoD, has proven most controversial. Canadian tests of the early models showed that they did not work satisfactorily under some very common conditions and were therefore unacceptable. No nation has adopted the technique to date. However, as one Canadian naval DG officer commented: 'The two sensor, self-ranging configuration is undoubtedly better than having no range at all in a zone of operations!'

Internationally, and outside the UK/USA/Canada efforts, the German navy, which adopted quite a different approach to many aspects of signature control, still dominates the navies of continental Europe, aside from France. In many experts' opinions, the Germans will continue to be the best in the field of mine countermeasures for some years to come. And let us not forget the Soviets, consummate mine warfare experts since the Russo–Japanese War at the turn of the century. They have developed some of the very best in magnetic signature control and are past experts at magnetic mine design.

As can be seen, degaussing went from the very first crude attempts to counter magnetic mines in 1939–40, to sophisticated, semi-automatic systems, capable of applying themselves as course changes and differing circumstances demanded. Most of this came about through the tireless efforts of the scientists of the Ship Degaussing Department within the Admiralty, the US Naval Ordnance Laboratory in Silver Springs, MD, and Canadian Naval Research Establishment (later, Defence Research Establishment, Atlantic), but the initial credit has to go to Charles Goodeve and his tiny band, who ignored the odds and brought the theories of degaussing to reality.

References
Manual of Degaussing, CB (R) 3139, Vols 1 & 2, SDG Admiralty, June 1944.
Manual of Degaussing, BR 825 (1) & (2), SDG Admiralty, Revised to 9 July 1952.
CAFO P6/46 revisions to above
AFO P233/46 revisions to above
AFO P289/46 revisions to above
AFO P306/46 revisions to above
Canada At War, 1939–45, Vol 2 (Toronto 1969), p573.
Naval Forces XI (111/1990), 'Degaussing Techniques', pp52–59.
Navy International (May 1991), 'Signature Management', pp152–158.
Correspondence with Mr Eric Westman, Director, Naval Architecture & Specialty Engineering, NDHQ, Ottawa, Ontario, April–July 1991.

WARSHIP NOTES

This section comprises a number of short articles and notes, generally highlighting little-known aspects of warships history.

AUSTRALIA'S FIRST NAVAL CASUALTY REMAINS A MYSTERY

Chris S Fuqua and Rick Kennett analyse the possible explanations for the unsolved mystery of the loss of the submarine AE 1.

In July 1914 the Royal Australian Navy was still in the embryonic stages, its forces limited and minuscule in comparison with the navies of the world powers. The RAN's strength lay in its battlecruiser, five light cruisers, three destroyers and the newest members of the fleet, the two 'E' class submarines *AE 1* and *AE 2* which had arrived in Port Jackson, Sydney, on Sunday 24 May, after a three-month delivery voyage from England. The arrival of the two submarines completed the RAN's fleet unit which had been building its strength for the seemingly inevitable war with Germany.

Over the next four years Australia would suffer its share of wartime casualties, but none as mysterious as its first naval disaster – the disappearance of the *AE 1* and her crew of thirty-four.

In total, fifty-eight 'E' class submarines were built prior to and during the First World War. The *AE 1* and *AE 2* (the 'A' prefix differentiated these two from their fifty-six Royal Navy sisters) were built by Vickers at Barrow-in-Furness. They had a surfaced displacement of 660 tons and submerged of 800. They could reach 16kts on the surface, propelled by two sets of 8-cylinder twin screw diesel engines producing 1750bhp. Although lacking a deck gun, the 'E' class were well armed with four 18in torpedo tubes – one bow, one stern and two beam.

When word of imminent war reached Australia in late July 1914, the *AE 1* and *AE 2* were undergoing a refit after their voyage from England. With war at hand, work on the two boats was speeded up considerably. On August 4 Britain declared war on Germany. The RAN were ready, their warships (except the old cruisers HMAS *Encounter* and *Pioneer* and the two submarines) already at sea on the way to their war stations. In Port Jackson work on the submarines continued. *AE 1* was ready by 8 August and *AE 2* by 10 August, both ahead of schedule. On 2 September the submarines sailed out of Sydney, accompanied by the gunboat *Protector* and the submarine depot ship *Upolu*, and set course north for Palm Island off the coast of Queensland. There the submarines received orders to join a force whose task would be to occupy Rabaul on the northern coast of New Britain, Germany's centre of government for its Pacific colonies.

On 9 September the RAN's occupation force assembled, comprising the battlecruiser *Australia*, light cruisers *Sydney* and *Encounter*, destroyers *Yarra*, *Warrego* and *Parramatta* (arriving late), auxiliary cruiser *Berrima*, storeship *Aorangi*, the oiler *Murex*, and the colliers *Koolonga* and *Waihora*. Another collier, the *Whangape*, arrived the following day.

By day the fleet were to steam in two columns, 1 mile apart; by night the columns were to be 6 miles apart. Initial plans called for the detachment of the *Sydney* and the destroyers at dusk on 10 September to reconnoitre Simpson Harbour before dawn on the 11th. But due to the late arrival of the *Parramatta* and to the slow speed of several of the other vessels, the cruising order had to be changed and the fleet dispatched in three sections. At 06.00 on 10

September, *Sydney* and the destroyers set off on their task; *Australia* and *Berrima* followed them at 08.00. The rest of the convoy came along slowly, escorted by *Encounter* and the submarines. By 06.00 on 11 September, Blanche Bay, Talili Bay and the channel on both sides of the Duke of York island group had been searched without finding any enemy vessels. The Rabaul jetty had been found to be clear, and picket boats had begun a sweep of Karavia Bay for mines. Except for a skirmish ashore while capturing the German headquarters, the operation went off without a hitch. However, the occupation would soon take its toll. Three days later the RAN would suffer its first major loss, one which would haunt the Australian navy with endless speculation to the present day.

At 07.00 on 14 September 1914, the *AE 1* left Rabaul harbour to patrol east of Cape Gazelle with the destroyer *Parramatta*, which had come from her previous night's patrol area off Raluana Point. General orders for both vessels were to patrol the vicinity for enemy vessels and return to harbour before dark.

At 14.30 the submarine and destroyer were in sight of each other. *AE 1* signalled *Parramatta* by wireless, requesting visibility information. The day had begun clear, but haziness had by mid-afternoon restricted visibility to 5 miles. The sea, however, had remained smooth, although strong currents were evident. At 15.20 *AE 1* was lost sight of in the mist, approximately 1½ miles south-south-east of Beard Point, Duke of York Island, and apparently heading back towards Rabaul harbour. *Parramatta* turned and steamed in the same direction, keeping close to the coast, but saw no further sign of the

HMA SUBMARINE AE 1, *with battlecruiser HMAS* Australia *and destroyer HMAS* Yarra *at a rendezvous off Rossel Island in September 1914, taken from the bridge of HMAS* Encounter. *The AE 1 was lost with all hands off Duke of York Island shortly after. (*The Australian War Memorial AWM J 3241*)*

submarine. *Parramatta* proceeded to the north-west and rounded Duke of York Island, anchoring off Herbertshöhe at 19.00.

By 20.00 *AE 1* had still not reached port. *Parramatta* and *Yarra* set off in search, using flares and searchlights. *Encounter* and *Warrego* joined the following morning. Motor and steam launches from Rabaul and Herbertshöhe were also engaged. The waters where the submarine was last seen were searched. Even the coasts of New Ireland and New Britain were investigated, as were all neighbouring waters for 30 miles north-west of Duke of York Island. But no trace of the *AE 1* was ever found.

Speculation and rumour began almost immediately. After all, the *AE 1*'s skipper, Lieutenant-Commander Thomas F Besant, RN, was well known for his skill and alertness. And yet the submarine had disappeared. The fate of Besant, Lieutenant The Honourable Leo Scarlet, RN, Lieutenant Charles L Moore, RN and the thirty-six men of the crew – a mixture of Royal Navy and Royal Australian Navy – remains a mystery, though not one without theories.

Many hypotheses arose immediate-ly, but the explanations considered most plausible emerged from those closest to the incident, and were set forth in a report by Lieutenant H G Stoker, RN, skipper of the *AE 2*. Stoker's first theory held that the *AE 1* had broken down and was subsequently carried away by the strong currents in the area. But the search following the disappearance eliminated that possibility when no debris or bodies were found.

Stoker's second theory suggested the *AE 1* could have been sunk by enemy action. However, no enemy ships had been sighted in the area, and if gunfire from Duke of York Island had sunk the submarine, the shots would have been heard by other ships in the Australian squadron.

Stoker's third theory – that the submarine suffered an internal explosion – also fell down because evidence of an explosion literally never surfaced. Still, this theory has its proponents. Edwyn Gray, in his book on submarine disasters *Few Survived*, maintains that the lack of wreckage suggests nothing but an internal explosion, of hydrogen gas.

Most experts agree, however, that Stoker's fourth theory is the most probable: that while on an unscheduled practice dive, the submarine struck a reef close in toward shore, possibly off Duke of York Island. As to the lack of oil and other debris, some suggest *AE 1* might have actually been caught under an overhang formed by the reef.

While mechanical failure quickly springs to mind as a possible cause of a diving accident, it is unlikely. *AE 1* had been in good working order when she left harbour that morning. The only problem reported was with the starboard electric motor which had been scheduled for repair on return to harbour that evening. The defect would not have adversely effected the submarine's standard operation. It would only have prevented the starboard propeller from being used during a dive, limiting submerged speed.

After years of pondering the possible causes of the disappearance, Stoker, in his 1925 book *Straws in the Wind*, admitted that each of his four theories had 'more arguments against it than for it. But the only solution which could account for the complete and absolute disappearance of the boat and its crew was an accident while diving.' If the *AE 1* did indeed submerge on an unscheduled dive, the question changes from 'What happened to the *AE 1*?' to 'Why did Besant dive when he had neither reason nor time?' The submarine was some 25 miles out of harbour when it was last seen, just three hours before scheduled anchor time. Besant had already expressed complete satisfaction with the capabilities of his officers and crew and with the diving ability of his boat. No enemy ships had been reported in the area which would have caused *AE 1* to dive for investigation. Stoker continued:

> If, however, the objections were brushed aside and one accepted as a fact that she dived and became out of control while diving, the end is plain to see. The sinking submarine would slip away down in the vast depths existing in those parts, rapidly filling through the hull, bringing a quick and clean death to the crew whose end might well have come before their steel tomb had reached the ocean's bed – there to rest undisturbed by man and his investigations.

This theory had been posited before to explain the disappearance of the British steam-driven submarine *K 5* near the Scilly Isles on 20 January 1921. The problem when applying it to the disappearance of the *AE 1* is that wreckage from the *K 5* was found, along with an oil slick – clear evidence of the disaster. On the same day the *K 5* sank, her sister the *K 22* (formerly *K 13*) added further support to the theory when, participating in the same exercises as the *K 5*, the *K 22* took on such a steep bow-down angle when she dived that her skipper promptly threw the motors into reverse and blew all tanks at full pressure to get her back to the surface as quickly as possible. Assuming such an incident occurred to the *AE 1*, the method used by the *K 22* to save herself would have been partially denied to the Australian boat as her starboard electric motor was out of action.

As to the lack of evidence, it must be remembered that whatever accident overtook *AE 1* probably happened no later than 18.00 and possibly as early as 15.30. The search did not get underway until 20.00 that night – two ships using flares and

searchlights to try and cover an area of over a hundred square miles of sea. By morning the strong currents in the area had had twelve hours or more – most of them in darkness – to disperse any wreckage.

Despite her mysterious fate, the *AE 1* must lie somewhere in the 25-mile stretch of water between the eastern side of Duke of York Island and Rabaul harbour, most likely at an extreme depth. If the resources of an organization such as the Wood's Hole Oceanographic Institute, who found the *Titanic* and the *Bismarck*, were applied to this short stretch of water, the 'where' aspect of the mystery would be cleared up, although the 'why' would probably remain forever the secret of Lieutenant-Commander Thomas F Besant, RN.

'To us, their companions and fellows and jesting rivals over many a mile of sea,' wrote Stoker in *Straws in the Wind*, 'their friends and messmates in harbour; who had daily shared with them every interest, joy and sorrow of many months crowded with incident and adventure; who were also losing, in many cases, friends of long years' standing; whose hopes and ambitions had framed no thoughts in which the *AE 1* did not share with *AE 2* – our loss was a loss indeed. May their rest be peaceful.'

TWO OLD NAVAL CUSTOMS THAT DIED HARD
Commander H St A Malleson reflects on two curious capital ship survivals – the Admiral's sternwalk and the submerged torpedo flat.

In different ways, the prolonged survival of these unrelated installations implies a lack of opposition in successive Admiralty Boards to what had become established practice – in other words, a 'naval custom'.

The sternwalk was of no possible wartime use. It was a direct descendant from the stern and quarter galleries of wooden warships, but its use in later years was to enable the admiral (or captain, in private ships) to escape visitors or even his staff, or to conduct private conversations with

other admirals and senior officers. More systematically, it was an excellent retreat from which the various ships in company could be directly inspected for faults of several kinds, such as sloppy flags and ensigns, untidy or dirty members of a ship's company, guns, derricks or searchlights not lined up and, perhaps most frequently, ill-kept and inefficient boats.

Thus, from the 1860s on, it was normal practice to specify sternwalks for battleships and First Class cruisers, wherever freeboard and other considerations (discussed below) permitted, and this custom prevailed up to and including the *Revenge* class of 1916. During the 1914–18 war, most ships had their sternwalks removed or even cancelled before completion (in the case of *Ramillies* and *Royal Sovereign*), but no time was lost in replacing them after the armistice (with the odd exception of *King George V*). It says something for tradition or habit that when the *Warspite* had her last major refit in the late 1930s, she emerged with her sternwalk unscathed.

As for the 'other considerations', it may have been forgotten that among the innovations adopted in the *Dreadnought* was the transfer from aft of the admiral's/captain's quarters to a more central part of the ship, together with the wardroom, gunroom and warrant officers' mess, officers' cabins, etc; the ship's company was accommodated both aft and forward of the officers' accommodation. This represented advanced (or heretical) views in the Admiralty Board of the time, but it continued as a policy up to and including the *Orion* class of 1910.

One effect of this policy was to remove any necessity for fitting sternwalks in some fourteen battleships and the earlier battlecruisers. It also made possible the fitting of a stern hawsepipe and anchor, etc, instead of a stream anchor mounted on the ship's side aft. But, although there were certainly operational advantages in the new scheme, it was not liked by the majority of those principally involved, either quarterdeck or lower deck. So, back came the sternwalk with the four '*KGVs*' and later classes of battleships, as noted above (and with the three *Lion* class battlecruisers) too. But the writing was on the wall – neither the *Tiger* nor the *Hood* were given sternwalks and this quaint link with the past ceased to be incorporated in DNC's drawings.

Contemporary with the *Dreadnought* were the last of the pre-dreadnoughts, *Lord Nelson* and *Agamemnon*, and they and the majority of their predecessors (amounting to some sixty-eight) all had sternwalks. I am sure that they and their successors could have told some intriguing stories. A summary of sternwalk fitting policy, as far as it is known, in the Royal and other navies is given in Appendix 1.

Submerged torpedo tubes and associated compartments (flats). Ever since the advent of the Whitehead torpedo, there had been agitation to fit torpedo launching arrangements in most classes of warships by the principal nations, as the torpedo was considered a more certain method of damage and destruction than the shot and shell of those days, though the erratic behaviour of the average torpedo was to continue for many years.

Reliable submersibles (the most

effective vehicle of discharge) were not to appear for many years, but most maritime nations lost no time in incorporating both above water and submerged torpedo tubes in their battleships and cruisers (the 'spar' torpedo was quickly replaced by the 14in self-propelled torpedo, carried by steam picket boats with suitable release gear).

Ranges achieved by these early torpedoes were moderate, as were speeds and, when they were used in action for the first time in a fleet action at the Battle of Tsushima in 1905, the verdict at the time was that the gun was paramount and the torpedo 'ineffectual'. The 18in torpedoes in use were of course propelled by plain compressed air, but after the invention by Charles Gordon Curtis of the USA of the 'heater' torpedo engine in 1904, there was a rush to incorporate the system in all 18in and 21in torpedoes, as it more than doubled speeds and ranges. (The power generation cycle devised by Mr Curtis was a forerunner of the gas turbine and the inventor did, in fact, patent and build a working gas turbine in 1899.)

This new development encouraged all navies to continue the fitting of submerged torpedo flats in their major warships (above-water tubes had been given up some years before). The last cruisers with submerged flats were the *Minotaur* class of 1908 and the *Nelson* and *Rodney* of 1927 were the last battleships.

The submerged flat. This compartment, which in the more modern ships was duplicated (one forward of 'A' turret and the other aft of 'Y' turret) was fitted with tubes for discharge on each beam. To prevent torpedoes being damaged when discharged, a girder-like 'bar' was run out from the forward end of the tube, to which the torpedo latched on, giving it a fair run away from the ship's side. After a torpedo had been loaded into the open tube and the top and rear covers secured, the front cap would be opened to flood the tube; after firing (by high pressure air) the front cap would be closed and the residue of water in the tube allowed to escape (seaboots were obligatory) and reloading could commence.

The flat also accommodated reloads in racks (up to ten per tube),

The form of the sternwalk was a direct descendent of that fitted on the last generation of sailing warships – a platform supported on light brackets with an ornamental mesh railing and an awning covering the platform. This is the ironclad HMS Northumberland *of 1868, but the features of the sternwalk were essentially the same forty years earlier or forty years later. (CMP)*

with compressors and pressure vessels, equipment for servicing and preparing torpedoes, together with suitable bilge outlets and pumping arrangements to cope with the large amounts of water involved.

At action stations there would be some fifteen to twenty men present, together with a torpedo gunner or senior torpedo rating in charge. Orders could come from the bridge or from the torpedo control, usually in the after conning tower, with its own rangefinder. Clearly, if the enemy presented himself within the eventual range and kept a steady course, there would be a chance of a hit, provided the torpedoes performed perfectly, with settings for depth and course (gyro angle) being obeyed exactly.

Unfortunately, these conditions seldom occurred, even in peacetime exercises; as a midshipman in the old '*KGV*' in 1920, I witnessed what were considered normal failures in quite simple situations.

In one case the target was our own picket boat on parallel course, range 1000yds, depth setting 18ft, ship's speed 10kts. The first torpedo broke surface at about 150yds but off course, and surfaced at set range, far off target. The second torpedo also broke surface, but nearer target and on course. After giving the picket boat's crew quite a turn, the missile plunged down and never reappeared, until reported three months later by a Turkish fisherman on a beach on the south coast of the Sea of Marmora (necessitating a special trip from the anchorage at Constantinople (Istanbul) and a suitable 'sweetener' for the fisherman.

This particular incident (which was more or less private) persuaded the Captain to cancel torpedo firings for the time being, but the Squadron Competition could not be avoided some weeks later. The C-in-C in the *Iron Duke* led the squadron of four in line ahead, speed 14kts, target cruiser *Centaur*, similar course and speed, range about 5000yds, each ship to fire in succession two torpedoes each (accompanying destroyers to follow tracks when seen). *Concord* later reported one hit out of the eight fired, but it was not ours, which both suffered from gyro trouble.

There are still many readers of *Warship* who could possibly remem-

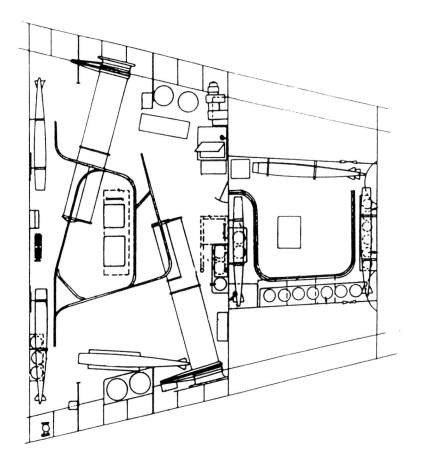

Dreadnought's *forward torpedo flat. Note how the restriction in athwartship space required the tubes to be offset; it also meant that part of the top of each tube had to open in order to load a torpedo.*

From The Battleship Dreadnought *by John Roberts.*

ber examples of erratic behaviour of torpedoes fired from submerged tubes. This is not to say that all torpedoes fired from the above-water tubes in cruisers and destroyers behaved perfectly, but the people concerned had much more continuous experience and it was often the fault of the torpedo control officer (and sometimes the captain too) when no hits were obtained in a straightforward practice.

In 1921, during a Combined Fleet exercise, the 1st Battle Squadron of four ships (*Revenge*, flag) discharged ten torpedoes each in 'rapid fire', more to test the submerged flat parties than to obtain hits, I suspect; the recovery destroyers had a field day and much water had to be pumped out from the flats afterwards! But my guess is that one or two torpedoes – at least – were lost as one of the results.

In fairly modern times, the *Bis-*

marck, after being brought to bay by lucky hits by the Fleet Air Arm and *Prince of Wales*, came under the guns and torpedoes of, among other battleships, cruisers and destroyers, the *Rodney*, with her 16in guns and 24½in torpedoes. She dealt out severe punishment (not without some fairly serious blast damage to herself) to the *Bismarck* and also fired her entire outfit of torpedoes at what must have been an easy target, without making any reported hits.

Conclusions. Sternwalks were strictly for a peacetime navy. As there was no serious naval warfare (as opposed to bombardments) between Trafalgar and the Russo–Japanese War, perhaps it is no wonder that they continued to be installed, as a civilised provision that did no harm to anyone.

Submerged flats are a very different subject. Without any evidence that they were worthwhile, very large volume spaces were allocated in building plans for battleships, battle-cruisers and heavy cruisers for several decades – spaces which could have been put to much better use (for instance, extra gun ammunition, fuel in particular or possibly extra boilers; various other alternatives could be suggested).

I have read no evidence anywhere of any proved hits from any ship firing torpedoes from a submerged flat in wartime and it is not unreasonable to ask why successive Boards of Admiralty allowed such a policy to continue, especially when the verdict of the participants in the Battle of Tsushima was so adverse.

APPENDIX 1: STERNWALKS
Austria–Hungary. Up to and including *Erzherzog* class sternwalks were fitted; later classes had large flush-fitting vertical stern ports instead.
Argentina. Never fitted (following US practice).
Brazil. In accordance with British custom, Brazil's two battleships of 1910 (built by Vickers) had sternwalks.
France. Up to 1903, with the completion of *Suffren*, sternwalks had been fitted; indeed, these were the most capacious ever seen and the change to plain sterns was thus more marked.
Germany. After the *Wittelsbach* class (1903), sternwalks ceased to be fitted.
Great Britain. Up to and including the two *Lord Nelsons*, all battleships (and First Class cruisers) had sternwalks, the only exceptions being those with very low freeboard or fitted with stern-chasers; the total came to about fifty-two battleships and represented what must have been a firm policy. However, it changed with the appearance of the *Dreadnought* and her successors up to and including the four *Orions*, for reasons noted above. Adding in the 12in battlecruisers, the total of capital ships never fitted with sternwalks (up to the outbreak of the First World War) comes to nineteen, whereas the 'KGVs', *Iron Dukes*, *Lions*, *Queen Elizabeths* and *Revenges* (totalling twenty) reverted to the original policy and fitted sternwalks. Wartime photographs show these were removed during hostilities but re-

installed afterwards (excepting 'KGV' herself).

There were special cases: *Erin* and *Agincourt* (originally destined for Turkey and built in England) had sternwalks, whereas *Tiger* and *Canada* (later Chilean *Admiral Latorre*) had not. Nor had the battlecruiser *Hood*, the last capital ship built for the Royal Navy before the *Nelson* and *Rodney*.
Italy. *Dante Alighieri* (1913) was the last Italian battleship to have a sternwalk.
Japan. Until 1906, Japan relied on foreign countries (mainly Great Britain) for her capital ships and these all had sternwalks, as did the prizes taken in battle from the Russians. The practice was continued until the completion of the *Hyuga* class in 1917–18, but was dropped in later ships.
Russia/USSR. Although some earlier pre-dreadnought battleships had sternwalks, none of the more modern ships carried them (*eg*, those completed from 1905 on).
Spain. Her three modern battleships (*Espana* class, 1915–20) all had sternwalks.
Turkey. See above (special cases, under Great Britain).
USA. Never adopted.

APPENDIX 2: SUBMERGED TORPEDO FLATS
The fashion for installing submerged torpedo flats in major warships was universal in all leading navies and, indeed, in minor navies too if in possession of ships of adequate size.

Never fewer than one tube on each beam was installed, accommodated in one flat; thus, in the Royal Navy, and up to 1910–11, one flat sufficed, with two 18in tubes. Subsequently, 21in tubes were standard, the *Iron Duke* class having duplicate flats, one forward of 'A' turret and the other abaft 'Y' turret. The last ships of the Royal Navy to be fitted with submerged tubes were the *Nelson* and *Rodney*, one 24½in tube each side; the torpedoes concerned used enriched air, as did Japanese weapons of later years.

The German Navy was much addicted to the fashion, some of their battleships having two tubes on each beam, as well as single bow and stern tubes.

In British light cruisers, submerged tubes continued to be fitted up to and including *Birmingham* and *Southampton* classes (1913–14), which could exceed 25kts, but these tubes were wisely superseded by trainable 21in tubes in later classes, no less than twelve tubes being provided in the 'D' and 'E' classes.

During the 1914–18 war, practical tests at high speeds, (*eg* in the *Renowns*) had demonstrated the failure of the bar to stand up to the stresses involved, with ensuing torpedo failure. And, in the late 1920s I remember discussions with other specialists about the relative effectiveness of weapons; the torpedoman's unofficial view was that at ship's speed over 20kts reliable running could not be certain. As peacetime exercises, because of the need for economy, took place at low speeds – 14kts or so – results tended to be optimistic and unrepresentative of wartime conditions.

Altogether, in the Grand Fleet alone, I estimate that there were 120 submerged torpedo tubes, calling for a total outfit plus spares of about 1200 torpedoes, large bodies of men and some thousands of cubic yards of space. The net result – zero.

LENINGRAD CLASS DESTROYERS
Arnold Hague offers the following amendments to Pierre Hervieux's article in Warship 1991, based on a document turned up in the Public Records Office

The British tanker *Hopemount*, which had been in Murmansk since April 1942, was detailed as the oiler for the 1942 eastbound Arctic Convoy, and her Master, Captain W D Shields, made a thorough report which is now in the Public Record Office in the Adm 199 series.

In his report Captain Shields states that his ship arrived at Tiksi on 31 August, and that the three Russian destroyers did not reach there to oil from him until 16 September. He further states that he was told by the Russian Admiral on board *Baku* that ten such ships had started and seven returned. Probably this was a misinterpretation, the seven ships being the balance of the convoy, not destroyers.

Captain Shields goes on to report that the Russian ships sailed on 18 September and outpaced him so that he went on alone. This discrepancy of one month in dates probably accounts for M Hervieux's statement that the destroyers took 5 weeks to pass Cape Chelyuskin; in fact the ships went straight through, *Hopemount* herself passing the Cape at 1800 on 22 September in clear water!

Hopemount arrived at Dickson on 26 September, and oiled the three Russian destroyers during the following four days. Passage was then made to Yugorski Shar where again the destroyers were fuelled. There is no further report of their presence after that date.

Captain Shields' report was dated 28 January 1943 on his return to Britain, and I feel that his dates must be accurate.

Pierre Hervieux says that his information is based on Friedrich Ruge's The Soviets as Naval Opponents 1941–45 *and* Chronology of the War at Sea *by J Rohwer and G Hummelchen, which both agree on the August date. A possible explanation is that the destroyers were held up by ice between 14 August and 16 September before reaching Tiksi rather than after. Cape Chelyuskin may have been clear of ice on the 22nd but the convoy eventually had to turn back and this was probably because of the dangers of ice.*

SOVIET CAPITAL SHIPS
Technical data on the capital ships of the pre-war Soviet naval programme, the Sovyetskiy Soyuz *class (Type 23) battleships and the* Kronshtadt *class (Type 69) large cruisers, were published in the early 1970s and are well established. In contrast,* authentic illustrations were confined to photographs of incomplete hulls, and an oblique (and far from orthogonal) sketch of Sovyetskiy Soyuz *in the magazine* Morskoi Sbornik. *General arrangement drawings of both classes were, however, published recently in the magazine* Sudostroenie *('Shipbuilding'). The accompanying text generally confirmed earlier accounts and data, but contained the additional information that the* Kronshtadt *design was modified in mid-1940 to allow substitution of German twin 15in turrets for Soviet triple 12in turrets (the eight twin turrets, ordered from Krupp, were never delivered). Ian Sturton based the following drawings on the latest information.*

1:1500 elevation of a Sovyetskiy Soyuz *class battleship; drawings of this type and photos of an official model released recently are in good agreement. Construction of this class was slowed in October 1940, when, reflecting changed national priorities in the allocation of steel and other resources, projected launch dates were put back to 1943.*

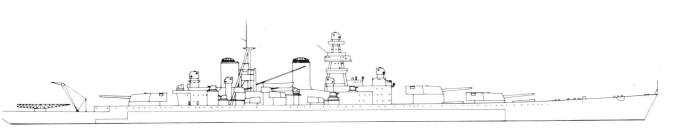

1:1500 elevation of a Kronshtadt *class large cruiser, showing the final design stage, Type 69.1, with twin 15in turrets. The 15in turrets increased displacement to 42,831 tonnes (full load) and one quadruple 37mm mount was eliminated; in October 1940, proposed launch dates were in the third quarter of 1942, which would have brought them into service ahead of the* Sovyetskiy Soyuz *class.*

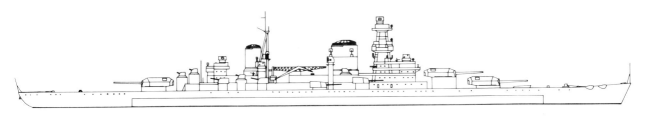

THE US SUBMARINE O 12 (SS–73) AND THE 1931 WILKINS-ELLSWORTH TRANS-ARCTIC EXPEDITION

Nowadays a submarine surfacing at the North Pole is relatively commonplace, but as David Miller explains, it was first attempted by an old ex-US Navy Lake boat in 1931.

The US Navy submarine *O 12* (SS-73) was one of the sixteen-strong 'O' class launched in 1917–18 and commissioned in the latter part of 1918, just too late to see war service. As was the case with a number of classes of US Navy submarines at that time, the 'O' class was actually two separate groups, with one series (*O 1* to *O 10*) being designed by the Electric Boat Company and the other by Simon Lake (*O 11* to *O 16*). The Electric Boat submarines served until 1945, being used in the Second World War as training boats, apart from *O 5* which was lost in a collision with a merchant ship in 1925, *O 1* which was scrapped in 1938 and *O 9* which

foundered in 1941. The entire Lake group was, however, decommissioned in 1924 and scrapped in 1930, with one exception – *O 12* (SS–73).

O 12 was built by the Lake Torpe do Boat Company at Bridgeport, Connecticut, being launched on 29 September, 1917 and commissioned on 18 October, 1918. She was 175ft (53.34m) in length and had a beam of 16ft 7in (5.05m), a draught of 13ft 11in (4.24m), and displaced 491 tons surfaced and 566 tons submerged; 500bhp Busch-Sulzer diesels were installed and there was a 120-cell battery driving two 200shp Diehl electric motors. Surface speed was 14kts and she was capable of a relatively high submerged speed (for the period) of 11kts. She was of single-hull design and had an operating depth of 200ft (61m). The armament consisted of four 18in torpedo tubes and one 3in/23 gun in the unique US Navy, semi-disappearing mount in which the gun retracted through 90° into a well, with some 2ft of the muzzle protruding vertically above the deck.

O 12 spent most of her service life in Submarine Squadron No 1 (Sub Ron-1), based at Coco Solo in the Panama Canal Zone, but after an

uneventful, albeit short, career she returned to the United States in 1924, being decommissioned on June 17 of that year. She was then placed in reserve in the Philadelphia Navy Yard.

O 12 was scheduled for scrapping, along with the rest of the Lake group, when onto the scene came the Australian Sir Hubert Wilkins. He is one of those men whose obituaries leave the reader breathless and wondering how a man could fit so much into one life-span. Born in 1888, he was trained as a mining engineer, but went to Europe in 1908 and first came to prominence as the official photographer for the Turkish Army in the 1912 Balkan War. He went to the Arctic in 1913 with the Stefansson Expedition, but joined the Australian Flying Corps in 1917 where he trained as a pilot, giving him a life-long interest in aviation. He took part in the 1920 British Imperial Expedition and then served as an ornithologist on Shackleton's last expedition to the Antarctic in 1921. Changing tack somewhat he then led an expedition for the British Natural History Museum into the deserts of Central Australia between 1923 and

O 12 (SS–73) in her original guise as an operational submarine of the US Navy. Built by Lake, she was commissioned in 1918 and spent most of her brief operational service defending the Panama Canal. (All photos by courtesy of the US Submarine Force Library, Groton).

Sir Hubert Wilkins (1888–1958), the Australian explorer and adventurer, with a painting of his unique submarine Nautilus, *formerly* O 12 *(SS–73).*

1925. His major love was, however, cold rather than hot climates and he went to the Arctic again for three years between 1925 and 1928, where he undertook a number of pioneering flights, becoming the first man to land an aircraft on ice and take-off again, the first to use an aircraft to make soundings of the Polar sea and the first to fly from Alaska to Spitsbergen across the Polar icecap.

In 1928 he was appointed leader of an Antarctic expedition, which was sponsored by the American Geographical Society and financed by the US millionaire William Randolph Hearst. Equipped with two Lockheed Vega aircraft, the Wilkins-Hearst expedition carried out numerous successful flights.

But, in addition to seeing so clearly the advantage of aircraft in Polar work, this intrepid explorer, by now knighted as Sir Hubert Wilkins, had also conceived the idea of using submarines to explore under the Arctic ice-cap and he was one of those men for whom the thought quickly leads to the deed. So, employing his formidable administrative skills he set about organising his next undertaking: the Wilkins-Ellsworth Trans-Arctic Submarine Expedition. He obtained sponsorship from a long list of organisations and people, including the American and Norwegian Geographical Societies, the Carnegie Institution and William Randolph Hearst, while numerous commercial companies, as disparate as Texaco and Horlicks, seem to have been very happy to contribute their products.

The ideal solution would doubtless have been to construct a submarine specifically for the undertaking, but it would also have been prohibitively expensive – at least $1 million, according to a contemporary estimate. The only other solution was to adapt a naval submarine and one of Wilkins' greatest coups was to persuade the US Navy, apparently without too much difficulty, to lease him a submarine (*O 12*) for five years at a rental of $1 per year, the only stipulation being that she must be used only for scientific research. The bureaucratic process was somewhat involved as the navy struck the boat off the register on 29 July 1930 and assigned her to the US Shipping Board. This body then chartered her to Lake & Danenhower Inc, which sub-chartered her to the expedition's official body, the Trans-Arctic Submarine Expedition Inc, but the end-product was very satisfactory – Wilkins got his submarine!

Wilkins and his advisers, among whom was Simon Lake the submarine's designer, had thought the project through with great care and *O 12* was taken to the US Navy Yard at Brooklyn for conversion, Wilkins' main concept was that the submarine would slide along the underside of the ice-cap, using positive buoyancy to maintain an upwards force, and this led to the main visual change to the boat – the addition of a large, smooth, convex upper deck. Also, numerous safety devices were built-in to cope with the Arctic conditions.

One possibility was, of course, that of hitting icebergs or floes and so an extending, collapsible bowsprit was fitted to absorb the shocks, while the bow was also strengthened internally with oak blocks and cement.

It was also envisaged that there was a possibility that they might be unable to find a gap in the ice through which to surface. So, a special escape device was installed which was essentially a 13ft (3.96m) long, 28in (71cm) diameter telescopic tube, fitted with a rotary cutting head. This would drill through the ice at a rate of about 1ft/minute (0.3m/min) and then allow the crew to escape onto the ice.

Another possibility was that the submarine could find itself under a large expanse of thick ice, with the battery running low and in need of recharging. This, too, had been thought of, and two 8½in (21.6cm) air-drills were installed which could penetrate up to 100ft (30.5m) of ice. In operation, one would provide an air-intake for the diesels and the other an exhaust, enabling the engine to be run to recharge the battery, following which the boat could move on to discover a place where it could surface properly. The similarity in concept with the later *schnorkel* is clear! Other safety devices included propeller guards and Momsen escape lungs.

The expedition's main purpose was, however, scientific and considerable thought was given to ensuring that they would gain the maximum value from the undertaking. Portholes were installed and powerful external lights fitted in the bow to enable those inside to see something of the underwater world they were travelling through. The forward torpedo-room was converted into a diving compartment with an airlock and there was an external connection for a 5000-watt portable lamp for the divers' use, who were also supplied with a specially-adapted underwater movie camera. A second, smaller airlock was installed further aft, above the living quarters. There was, of course, a laboratory and the extensive scientific apparatus included a variety of depth-finding devices and a photographic balloon.

The expedition was obviously potentially hazardous and so Wilkins insisted that the submarine carry six

The Nautilus *pulls away from the jetty for trials following her conversion. The protrusions atop the long superstructure were dismantled before submerging and the strake was designed to act as a runner along the underside of the polar icecap. The cylindrical object in the bow was an extending bowsprit, intended to soften the impact of any collision with an underwater obstacle.*

Nautilus *in the environment for which she was intended. The picture was taken from the outboard motor-launch which was carried aboard.*

months supply of food, plus emergency supplies for another full year, together with tents, packs, cookers, and even smallarms and ammunition. There was also a fully-equipped radio room with a 200-watt high frequency (HF) transmitter and a number of receivers.

From all this it is apparent that this was no extemporised undertaking, but rather a very serious, carefully thought-out, and properly-funded and -backed expedition.

The crew for this undertaking was also carefully selected. The captain was Lieutenant-Commander Sloan Danenhower, USN Retired, a former submariner and partner with Simon Lake in the firm of Lake & Danenhower, Inc. Wilkins was the joint-leader with Lincoln Ellsworth, another noted Arctic explorer, while the chief scientist was Professor Sverdrup, who had been a senior member of the 1917–1925 Amundsen expedition. The majority of the crew were, however, former US Navy submariners, most of them with experience on the O-boats, one of whom was the expedition's only fatality, falling overboard and disappearing during the initial short voyage from Philadelphia to the New York Navy Yard.

The conversion completed, the submarine, now a civilian boat, was christened the *Nautilus* on 24 March 1931 by Lady Wilkins, supported by Jean Jules Verne, grandson of the author. Final preparations were completed in April and May, and then she was ready for the great adventure. She moved up to the New England coast in easy stages and then set out on a surface voyage across the Atlantic from Provincetown. Unfortunately, she was hit by a storm in mid-ocean and wallowing very badly, she pressed on for several hours until the starboard diesel packed up. The situation was serious although not desperate, but then water got into the fuel line to the port engine. This problem was rectified, but then the armature on one of the electric motors disintegrated, scattering sparks all over the engine compartment. Fortunately this did not start a fire, but the captain decided that the time had come to transmit an SOS. This was answered by USS *Arkansas* (BB–33) and *Wyoming* (BB–32), which happened, by chance, to be in the vicinity, and, with a high degree of seamanship the mighty battleship *Wyoming* took the battered submarine in tow, delivering her to Cobh in Ireland some days later.

Repairs were attempted at Cobh, but it was found that the diesels could not be started and so *Nautilus* was towed to Plymouth, where she was put into drydock. The repairs were quickly completed and she then made her way to Bergen in Norway. She was then refuelled from drums, a lengthy and arduous undertaking, but when it was completed an underwater oil leak was discovered. So, all the fuel had to be pumped out into a barge lent by the Norwegian Navy until the leak was above water, and once it had been repaired the fuel was pumped back into the *Nautilus* again.

They then made their way up the coast to Tromso, where more repairs to the engines were necessary. However, the submarine was an object of such interest and the number of inquisitive visitors so great that they found it necessary to sail up to the head of a deserted fjord in order to allow the engineers uninterrupted access to their own engine room. Finally, however, they were as ready as they ever would be and they sailed for the Arctic.

All these delays meant that they arrived in the Arctic far later than scheduled, but fortunately the season was relatively mild and the leaders, in conference with Danenhower, estimated that they still stood a good chance of reaching their objective – the North Pole. After passing Bear Island and making a refuelling stop at Spitsbergen they pushed on to the edge of the ice-pack where they made the discovery that somewhere on their travels the *Nautilus* had lost her hydroplanes. It seems extraordinary (admittedly with the benefit of hindsight) that nobody had noticed this before, but, of course, all was by no means lost, since they could still submerge using the main ballast tanks, with the trim tanks providing fine adjustments.

So, Captain Danenhower was at long last able to take her under the ice for the first time and they watched this new world with great excitement through the strengthened portholes.

They were the first men ever to see the underside of the ice, which they discovered was not smooth, as they had expected, but very uneven, with great masses hanging down like stalactites. Despite the excitement they did not forget the scientific purpose of their voyage and collected samples from the ocean floor. They also discovered that there were four distinct layers of water under the ice: a warm layer near the bottom, then a cold layer, then a warmer layer and, near the surface, another cold layer.

They also surfaced on several occasions, spotting seals and birds, and obtaining samples for the museums that had taken an interest in their project. In all, they remained in the area for some two weeks, despite problems for both the men and the machinery from the cold, and several leaks in the hull. They maintained communications with the outside world, although at one stage their transmitter was off the air for five days, while a technician carried out repairs, which caused some alarm in the outside world. Indeed, when they re-established communications Hearst sent a message telling Wilkins that they should now return to plan another expedition incorporating the many lessons they had learned from this one.

Wilkins had, in fact, already decided to turn back. He had got within 450 miles (724km) of the Pole, but it was obvious that the old and by now somewhat battered submarine was in no state to approach any closer. So, they turned back and reached Bergen safely. They returned the submarine to the US Navy, which saw little purpose in bringing her back across the Atlantic, so the hulk was formally restored to the navy's books and then scuttled in a Norwegian fjord on 20 November 1931. Presumably, the hulk is still there.

After this expedition Wilkins and Ellsworth worked together in the Antarctic for some years, and then during the war Wilkins was an adviser on cold-weather conditions and equipment to the US Navy. He died in 1958 and in a very fitting tribute USS *Skate* (SSN-578) took his ashes and scattered them on the ice at the North Pole. So the gallant explorer reached the Pole by submarine after all.

NAVAL BOOKS OF THE YEAR

The reviews are divided into three main sections: first,
a selection of full reviews; then short notices; and finally,
a straightforward listing of books announced but not received.
In all sections the order is alphabetical by author.

CARRIER-21 Future Aircraft Carrier Technology. Volume 1: overview, *published by National Academy Press (Washington, DC), 1991. 129 pages.*
Price not quoted.

This is a most interesting book, with implications far beyond the future of the USN's enormous fleet carriers. In 1990, Congress required the Department of Defense to obtain an outside study of future carrier development and a contract for this work was given to the US National Academy of Science (National Research Council). It became a major task with 106 engineers and scientists involved and groups meeting for a combined total of 112 days; 70 of the team went to sea for a day. The working party saw the need for large fleet carriers as self evident, the Gulf War having clearly shown the value of world-wide power projection. Consideration of 'small' carriers (40,000–50,000 tonnes) is dismissed as the unit cost per plane is higher. For the big ship, they saw no alternative to nuclear power though new reactors with a higher power density should be developed. Budgets and the number of ships were outside their terms of reference though they did quote costs for the proposed options.

Their individual recommendations seem well founded and properly thought through; *eg* the cost of new dry-docks is considered for the bigger options. The main design drivers were seen as:

Increasing size and weight of aircraft;
The need for increased survivability; and
Technical developments which, to some extent, offset the effects of the first two drivers.

Existing USN aircraft will all end their service life early in the next century and their successors are likely to be heavier, requiring new arrester gear, and with greater external dimensions, requiring a bigger flight deck and hangar. The need for improved survivability derives from the increasing threat from improved weapons. There is little attempt to justify any particular level of survivability but it is implied that a 15 per cent rise in first cost is reasonable. They suggest a blend of active and passive defence using very advanced weapons (lasers, particle beams and electro magnetic guns), hard kill anti-torpedo measures, and much attention to emission control and signature reduction together with many measures to resist damage when hit.

The non-contact torpedo exploding under the keel is seen as by far the most important and difficult threat to counter. Defence using hard structure may be possible but a compliant structure, partially water filled and projecting 40ft below the keel is preferred. This is described in a classified volume 2, not available to the public.

There are many detailed technical recommendations, mostly sensible, and some intriguing suggestions such as that a SWATH makes less wake than a monohull, and is hence less vulnerable to homing torpedoes. To give a flavour, a few other points are listed below:

Some 350 tonnes of paper and 10,000cu ft could be saved by putting records on computer.
The overall space per man is 500cu ft, and a 20 per cent saving in crew numbers is realistic.
C^3I should be adaptable to accept new allies and to exclude old friends.

All this leads to a number of preferred options. The first is a *Nimitz* hull and machinery incorporating as much new technology, particularly in survivability, as possible. This option would add about 10–15 per cent to the cost of a *Nimitz* but is not favoured as its capability to operate new aircraft would be limited by its size.

A large new monohull from 105,000 tonnes to 215,000 (1500ft) costing 10–100 per cent more than *Nimitz* seems the preferred option. A third option is a SWATH which would ballast at sea to bring the propellers down to 125ft draught but, without ballast, would enter harbour at 40ft. Displacement at sea would be 660,000 tons and 325,000 light. It is thought that there might be problems in extrapolating from existing designs. Cost would be up to four times that of *Nimitz*.

These options make the DoD proposals seem modest: perhaps that was the intention. The conclusions also show that a good design is not the straightforward sum of all desirable features but a compromise. An advisory Committee, however well informed, is ill adapted to produce a detailed technical solution.

D K Brown, RCNC

Norman Friedman, The Naval Institute Guide to World Naval Weapon Systems, 1991–92, *published by Naval Institute Press (Annapolis) 1991. UK Distributors, Airlife Publishing.*
300 × 250mm, 928 pages, 1300 illustrations.
£80.00.

This is the second edition of what is to be a biennial publication. The new edition has nearly twice as many pages as the first, although a few systems, no longer in service or not developed, have been removed. The book is organised in the same way with some most useful introductory material followed by six main headings – Surveillance and Control, Strategic Systems, Strike/Surface Weapons, Anti-Aircraft Warfare, Anti-Submarine Warfare and Mine Warfare. Each of these main sections has a lengthy and interesting introduction, followed by detailed notes arranged first under category, such as surface to air missiles, and then by country of manufacture. Experience with the first edition has shown that, thanks to a good index, it is easy to find specific information but much less easy to obtain an overall view of an integrated system such as AEGIS or FAMS where available information is split between sensors, missiles etc.

In this new edition, most sections are 50 per cent longer than previously and most of the illustrations are new. The author has made excellent use of his own photographs taken at naval exhibitions, particularly at the 1991 US Navy League show, which fills much of the long addendum. This also contains a valuable section on SOSUS, based on recently declassified material.

The first section, Survelliance and Control, has almost tripled in length thanks to some 21 new pages on computers and Command and Control Systems, such as ADAWS and SSCS. The need for such systems is clearly presented, as are the difficulties in achieving a good result. Dr Friedman suggests that major navies will be disposing of older ships, lacking such systems, and lesser navies will have to weigh the low asking price against the limited capability of such ships. He also discusses the extent to which standard commerical computers can be used instead of the very expensive, purpose-built hardware.

In his introduction, the author raises the point that he is largely dependent on manufacturers for information and hence some of the systems mentioned may have no existence outside the glossy brochure. This book is so authoritative and comprehensive that many smaller navies will use it as the basis for their shopping list and may receive a shock when they find their chosen system has yet to be developed and that the cost will fall on the customer. A similar difficulty is that few of the 'Advanced' weapons displayed by Iraq before the war were used and most were probably dummies.

As usual, Dr Friedman's views expressed in both the general introduction and in the introductions to sections are stimulating. The main introduction was written during Desert Storm and makes several interesting points. The success of US clever weapons such as Tomahawk and SLAM is rightly praised but one may see a US slant in that Sea Skua, with which three Lynx disabled about half the Iraqi navy, is dismissed because its warhead was too small to sink its targets. He also points out the need for a deep penetration bomb against bunkers and the fallability of mathematical simulation of weapon performance. This introduction must have been written before the mining of *Tripoli* and *Princeton* which would have encouraged greater attention to mine warfare.

The first edition has proved a valuable and accurate reference book and the new book is even more comprehensive. The price is not unreasonable for a book of this size and content but the publishers will have to avoid any further escalation at a time when budgets in the defence world are being cut.

D K Brown, RCNC

Group Captain B C Laite, RAF, Maritime Air Operations, *published by Brassey's (UK) Ltd, 1991. 256 × 177mm, 144 pages, 35 photographs, 23 drawings. £23.50; £11.50 paperback.*

During the past five years Brassey's (UK) have published three series on contemporary Sea Power, Land Warfare and Air Power respectively, each comprising about a dozen books. Publication began with a lead book by each Series Editor giving an overview. *Modern Sea Power*, Vol 1 was written by Geoffrey Till and reviewed in *Warship* No 47. Succeeding books, by a variety of authors, each cover one aspect of the series subject. The book under review covers Maritime Air Operations which is the last of the Air Power series.

As the author acknowledges, in many countries Maritime Air Operations would figure under Sea Power as a naval function performed by naval aircraft, but this book takes 'the activities of the Royal Air Force to exemplify maritime air operations' and is confined to the maritime activities of aircraft operating from shore bases, whether USN, Red Fleet or RAF. Roles therefore comprise Anti-Submarine, Anti-Ship, Air Defence and Air Sea Rescue, with a glance at Electronic Warfare and Airborne Early Warning and some basic Soviet warship data.

Clinging to the RAF example unfortunately distorts the historical background. In tracing the development of attack against ships by shore based aircraft the book ignores the most potent performers during the critical first half of the Second World War, the Luftwaffe's Ju 87 and Ju 88 divebombers whose 30yd to 40yd average bombing accuracies exacted a frightful toll of Allied ships sunk or disabled.

These Brassey publications are 'aimed at the international officer cadet or junior officer'. It cannot be easy to maintain a constant level of sophistication over eleven books, and after sampling some others I would judge that this author has undershot his target. He could well have cut the elementary generalities and pruned the equipment listings. I would have preferred more explanation of how the gear is used and of its pros and cons.

Sonic systems in general are discussed, as are the characteristics of individual makes of sonobuoy, but there is little on the selection of the type to be used and where to place it in various tactical situations, nor on sonobuoy economics; the USN 'DIFAR (directional buoy) only' policy is mentioned without comment.

Another matter would have been worth discussion: fuel consumption is the most important and highly variable constraint in anti-ship and air defence operations beyond coastal waters since fuel per minute and per mile can vary by factors of ten times or more. Supersonic capability is no use if it runs you out of fuel. Surely this factor merits acknowledgement; representative consumption curves are common knowledge.

Although pitched somewhat low in the readership scale by *Warship* standards this book could be useful to those needing an introduction to its subject.

David Stanley

Andrew Lambert, The Crimean War: British grand strategy against Russia, 1853–56, *published by Manchester University Press, 1991.*
216 × 138mm, 390 pages.
Paperback £13.95.

In this first modern study of the 'Crimean War' the author shows that the usual name is wrong: it was a maritime war fought primarily in the Baltic. Indeed it can be argued that

the impending attack on Kronstadt and the ensuing threat to St Petersburg was the main cause of the war's end. It involved the use of sea power to contain an expansionist land power and, as such, has many parallels with late twentieth century limited wars.

The book concentrates on overall strategy but has much to say about naval operations which saw the introduction of much new technology – steam ships, armour, mines and the mass production of specialised coastal attack vessels. The latter featured strongly in the Victory Review, seen by the author as a demonstration of power and an implied threat.

It is a very well researched book, hard going at times but, now that it is available at a reasonable price, well worth reading.

D K Brown, RCNC

T M Melia, 'Damn the Torpedoes': A Short History of US Naval Mine Countermeasures, 1777–1991, *published by US Naval Historical Center (Washington, DC), 1991.*
242 × 168mm, 232 pages, 58 illustrations, paperback. No price quoted.

This is another in the excellent series 'Contributions to Naval History', covering USN mine countermeasures from 1777 to 1991. It begins with Bushnell's attack on HMS *Cerberus*, but mine warfare in American waters began during the Civil War (1861–65).

The US Navy seems even more prone than the British to forget mines between wars and, despite some activity during the Spanish–American war (little known outside America) there were few developments until the USA entered the First World War. Their MCM capability was largely adapted from RN methods and equipment until they laid the Northern Barrage with antenna mines – and almost immediately had to clear it as the war ended. The antenna would activate the mine on contact with a steel hull but, for sweeping with steel ships, the

USN devised a most ingenious 'impressed current' protection system.

Attention lapsed again until the US entered the Second World War. Their equipment was again largely based on that of the RN though the USN produced some excellent ships in the big *Raven* class and the small YMS, many of which served in the RN. The US also built some ingenious pressure mine sweeps – 'egg-crates' – some of which were used, unsuccessfully, by both navies. Later chapters deal with the Wonsan landing and other operations up to 'Desert Storm'.

The author suggests, and few would disagree with her, that the USN's greatest problem has been the lack of a career stream of MCM specialist officers who can lead both training and material development. Though the RN is better off, one may also wonder if the MCM world has sufficient influence in Whitehall.

The author frequently mentions and praises RN work (not always accurately) for which she is, perhaps, too kind. Overall, the book is commendably free of error, easy to read and describes several operations unfamiliar to British readers. It should be read by all concerned with MCM work as it offers a different viewpoint and particularly by anyone involved with liaison on MCM with the USN.

D K Brown, RCNC

Norman Polmar and Jurrien Noot, Submarines of the Russian and Soviet Navies, 1718–1990, *published by Naval Institute Press (Annapolis), 1990. Distributed in the UK by Airlife Publishing, Shrewsbury.*
278 × 210mm, 384 pages, 194 photographs, 75 line drawings.
£37.95.

The first 220 pages of this fascinating book describe the technical development and the operations of Russian submarines from mythical beginnings to 1990. One may see 1906 as the end of the experimental period, when thirteen boats were deployed in the Pacific at the end of the Russo-

Japanese war. At the start of the first World War the Russians had a force which was numerous but largely obsolescent. The main theatre of operations was in the Baltic where the British submarines were much more effective, the 'E' class entering the Baltic directly while the smaller 'C' class boats were transported on barges down the canal from Archangel. (There is a photo of *C 32* on her barge.)

The Revolution interrupted building and largely removed the officer force but recovery was quite rapid and by the time that the Soviet Union was forced into the war they had many submarines whose capability was judged to be only somewhat less than those of other navies. Their operations were mainly in land-locked seas, dominated by Nazi forces, which made success difficult.

However, there were problems, mainly due to the lack of training and poor morale of commanding officers. In the Arctic, the few British submarines achieved much better results than Soviet boats even though one Soviet officer described the British boats as being dirty with ill disciplined crews!

As soon as the war was over, Stalin initiated an enormous building programme of submarines and surface ships. The authors try hard to dis-tinguish between Soviet aspirations, US intelligence estimates and what was actually built. There were frightening estimates of 1200 modern submarines available by the mid-1960s and such figures do seem credible given Soviet shipyard capacity; there are Soviet publications suggesting a similar target.

Production peaked in 1955, when eighty-one boats were completed, and was then cut back. After a maximum of around 500, the force level dropped to about 350–380 from 1965 to the 1980s. Recent widely publicised cuts in submarine numbers are in obsolete craft and the ex-Soviet force, with very uncertain control, is still a major potential threat.

Nuclear submarines entered the fleet only four years after USS *Nautilus* with thirteen of the 'November' class followed by eight 'Hotel' class SSBNs. These early boats were accident-prone and some were lost.

Later developments are fully covered and the authors even offer a diagram showing broad band noise levels for Soviet and US submarines from 1960 (when the Americans had a big lead) to the present day (when their advantage is much reduced).

The main text is followed by a lengthy tabular section listing the particulars of every submarine, including its fate. There are sections on foreign submarines used by the Soviet navy, on Soviet shipyards and on missiles. The authors are to be commended for including the diving depth of most classes and for defining it.

The value of a book like this depends entirely on its accuracy. The authors have used a very large number of sources including recently declassified USN and Soviet material – the bibliography runs to over 8 pages – but as many are hard to find it has not been possible to make many direct checks. However, the text makes technical sense and is consistent, the authors are well qualified and this gives good ground for confidence.

There are two topics on which the authors are muddled; they confuse the Walther HTP turbine with recycle diesel propulsion and, indeed, credit *Explorer* with the latter. They also confuse contra-rotating propellers and co-rotating (tandem), with two propellers on the same shaft. Both words are used in the same sentence describing the 'Victor III'.

The book is very readable and well illustrated, using unfamiliar photographs where possible. One can only wonder what the next edition will have to say.

D K Brown, RCNC

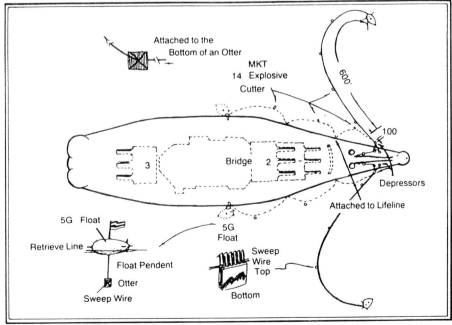

A diagram of the makeshift bow protection system set up aboard USS Iowa *in 1987 prior to her entry into the Persion Gulf. From T M Melia's* 'Damn the Torpedoes': A Short History of the US Naval Mine Countermeasures 1777–1991.

Courtesy Bobby Scott and Wilfred Patnaude

SHORT NOTICES

'Anatomy of the Ship' series:
John McKay and Ron Coleman, The 24-Gun Frigate Pandora 1779
Xavier Pastor, The Ships of Christopher Columbus
John Roberts, The Battleship Dreadnought
all published by Conway Maritime Press, 1992.
Each: 240 × 254mm, 128 pages, approx 20 photographs and 300 line drawings
(Dreadnought *256 pages, 40 photographs, 650 line drawings*).
Pandora *and* Columbus' Ships £20.00
Dreadnought £25.00.

The *Dreadnought*, which is probably the most interesting of these titles to *Warship* readers, is not only the first new book by John Roberts for some years, but is also the most extensive and comprehensive contribution to this well known series of monographs. As befits such an important ship, virtually every aspect is covered in the most minute detail with a quality of draughtsmanship that few can equal, including some spectacu-lar perspective views of complicated areas like the engine and boiler rooms. For such an apparently well known ship, there is a surprising amount of new information in the introduction, while the drawings often depict much discussed but rare-ly illustrated items of equipment like the Dreyer fire control table.

The other volumes are devoted to the Sixth Rate that was sent to round up the *Bounty* mutineers (the wreck of which has been investigated by an underwater archaeology team in Au-stralia); and reconstructions of Col-umbus' *Santa Maria, Niña* and *Pin-ta*, based on the latest evidence.

Siegfried Breyer, Soviet Warship Development. Volume I: 1917–1937, *published by Conway Maritime Press, 1992. 270 × 200mm, 288 pages, 350 photographs, 280 line drawings.* £35.00.

The first of a mutli-volume survey of Soviet warship design and construc-tion from the Revolution – although there is also a prelude covering Czar-ist achievements – to the present day. It is more detailed than anything previously published, and later volumes may benefit from the new openness that has come over Russian archives to give a clearer picture of Cold War naval developments. Heavily illustrated, although like so many Soviet photos, the quality is not impressive; the line drawings are better. Essentially a revised transla-tion of the German *Enzyklopädie des Sowjetischen Kriegsschiffbaus*, it seems to be based mainly on Soviet technical literature, although there are hints that Breyer has other sources. A valuable book, but it will be the later volumes that will deter-mine the work's true status.

Peter W Brooks, Zeppelin: Rigid Airships 1893–1940, *published by Putnam Aeronautical Books, 1992. 270 × 200mm, 224 pages, 250 photographs, 50 line drawings.* £35.00.

Clearly an aviation book, but given the contribution of airships to naval history – and the contribution of navies to airship development – worthy of inclusion here. As with most Putnam books the emphasis is on the characteristics of the flying machines themselves, but this volume is organised to tell a more coherent story than most. As its title suggests, this story is dominated by Germany, but other countries' efforts are also well documented.

John C K Daly, Russian Seapower and 'The Eastern Question' 1827–41, *published by Macmillan, London, 1991. 215 × 138mm, 336 pages.* £45.00.

An academic study of the uses to which the Russians put the Black Sea fleet, but including valuable appen-dices listing Russian shipbuilding programmes (with precise laying down and launch dates), warship losses, naval expenditure and even abstracts of merchant ship construc-tion in Black Sea ports.

Dreadnought *coaling. One of the illustrations from John Roberts' new 'Anatomy of the Ship' volume on the ship.*

Vice-Admiral Sir Louis le Bailey, From Fisher to the Falklands, *published by Marine Management Holdings Ltd (the Institute of Marine Engineers), 1991. 216 × 128mm, 249 pages, 27 photographs, £17.50.*

A complement to, rather than a continuation of, the author's previous autobiographical book (noted in *Warship 1991*), this volume is a rather polemical survey of engineering in the Royal Navy since the beginning of this century. It is unduly harsh on Admiralty decision-making in the earlier sections, but once the author's personal experience comes into play, it makes illuminating reading. British warship machinery obviously failed to keep up with innovation between the wars, probably due to basic industrial decline, but the author also blames the lack of service prospects for engineering officers which led to a poor standard of candidates. The result was machinery that could be maintained with the right combination of skill and dedication – unlike so much of the 'high tech' German engineering – but the old idea of reliability obviously needs qualifying.

The author's firmly-held views played their part in the rapid strides made by the RN after the war and the service which did so much to pioneer marine gas turbines was clearly very different from that which in an earlier age had banned labour-saving chemical treatments in boiler cleaning.

Shizuo Fukui, Japanese Naval Vessels at the End of World War II, *published by Greenhill Books, 1992. 286 × 219mm, 192 pages, 108 photographs, 300 line drawings. £25.00.*

Fukui is perhaps best known to present-day naval enthusiasts as the possessor of a near-legendary collection of photographs, some of which have been beautifully published in volume form in Japan. He had been

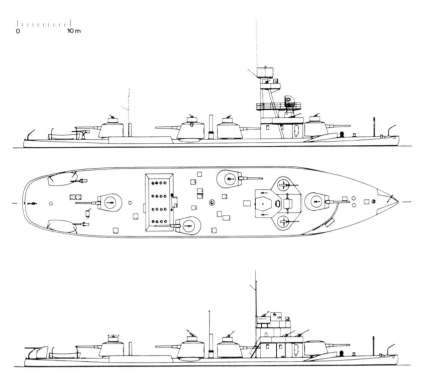

Soviet river monitors Sverdlov, ex-Vyuga *about 1940 (above) and* Kirov, ex-Smerch *about 1945. Drawings by S Breyer from* Soviet Warship Development.

an IJN constructor and the collection of this material must have been facilitated by his postwar work for the US Navy compiling a comprehensive report on all of Japan's surviving warships and naval auxiliaries. This was originally issued in 1947 and consisted of numerous detailed line drawings with the compiler's notes on the characteristics of the ships, all meticulously hand lettered in fractured English. The value of the report was the exhaustive nature of its coverage, which included auxiliaries and harbour craft, types of Special Attack (kamikaze) weapons and even some Army vessels and amphibious tanks.

Because of the mass destruction of official documents in 1945, this mine of information has been the starting point for most recent studies, and was itself reprinted about twenty-five years ago in the United States (combined with wartime US Naval Intelligence data). This volume has been out of print for some time and is now very difficult to obtain, so the new Greenhill edition is to be welcomed, particularly as it has an additional photographic section of over 100 views.

German Warships of World War One: The Royal Navy's Official Guide to Capital Ships, Cruisers, Destroyers, Submarines and Small Craft, *with an introduction by Norman Friedman, published by Greenhill Books, 1992. 290 × 210mm, 416 pages, 98 photographs, 142 line drawings and 133 silhouettes. £35.00.*

A compilation of Naval Intelligence Confidential Books that were issued to the Royal Navy during the Great War, the resulting work is both a remarkably detailed guide to the ships themselves and, more importantly, an insight into how much the British knew about their enemy. This turns out to have been quite a lot, but besides the quantity of information, the quality is also impressive, suggesting a successful intelligence gathering operation 'on the ground' in Germany. Besides the technical details of the ships, the information includes such matters as U-boat tactics in attack and defence, and is illustrated with sketch plans and photographs (most of these are actually paintings by Oscar Parkes, and in the Introduction Norman Friedman speculates that these were preferred to genuine photographs where the backgrounds might reveal how, when and hence by whom the pictures were taken).

John Harland, Catchers and Corvettes: The Steam Whalecatcher in Peace and War 1860–1960, *published by Jean Boudriot Publications, 1992.*
309 × 237mm, 448 pages, 200 photographs, 380 line drawings, 40 plans.
£65.00.

Although this book is predominantly devoted to the mercantile whale-catcher, it does contain some information on the wartime conversions of such boats, and also their naval derivatives. Chief among the latter are the famous British 'Flower' class corvettes, but space is also devoted to the First World War Z-whalers and German *Vorpostenboote* of whaler origin. The degree of detail relating to the mercantile whalecatchers is outstanding – and

some aspects such as the steam machinery is equally applicable to naval types – but corvettes and naval craft are not central to the book's concerns.

'History of the Ship' series:
D K Brown (Consultant Editor), Eclipse of the Big Gun: The Warship 1906–45
Professor Alistair Couper (Consultant Editor), The Shipping Revolution: The Modern Merchant Ship
Andrew Lambert (Consultant Editor), Steam, Steel and Shellfire: The Steam Warship 1815–1905
Brian Lavery (Consultant Editor), The Line of Battle: The Sailing Warship 1650–1840.
Each: 295 × 248mm, 208–224 pages, 250 photographs and line drawings.
£28.00.

Three of the first four of this new series are devoted to warship topics, between them covering the evolution of fighting ships from the introduction of the line of battle ship to the

end of the Second World War. The express purpose of the 'History of the Ship' is not to break new ground and so the ultra-specialist is unlikely to find very much that he did not already know; the real aim is to employ all the latest research and modern interpretation to produce a well-balanced overview that covers the whole field – even the less well ploughed furrows – in a single volume. This is not to exclude original contributions, and the historically earlier volumes incorporate some significant new work, particularly on smaller vessels.

Each volume is a series of essays, mainly on ship types, but also covering more general aspects such as guns and gunnery, written by a wide range of authorities, most of whose names will be familiar to readers of *Warship.* Some are an obvious choice – Dr Ian Buxton on monitors, for example (although inadvertently omitted from the list of contributors to *Eclipse of the Big Gun*) – and although style and quality varies somewhat, all manage to pack a lot of information into a restricted extent. The best are also able to suggest the driving forces behind technical advances, and in this respect *Steam, Steel and Shellfire* is particularly successful, for the first time presenting a coherent picture of the introduction of all the nineteenth century technical innovations, with due

John McKay's drawing of the Vorpostenboot *(patrol boat)* Falkland, *one of the excellent plans in* Catchers and Corvettes.

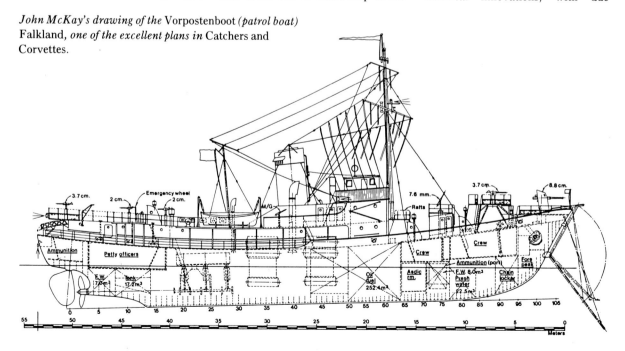

weight being given to the political and economic background. The old view of the dyed-in-the-wool conservatism of nineteenth century navies is so clearly revealed to be a fallacy that this book's more positive opinion is likely to become the new orthodoxy.

The scope of the series is such that some generalisation is inevitable, but care has been taken to pin developments to specific ships or classes. Of course, even for the largest types, not every vessel can rate a mention, but specification tables list significant or typical ships for each relevant chapter, allowing the reader to follow, say, the growth in size, or to note differences between the various navies' design practices. The illustrations, with their lengthy captions, also emphasize the particular over the general, while extensive descriptive bibliographies direct the aspiring reader to more detailed further reading.

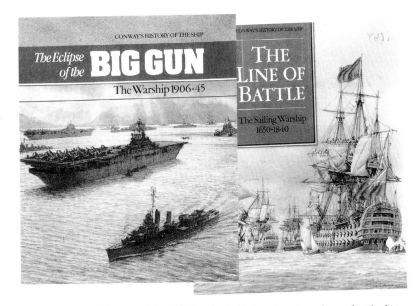

A feature of the 'History of the Ship' series is that each volume has a dustjacket painting by Mark Myers. These are the first two titles.

Stephen Howarth, To Shining Sea: A History of the United States Navy 1775–1991, *published by Weidenfeld & Nicolson, 1991.*
234 × 154mm, 620 pages, 49 photographs and 12 maps.
£25.00.

A competent and readable general history, but it is big subject for a single volume and does not offer any strikingly original material. Unfortunately, despite its '1991' dateline, it was completed too early to include the US Navy's Gulf War operations.

James A Mooney (ed), Dictionary of American Naval Fighting Ships, Volume I – Part A, *published by the Naval Historical Center, Washington, 1991.*
260 × 200mm, 542 pages, c300 photos. No price quoted.

The original *Dictionary* began publication in 1959 and as the volumes progressed the bare career outlines gradually expanded into lengthy biographies of each ship. This volume, which covers all those vessels whose names begin with 'A', is entirely revised, not only including ships built since 1959 but augmenting the entries for earlier vessels in line with the standard of later volumes. A revised edition of the 'B' volume is in preparation.

It is hardly easy reading – although it is a browser's delight – but the *Dictionary* is a major achievement of scholarship and a prime reference source.

Captain John Moore (ed), Jane's American Fighting Ships of the 20th Century, *published by Studio Editions, 1992.*
317 × 250mm, 320 pages, 1,000 illustrations.
£16.95.

A compilation of pages from various editions of *Jane's Fighting Ships* reproduced in facsimile, this book has only one merit: its cheapness. Its disadvantages are legion, from the miserable quality of the halftone printing to the highly variable information presented, depending on which edition was its source. Because a yearbook presents only the current position, it is almost impossible to give an adequate sense of development so, for example, to cover FRAM conversions to wartime destroyers it is necessary to cover the classes at least twice, using pages from different editions, with all the risks of duplication and/or omission, not to mention inconsistencies. It is never clear which year is being represented, and since annuals are not concerned with the past the fates of virtually all ships are omitted. The volume is also confined to major warships, ignoring auxiliaries and all but a representative selection of the US Coast Guard.

Michael A Palmer, On Course to Desert Storm: The United States Navy and the Persian Gulf, *published by the Naval Historical Center, Washington, 1992.*
241 × 168mm, 224 pages, 45 photographs, paperback.
$11.00.

No 5 in the 'Contributions to Naval History' series is an in-depth analysis of the US Navy's gradually expanding role in the Gulf since 1945. It is mostly pitched at the level of strategic policy, but the operations are described in some detail, particularly those carried out during the so-called 'Tanker War'. However, the book does not cover 'Desert Storm' or even the immediate build-up to it, but finishes with the Iraq–Iran ceasefire.

A J Pelletier, Bell Aircraft since 1945, *published by Putnam Aeronautical Books, 1992.*
270 × 200mm, 288 pages, 420 photographs, 40 line drawings.
£35.00.

Although Bell are not known for their naval aircraft, the company's great contribution to helicopter development justifies mentioning the book. Bell, or its associates, are also involved with the tilt-rotor V-22 Osprey so desired by the US Marines, as well as the LCAC, an operational hovercraft landing craft.

John C Reilly, Jr, The Iron Guns of Willard Park: Washington Navy Yard, *published by the Naval Historical Center, Washington, 1991.*
228 × 154mm, 116 pages, c60 illustrations, paperback. No price quoted.

This book combines a walk-around guide to preserved ordnance in the Washington Navy Yard with a brief outline of artillery development in the smooth bore era. Although some are earlier, the majority of guns date from the mid-nineteenth century, with examples of Union Dahlgren and Confederate Brooke weapons, as well as British imports like the Blakely and some early Whitworth muzzle-loading rifles. Photos of most of the guns and appendices of dimensions and proportions make this a useful little book.

J Rohwer and G Hümmelchen, Chronology of the War at Sea 1939–1945, *published by Greenhill Books, 1992.*
268 × 210mm, 416 pages, no illustrations.
£35.00.

A long-overdue revision of the classic work, not only correcting but expanding an already highly detailed text.

V E Tarrant, King George V Class Battleships, *published by Arms & Armour Press, 1991.*
245 × 185mm, 286 pages, c200 illustrations.
£19.95.

After an initial chapter on the design

A new history of the King George V *class by V E Tarrant is reviewed above. This photo shows the last days of* Duke of York *and* Anson *(in the distance) Lying in the Clyde in April 1957. (CMP).*

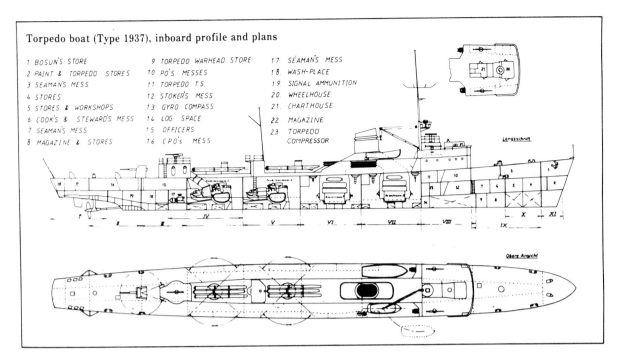

Torpedo boat (Type 1937), inboard profile and plans

1 BOSUN'S STORE
2 PAINT & TORPEDO STORES
3 SEAMAN'S MESS
4 STORES
5 STORES & WORKSHOPS
6 COOK'S & STEWARD'S MESS
7 SEAMAN'S MESS
8 MAGAZINE & STORES

9 TORPEDO WARHEAD STORE
10 PO'S MESSES
11 TORPEDO T.S.
12 STOKER'S MESS
13 GYRO COMPASS
14 LOG SPACE
15 OFFICERS
16 CPO's MESS

17 SEAMAN'S MESS
18 WASH-PLACE
19 SIGNAL AMMUNITION
20 WHEELHOUSE
21 CHARTHOUSE
22 MAGAZINE
23 TORPEDO
COMPRESSOR

An inboard profile of a German Type 1937 torpedo boat, one of the illustrations from German Destroyers of World War Two *by M J Whitley.*

of the class, this book settles down to its main theme which is a detailed biography of each ship. The design analysis is neither original nor penetrating, and tends to follow the over-critical opinions of some officers and men who served in the *KGV*s. However, once it embarks on its main task of describing the ships' careers, the book is greatly enlivened by the author's interviews and correspondence with survivors of their crews. Not only do their accounts give a first-hand impression of the ships, but many have supplied their own previously unpublished photographs which are reproduced in the book.

Stephan Terzibaschitsch,
Submarines of the US Navy,
published by Arms & Armour Press, 1991.
270 × 210mm, 216 pages, 300 photographs and line drawings.
£30.00.

This is the latest in a series of books

that have so far covered the larger surface combatants of the US Navy. Although the English language editions have been published under various imprints, the basic pattern remains the same – an emphasis on appearances changes and differences between ships, rather than an analysis of design or performance. With the large classes usually favoured by the US Navy, this approach has its value, which is always enhanced by a large selection of photographs.

M J Whitley, German Destroyers of World War II, *published by Arms & Armour Press, second edition 1992.*
246 × 244mm, 224 pages, 200 photographs and line drawings.
£25.00.

It was always a mystery why the first edition of this book was published in a mean little format, unlike the larger

page size of its companion volume on cruisers (and most of the publisher's other reference books, for that matter). However, this new and revised edition makes belated amends, adopting the traditional squarish format which has allowed photographs to be reproduced larger and integrated with the text.

Jordan Vause, U-Boat Ace:
the story of Wolfgang Lüth,
published by Airlife Publishing, 1992.
216 × 150mm, 256 pages, c50 photographs.
£15.95.

Apparently the first biography of Germany's second most successful submarine commander (after Kretschmer), this book is a portrait of a rather unattractive character – an ardent Nazi with little compassion for his enemy, but it is to the author's credit that he has been able to make the man interesting.

BOOKS ANNOUNCED

Philip Birtles, Supermarine Attacker, Swift and Scimitar, *published by Ian Allan, £15.95.*
Study of a family of jet aircraft designs including two rather neglected naval fighter types.

R Compton-Hall, Submarines and the War at Sea 1914–19, *published by Macmillan London, £18.99.*

Julian S Corbett, England in the Seven Years War, *published by Greenhill Books, 2 vols, £25 each.*
Reprint of an influential, and now very rare, book.

D G Crewe, Yellow Jack and the Worm: British Naval Administration in the West Indies, 1739–1748, *published by Liverpool University Press, £15.00.*

Mike Critchley, British Warships and Auxiliaries, *published by Maritime Books, £4.95.*
A new edition of the recognized 'spotters' guide.

J D Davies, Gentlemen and Tarpaulins: The Officers and Men of the Restoration Navy, *published by Oxford University Press, £35.00.*

Eric Grove (ed), Sea Battles in Close Up – 2, *published by Ian Allan, £19.95.*
Includes Narvik, Crete, Java Sea and *Tirpitz* attacks.

Michael Gunnon, Operation Drumbeat: Germany's First U-boat Attack against the American Coast in World War II, *published by HarperCollins, paperback, £8.95.*

Paul Hague, Naval Wargaming, *published by Patrick Stephens Ltd, £14.99.*
A brief introduction but outlining games for galleys, sailings ships, dreadnoughts, carrier warfare and even submarine attacks.

Stephen Howarth (ed), Men of War: Great Naval Leaders of World War II, *published by Weidenfeld & Nicolson, £25.00.*
Biographical essays by twenty-six historians covering thirty-one of the best known commanders.

John Jordan, Soviet Warships 1945 to the Present, *published by Arms & Armour Press, £25.00.*
With so much new information coming out of the old Soviet Union, the timing of this new edition may prove a little premature.

Arthur Mokin, Ironclad: The Monitor and the Merrimack, *published by Presidio Press, £14.95.*

L R L O'Connell, Sacred Vessels: The Cult of the Battleship and the Rise of the US Navy, *published by Westview, £16.95.*

The Royal Navy at Gibraltar, *published by Maritime Books, £25.00.*
A large format pictorial work like the previous volumes on the RN at Malta.

Don Sheppard, Riverine: A Brown-Water Sailor in the Delta, 1967, *published by Greenhill Books, £14.95.*
Personal experiences in Vietnam.

Michael Slackman, Target: Pearl Harbour, *published by the University of Hawaii Press, paperback, £11.95.*
An academic study of the prelude to the attack.

Admiral Sandy Woodward, One Hundred Days: The Memoirs of the Falklands Battle Group Commander, *published by HarperCollins, £18.00.*
Bestselling personal view of the South Atlantic conflict.

THE NAVAL YEAR IN REVIEW

The events covered by this review stretch from approximately May 1991 to May 1992, with some reference before and after. Compiled by Ian Sturton.

A. INTRODUCTION

The year was remarkable for the collapse of Soviet communism and the disintegration of the USSR, a much reduced Russia inheriting the former Union's problems and the bulk of its armed forces; strategic forces were controlled by a tenuous Commonwealth of Independent States (CIS). Yugoslavia split more abruptly amid chaos and bloodshed. One superpower remained, but in continuing military decline. New programmes continue to be cancelled, cut or deferred, although falling manpower totals release money for procurement; with much secondhand tonnage available, developing countries have less incentive to build new ships locally or place orders abroad.

In the Asia–Pacific ('PACRIM') region, the trend is towards reduced tension, with ideological rivalries declining, although potential areas of conflict like the Spratly Islands abound. Increased defence spending appears to be more the consequence of economic growth than a conscious arms race; Japanese GNP, already more than one half that of USA, is likely to grow to 75 per cent by 2000, when other industrialising Asian nations will be overhauling Western Europe.

The strengths of the major naval powers are listed in Table 1.

B(i). THE STRATEGIC BALANCE

The days of simple, single-threat force planning are over; NATO, with fewer new equipment choices, must consider responses to a wide range of ill-defined future scenarios. New guidelines replaced the old doctrines of 'forward defence', 'flexible response' and 'nuclear deterrence', with multinational naval task forces in all NATO areas; in the Mediterranean, the on-call NAVOCFORMED was replaced by STANAVFORMED, a new eight-nation standing naval force (30 April 1992). In a crisis, the modular standing forces, designated

Table 1. *MAJOR WARSHIP TYPES OF PRINCIPAL NAVIES, 1 APRIL 1992*

Type	USA	Russia	UK	France	China	India	Japan	Italy
CV (large)	14	1	–	–	–	–	–	–
CV (medium)	–	4	–	2	–	1	–	–
CV (small)	–	–	3	–	–	1	–	1
Battleship	–	–	–	–	–	–	–	–
Cruiser (helicopter)	–	2	–	1	–	–	–	1
Cruiser (missile)	49	27	–	–	–	–	–	–
Destroyer	40	38	12	15	17	5	39	3
Frigate (fleet)	80	41	30	3	38	10	18	14
(escort)	–	117	–	17	–	9	–	14
SSBN	25	59	4	5	1	–	–	–
SSGN	{87	38	–	–	–	–	–	–
SSN		62	13	5	5	–	–	–
SS (all types)	–	77	5	8	c44	18	15	8
MCMV (ocean and coastal)	17	217	33	17	c130	12	30	12

Note: The 14 US carriers include two in SLEP/overhaul. Russian (ex-Soviet) totals include many ineffective or unserviceable ships.

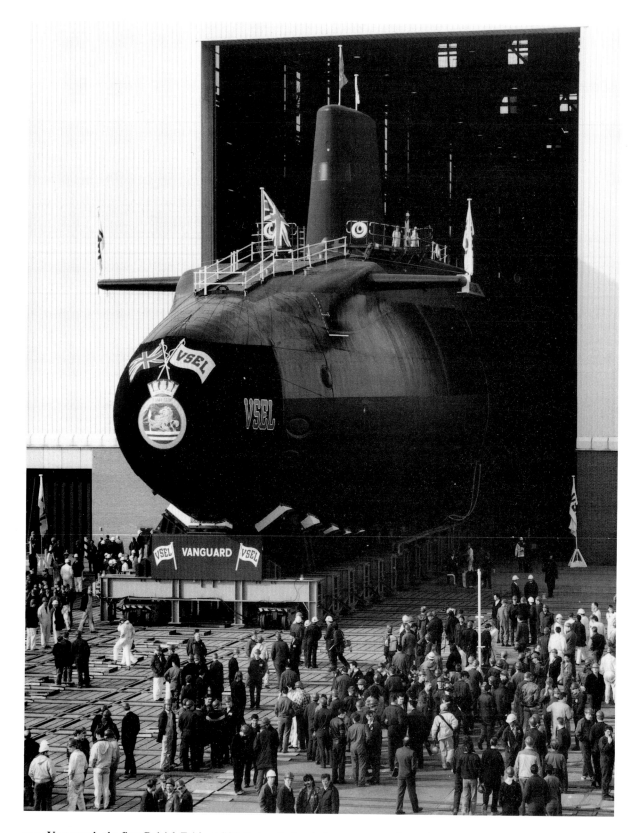

HMS Vanguard, *the first British Trident SSBN, is rolled out at one metre a minute from the Devonport Dock Hall, Barrow-in-Furness, 4 March 1992; she was lowered into the water by Synchrolift at 20cm a minute over three days from 5 March, and named on 30 April.* (Crown Copyright 1992/MOD reproduced with the permission of the Controller of Her Majesty's Stationery Office)

as Immediate Reaction Forces (IRFs), would be expanded to Ready Reaction Force (RRF) status by adding a cruiser and destroyers, and further escalation could add a carrier or carriers, an amphibious force and MCMVs, as required.

Closer defence integration within Western Europe is elusive, although a target of EC and WEU Treaty revisions. The EC failed to react in the Gulf, and has been ineffective in Yugoslavia; WEU nations co-operated more successfully in the Gulf conflict, and off Dubrovnik.

Elsewhere in the world, bilateral alliances generally replace regional security groupings. The Gulf Consultative Council is just that, and ASEAN is mainly an economic and political grouping, with no multilateral defence framework.

B(ii). DISARMAMENT

START reductions were agreed, cutting US and Soviet strategic weapon totals by about 30 per cent to 1998, with ship-launched cruise missiles (SLCM) limited to 880 missiles each by a side agreement. The treaty was initiated in Moscow; its ratification by the US Senate may require signatures of former Soviet republics with strategic weapons, unless the CIS is an effective control authority. Further US and Soviet proposals in September and October were accompanied by unilateral gestures; the US would remove 100 nuclear Tomahawk cruise missiles from USN submarines and surface ships, and an estimated 400 nuclear gravity bombs and depth charges (the older half to be destroyed, the newer to be stored),

USS Kearsarge *(LHD-3) after launch, April 1992. This class will replace the* Iwo Jima *class helicopter assault ships; the Marine Corps has requested a sixth LHD for FY96.* (Litton Systems)

and the removal was almost complete by February 1992; the Soviet Union/ Russia responded. Similarly, from September British nuclear depth charges were landed and stored ashore, and all RN non-strategic nuclear weapons were discarded in June 1992. In June 1992 also, a post-START agreement was completed: a fraction of American Trident weaponry was traded against all CIS land-based SS-18 missiles. By 2003, each side will be allowed between 3000 and 3500 warheads, of which 1700 to 1750 will be in submarines.

The French trials and research ship Monge, *as delivered by Chantiers de l'Atlantique, St Nazaire. Telemetry antennae and other electronic equipment will be fitted at Brest Naval Dockyard, enabling* Monge *to track M5 ballistic missiles.* (Alsthom)

C. BUDGET PROPOSALS AND NEW PROGRAMMES

C(i). USA, NATO and Allies

Major NATO Navies

(a) United States. The defence spending (authorisation and appropriation) bill for FY92, beginning 1 October 1991, was finalised at $291b. The Administration's budget authority request for FY93 was $267.6b, $9.9b below the FY92 figure of $277.5b (a decline of 7 per cent in real terms), reflecting part of the $50.4b cuts during FY92–97.

The Navy's budget allocation remained steady (the FY93 request of $84.6b was some $15b less than three years earlier) and the base force plan

of 451 deployable ships, including 12 carriers (and one training carrier) and 13 naval air wings (11 active), remains, but the level of new orders has been further slowed (see Table 2). The exceedingly expensive *Seawolf* submarine (SSN-21) programme terminated at one ship; a cheaper alternative, N-SSN or Project Centurion, is proposed.

The open ocean ASW threat has greatly diminished, to be replaced by more regional power-projection and support missions; in future, fleet submarines may be combined with cruisers or destroyers in joint task groups to fill the carrier gap, duties including minelaying, land attack by Tomahawk precision strikes, support of covert forces and reconnaissance. Sea control will give way to sea access.

The USN has left or is leaving Holy Loch, Scotland, the joint communications base in Western Austra-

lia, and (at the Philippines Senate's insistence) Subic Bay Naval Station. Seventh Fleet facilities from Subic Bay will go to Guam and Singapore; Malaysia and Indonesia have expressed interest in servicing US ships. There are no plans to leave Guantanamo Bay, Cuba.

The limitations of the fast sealift force and the Ready Reserve Force were shown in the Gulf conflict; Sealift Command will get more money for improving the deployment and supply of amphibious forces, and twenty fast new Ro-Ro ships will boost mobility requirements.

(b) United Kingdom. Defence spending for FY91–92 was £24.0b ($41.4b); spending, already down by a real 10 per cent over the last five years, will be further cut by a real 6 per cent in the next four. The 1991 Defence White Paper, in formalising

Table 2. *USN Shipbuilding Programmes, 1990–1995*

New Construction	Approved (authorised and funded)			Proposed (subject to amendment)		
	FY90	*FY91*	*FY92*	*FY93*	*FY94*	*FY95*
SSBN *Ohio*	1	1	–	–	–	–
SSN-688 *Los Angeles*	1	–	–	–	–	–
SSN-21 *Seawolf*	–	1	1	–	–	–
CVN	–	–	–	–	–	1
DDG-51 *Arleigh Burke*	5	4	5	4	3	4
MCM *Avenger*	3	–	–	–	–	–
MHC *Osprey*	2	2	3	2	–	1
LHD *Wasp*	–	1	–	–	–	–
LSD (cargo variant)	–	1	1	–	–	–

Notes: Proposals for FY93–FY95 provisional. The Navy will attempt to rescind funding of second and third of SSN-21 Seawolf class, funded in FY91 and FY92 but cancelled. $832m for long-lead items for CVN-76 is requested in FY93. MHC projected in FY95 will be of lengthened, improved type. The LSD authorised in FY92 was not funded.

USS Anzio *(CG-68), the latest AEGIS cruiser, commissioned 2 May 1992. This class continued in the news; reports indicate that* Vincennes *(CG-49) was within Iranian territorial waters when, under attack by Iranian gunboats, she shot down the Iranian A-300 Airbus, 3 July 1988. (*Litton Systems*)*

the 'Options for Change' review, set the defence pattern for the decade; the Soviet break-up will apparently not bring further major cuts, although total naval manpower, including Marines, will be 55,000, down by an extra 5000, to finance the new amphibious forces programme. Tenders for preliminary studies for the new AAW frigate with LAMS were invited (27 June), but SSN-20 was cancelled – a Batch 2 *Trafalgar* will be substituted – and orders for seven MCMV were not placed. Three Type 23 frigates were ordered from Yarrow on 23 January. In February, a £500m amphibious forces programme invited tenders for the design and construction of a new LPH (formerly ASS) and for the design of a new LPD. Rosyth will remain open, although operations will be reduced. Reserves are being cut, and two 'River' class MCMV laid up. From 1992, Wrens may serve aboard submarines.

(c) Canada. New equipment will be financed by reducing defence personnel from 84,000 to 76,000 overall. In the long term, Maritime Command will focus more on watching national waters than on protecting sea lines of communication. Instead of replacing the modernised 'Tribal' class from about 2005, new fast patrol corvettes will be built for EEZ patrols. The patrol submarine competition was further delayed to 1994, while an extra refit will extend the life of the existing boats. The contract for the twelve Maritime Coast Defence Vessels (MCDVs) went to Fenco Engineers in October.

(d) Germany. The 1992 defence budget proposals set spending at $29.16b, level with 1991; procurement cuts of $28.8b through 2005 will mainly affect the army. According to the Marine 2005 plan, the navy will still get the NH-90 helicopter and new maritime patrol aircraft, and the

Type 124 frigate programme is untouched, but a 'qualified freeze' was placed on Type 212 submarine orders; like the new patrol craft, Type 212 is not now expected until 2005.

(e) Italy. The 1992 defence budget totalled $19.0b, almost unchanged from 1991, but less by inflation. According to the new 'Defence Model' for the next eight to ten years, active defence personnel will be reduced – the navy from 49,000 to under 42,000 – to release funds for better equipment. The navy will have not less than twenty major surface combatants, of which sixteen will be kept operational. No firm orders for major combatant ships are scheduled for the near future, so the four ex-Iraqi frigates will be a welcome reinforcement.

(f) Netherlands. 1992 budget cuts left a final figure of $7.2b; further

The Canadian frigates Toronto, Vancouver *and* Montreal *in varying stages of completion at Saint John SB Ltd, Saint John, New Brunswick. (*Saint John Shipbulding Ltd*)*

THE NAVAL YEAR IN REVIEW

HMS Marlborough, *the third Type 23 frigate, built by Swan Hunter and commissioned on 14 June 1991. Units Nos 11, 12 and 13 of this class, ordered from Yarrow in January 1992, will be named* Somerset, Grafton *and* Sutherland *respectively.* (Swan Hunter)

naval reductions include a third *Kortenaer* to be sold by 1994, with three more in reserve by 1996, and two minehunters will go into reserve one year early. Defence requirements continue to include a viable surface fleet and a submarine force, although the submarine total will fall from six to four when the *Zwaardvis* class is deactivated.

(g) The South–Eastern Flank. Greece and Turkey continued existing programmes; construction of the three Greek *Ydra* class frigates was jeopardised by the bankruptcy of the shipbuilders.

Lesser NATO Navies

Norway. Proposed defence budgets showing 'zero growth' after inflation may reduce defence capability by 40 per cent in the next 20 years; in the short term, there will be fewer coastal escorts and fast attack craft.
Portugal joined the Belgian–Dutch monohull minesweeper programme.

France and Spain

Cooperate with NATO but are not full military members.

France. The proposed 1992 military budget was $33.9b, an actual reduction of 2.5 per cent after inflation; 1992–1997 military spending will allow an 1.5 per cent annual increase in funding (with annual inflation likely to be from 3 to 5 per cent, a reduction in real terms), ensuring that all major arms programmes continue. Development of the naval M5, the new strategic nuclear missile, will start in 1992 instead of 1995, but the Navy wil only get four or five new-generation ballistic missile submarines (SNLE-NG), instead of the six planned. Certain smaller naval bases are to be closed and fleet distribution revised, with the submarine deterrent force and protecting ships at Brest, and the surface task force at Toulon.

An artist's impression of the Type 212 submarine, designed by HDW/TNSW for the German Navy. A 125kW AIP fuel cell propulsion system and high energy sodium sulphide batteries are proposed. (HDW)

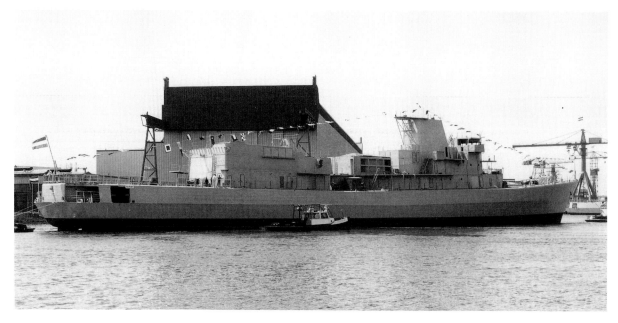

The launch of the Dutch frigate Van
Nes *at Flushing on 16 May 1992.* (L
& L van Ginderen)

Spain. The future structure of the
armed forces is set out in the FAS
2000 Plan, reducing overall numbers
to release funds for new equipment.
A cut of $1.0b in the 1992 defence
budget will cause further delays to
the Alta Mar naval programme; the
go-ahead for new GRP minehunters
was withheld and the first F-100
frigate may not be ordered until 1995.

The Swedish fast attack craft Göteborg, *first of four completed between 1990
and 1992.* (Karlskronavarvet)

Major US Allies

Japan. The FY92 (beginning April
1992) draft Defence Budget request
was for $36.2b, an increase of only
3.87 per cent, the smallest rise in 32
years, and representing only 0.941
per cent of GNP; equipment requests
were down by 4 per cent, to $6.8b.
There will be a full-scale defence
review in 1993, and spending is
expected to decrease from 1995. Requests in FY92 include the fourth
AEGIS destroyer, one patrol sub-

marine, three MCMV and nine smaller and support ships, at a cost of
$1.6b. Steps were taken to remove
the constitutional ban on use of
Japanese forces overseas.

Australia. The 1992/93 defence
allocation was $7.2b; a 'zero growth'
policy is planned through 1995, in
place of the previous annual real
increase of 1 per cent. Negotiations
began for six (or four plus two)
coastal minehunters, probably to be
built abroad; because of electronics
problems, the 'craft of opportunity'
concept of *Rushcutters* and trawlers
will not be continued.

C(ii). Neutral European Nations

(a) Finland's 1992 defence budget was $2.1b, up by two per cent from 1991; procurement allocations include continued funding for *Rauma* class FAC.

(b) Sweden. The $4.5b defence budget will be increased by about $1.2b over the next five years (3.3 per cent annually) but the increase is insufficient to prevent further cuts. The navy will get new submarines, an enhanced ASW capability and new amphibious units.

C(iii). Eastern European Nations

USSR, Russia and Successor States. Russia inherited the Soviet Union's 1918–1940 Baltic coastline, plus the Kaliningrad enclave, and a much reduced Black Sea littoral; the status of the Crimea is in dispute. Moscow wants to control the ocean-going fleets, with other new republics limited to coast defence forces and the Commonwealth of Independent States, set up 8 December, accepting

The Danish patrol frigate Thetis; *the rounded stern shown has since been modified to take a towed array, and struts now stiffen the mast.* (RDN)

ultimate responsibility for strategic forces; a very public dispute with Ukraine on the division of the Black Sea Fleet seemed likely to end with an allocation of 20 per cent of ships to the smaller republic.

Quantitative estimates of the USSR's rapid economic decline vary. GNP probably dropped by about 15

The French LSD Bougainville, *based in the Pacific at the nuclear test base, is classed as a transport and supply ship.* (Alsthom)

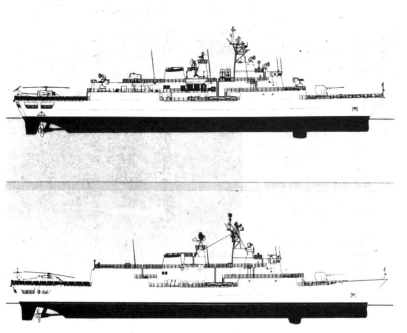

Elevations of the Meko 200 ANZAC and Barbaros *classes on order or building for Australia/New Zealand and Turkey respectively. (*Blohm & Voss*)*

per cent in 1991, and defence spending, after falls of around 6 per cent in 1989 and 1990, by a similar figure, with new weapon procurement down by 50 per cent. Analysts expect the military budget to drop progressively to an eventual 4 to 6 per cent of GNP, as in the West. Total personnel will be reduced from 1991's 3.7 million to between 2.0 and 2.5 million in 1994.

The very expensive carrier programme, set in train by Admiral Gorshkov more than a decade ago, was terminated at one ship; most new naval aircraft will not enter production. General plans to modernise the SSBN force are believed to have been

The Spanish replenishment tanker Mar del Norte, *a simple interim design. The Dutch* Amsterdam, *the first of two dedicated fast combat support ships designed jointly by the Netherlands and Spain, was laid down on 21 May 1992; the Spanish* Mar del Sur *will follow one year later. (*Bazan*)*

HMAS Brisbane *showing Gulf fit, with Phalanx CIWS either side of the funnel and ship's boats replaced by rigid inflatable craft.* (RAN)

frozen. Warship construction at most naval shipyards has stopped: although six submarines were launched in 1991, slipway work on nuclear submarines in the Pacific, on 'Victor III' SSN at St Petersburg, and on 'Delta IV' SSBN hulls Nos 8 and 9 at Severodvinsk has ceased. No new SSBN construction is now planned for the 1990s (although US Intelligence reported deliveries of hull plating for a new SSBN type at Severodvinsk in mid-1991), and annual production of other types will be about 1.5 SSGN/SSN and two 'Kilos', one 'Kilo' being for export. R & D for fourth-generation follow-ons to 'Sierra' and 'Akula' types continues, but orders are not expected for some years. Of surface ships, the *Sovremenniy* class will probably continue beyond 2000 for an eventual total of twenty-three, but the new frigate type may be halted at two ships. US Intelligence estimates of the future Russian navy indicate that it will be smaller and more modern, with new weapons and sensors, increasing the qualitative threat in Northern Norway and the Pacific; there will be smaller exercises, less training and reduced activity by general-purpose forces.

Ukraine plans to reduce defence expenditure from 30 per cent of GNP to 8.9 per cent within five years; the navy will have a coast defence role.

The Adriatic. Slovenia has two patrol craft, based at Koper; the **Croatian** Navy, founded 13 September 1991, seized about 25 per cent of the old Federal Yugoslav Navy and most naval shipyards (minus removable equipment), besides inheriting most trained personnel; some boats building for Yugoslavia were completed for Croatia. Almost half of the rump **Yugoslav** (*ie* **Serbo-Montenegrin**) Navy, restricted to a few bases in the south, has been laid up.

C(iv). Middle East

Iran, aiming at renewed regional superpower status, has started a major arms procurement programme; in 1990, a crew began training in Riga for the first of three 'Kilo' class submarines, and 'Scud C' SSM have been acquired from North Korea.

Israel's two HDW/IKL submarines, reinstated after the Gulf conflict, are due for delivery in 1997, the three Sa'ar 5 corvettes in 1993–94. The defence staff is trying to get its budget as a fixed percentage of GNP; it is currently 9.4 per cent but likely to fall to aboout 8 per cent.

Oman. Two missile corvettes will be built by Vosper Thornycroft; four smaller, simpler offshore patrol vessels (OPV) may be ordered later. **Saudi Arabia** released $2.7b for the second phase of the Anglo–Saudi Al Yamamah Programme, probably excluding the second *Sandown* class MCMV trio. **Egypt** would like to acquire submarines, but money for new construction is lacking. **Libya** is trying to update its 'Foxtrot' class submarines, and reportedly attempted to obtain 'Yankee' class missile boats before Russian ships finally left Libya in early 1992.

C(v). Pacific Rim ('PACRIM') and Indian Ocean

China. The 1992 Defence budget will rise by an official 12 per cent to $7.1b, but using NATO methods of calculation the total would be much higher. Numerical force totals, particularly support and administrative units, will be cut to free funds for equipment and to develop forces that can be projected well outside the country; May 1992 saw the first long-range naval exercise, about 5000km from the Chinese mainland in the Western Pacific. New destroyers and frigates are entering service; a first carrier, perhaps a mercantile conversion, is expected by the end of the decade.

India. The 1992–93 defence budget was set at $6.2b, a nominal 7 per cent increase over 1991–92 but an actual fall, because of 12 per cent inflation and devaluation of the rupee. Existing programmes continue slowly; an indigenous nuclear-powered submarine with an Indian PWR in a 'Charlie'-type hull is now first priority, ahead of the future carrier, which has shrunk to an ASW *Giuseppe Garibaldi* derivative. The navy is preparing to make spares for its Soviet equipment locally.

Lesser Navies

South Korea. In-country construction of Type 209 submarines has begun, and the first new KDX frigate will start in June 1992. Units four–six of the *Lerici*-derived MCMV are also building. **Taiwan.** Up to sixteen submarines are required, but the Dutch Government upheld the existing ban on construction in the Netherlands. Six *Lafayette* class frigates worth $650m were ordered in France, effectively reinstating the 1989 order; the sale is of 'unarmed hulls', to be completed and equipped in Taiwan, but equipment contracts from CSEE are also reported. In this context, it should be noted that four nominally civilian 'offshore oil rig support ships'

The Soviet carrier Admiral Kuznetsov *on passage from the Black Sea to the Northern Fleet. Escorted by a 'Krivak I' class frigate, the carrier passed the Bosporus on 2 December; deck markings were reported unchanged from 1990, during the passage only routine support flying was observed, and the 'Sky Watch' radar was not operational. The ship's departure from the Black Sea was pre-planned, not a sudden bid to prevent seizure by the Ukraine.* (USN)

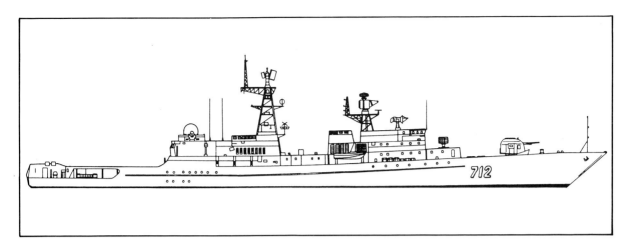

Elevation of the new Russian frigate Neustrashimy.
(Ships of the World)

The Indian corvette Khukri, *an indigenous design, seen
at Penang in May 1990. (*L & L van Ginderen)

delivered in 1991 immediately meta-
morphosed into naval minehunters.
The Philippines' ten-year programme to replace all Second World War
ships is underway, with six fast
attack craft on order in Spain and
Australia and two logistic support
vessels in China. **Thailand**. The
defence budget was increased by 13.5

per cent to $2.75b, around 14.9 per
cent of government spending; the
navy may buy four surplus *Knox*
class frigates, or additional frigates
from China if the initial six prove
satisfactory. The order for the
offshore patrol helicopter carrier
finally went to Bazan, and a support
and replenishment ship may be built

in China. The **Malaysian** submarine
contract with Kockums is 'on ice'
until at least 1995; two light frigates
were ordered from Yarrow at a cost
of $680m, the first to be ready in
1996, with an option on two more,
possibly with greater Malaysian participation. Tenders will be invited in
1992–93 for the first batch of six

1200t OPVs; the total OPV requirement up to 2005 is eighteen. **Brunei**'s planned missile corvettes were scaled down to OPVs, but orders remain frozen. **Indonesia** seems to have substituted corvettes for the indigenous frigate programme, as frigate requirements can readily be met by secondhand Dutch tonnage or Chinese new construction. **Pakistan**'s FY91–92 defence budget was $2.9b, an actual reduction because of inflation; conditions for the restoration of US military aid are unfulfilled. The navy has expressed interest in

Chinese submarines, including one 'Han' class SSN, and the tripartite minehunter order went to DCN, France, in January 1992. **Sri Lanka** continues to modernise and expand its navy, to contain the Tamil insurgency in the north and east of the island; three improved 'Shanghai' class FAC were acquired from China, and two landing craft are building. The **New Zealand** budget for FY92 was cut by 10 per cent to $697m, reducing the administrative 'tail'; according to the Defence White Paper, the country is heading for the

The Indian replenishment tanker Shakti; in 1991 and 1992, the Indian Navy abandoned almost forty years of self-imposed operational isolation, and held separate joint exercises with Australia, Indonesia, Britain, France and the United States. (Bremer Vulkan)

The lead South Korean 209 Type 1200 submarine, name not listed, built at Kiel; Daewoo is building five more at Okpo. (HDW)

An artist's impression of the Project Muheet missile corvette ordered for Oman; ASW sensors and weaponry are not included, but space and weight is available for their addition. (Vosper Thornycroft)

An artist's impression of the French light frigate Lafayette, *due to be launched in 1992 and completed in 1994. Six 'unarmed hulls' of this class are to be supplied to Taiwan; three enlarged AAW modifications are on order for Saudi Arabia. (DCN)*

concept of 'credible minimum force' in defence.

C(vi). Latin America

Argentina continued to reduce its navy's ocean-going capacity, in spite of Gulf conflict participation; the carrier, not fully operational since 1985, will apparently not be refitted. Work on new frigates and submarines, and on submarines in refit, has ceased, pending sale. **Brazil** is

similarly handicapped by lack of money; naval priorities are SSN, frigate upgrade, corvette construction, and the helicopter purchase. **Chile** continues to modernise 'Counties' and *Leander*s, but funding delays the indigenous submarine programme.

C(vii). Africa

With no external threat, **South African** defence spending dropped by a

real 30 per cent between the 1989/90 and 1991/92 financial years, and a further drop for 1992/93 is expected. The ASW capability has gone, and the submarines and patrol craft will be withdrawn around 2000–2005 after further refits. The planned missile corvettes were dropped, and new construction may be limited to six OPVs at the end of the decade.

D. WARSHIP BUILDING

D(i). New Designs and Principal Orders

Data on new warship types are listed in Tables 3 and 4.

(a) United States. The USN is to pay an extra $58m for weld repairs to cracks in the *Seawolf*'s pressure hull, increasing the boat's total cost to $784m and delaying the in-service date by one year, to May 1996; both Navy and contractor contributed to the problem. *Seawolf* will be the sole unit of her class, a very advanced boat, and probably a fully operational submarine rather than a R & D asset. The smaller, cheaper N-SSN, formerly Project Centurion, of less combat and computational power, is at the conceptual design work stage; she will be configured for multiple missions, but the optimum threat scenario is uncertain.

Later units of the *Arleigh Burke* (DDG-51) class will probably have an increased AAW capability to counter

low-flying supersonic missiles, with a two-helicopter hangar; ASW capability will be reduced. Only forty-nine units are currently planned.

(b) United Kingdom. *Vanguard* was ceremonially rolled out on 4 March. With work on the hull structure well advanced and £140m ($238m) already spent, the formal order for the fourth SSBN is expected shortly. Greenpeace estimated the real cost of the Trident programme at over £33b: the official figure of £10.5b omits development of the PWR 2 reactor, running and decommissioning costs, and new land facilities at Faslane, Rosyth and Aldermaston. Missile and warhead programmes remain on course, but *Vanguard* may put to sea without a fully operational command

Table 3. *NEW FRIGATE AND CORVETTE TYPES*

Country	South Korea	Malaysia	Oman	Turkey
Category	Frigate	Frigate	Corvette	Frigate
Class	KDX	–	Mod *Vigilance*	*Barbaros*
No in class	1+9	2+?2	2	2+?
Builder(s)	Daewoo	Yarrow	Vosper	Blohm & Voss
	Hyundai		Thornycroft	Golcuk, Kocaeli
Building dates	1992–?	c1992–1997	c1992–1997	1993–1995
Displacement (max)	c4000t	2200t	1400t	3350t
Lxbxd(max), metres	124 × 13.4 × 3.9	105.5 × 14.2.8 3.6	83 × 11.5 × 4.7	116.9 × 14.8 × 4.3
Missiles	8 Harpoon	8 MM 40	8 MM 40	8 Harpoon
	Sea Sparrow VLS	Seawolf VLS	Crotale	Sea Sparrow
Guns	1–5in/54	1–57mm/70	1–3in/62	1–5in/54
	2–30mm CIWS	2–30mm	2–20mm	3–25mm CIWS
ASW	6–12.75in TT	6–12.75in TT	–	6–12.75in TT
Aircraft	1 Super Lynx	1 Wasp	Platform only	1 AB 212
Machinery	CODOG	Diesel	Diesel	CODOG
Max shp/bhp	–	–	32,850	44,000
Speed (kts)	30	28	30	32

Table 4. *GENESIS OF THE THAI OFFSHORE PATROL HELICOPTER CARRIER*

Country	Thailand	Thailand	Spain
Design/builder	Bremer Vulkan	Bazan	Bazan
Name	–	–	*P de Asturias*
Displacement, max	7800t	11,500t	16,700t
Lxbxd, metres	156 × 32 × 5	182 × 30 × 8.5	195.9 × 24.3 × 9.4
Guns	1–5in/54	4–20mm CIWS	4–20mm CIWS
	6 or 8–40mm/70		
Aircraft	12 helicopters	12 helicopters	6–12 fixed wing
			16–10 helicopters
Machinery	2-shaft diesel	2-shaft CODOG	1-shaft gas turbine
Max shp/bhp	26,376	–	44,000
Speed (kts)	25	26+	26
Complement	350	455	555

system (SMCS). VSEL was awarded a £6m ($10.6m) study contract for a Batch 2 *Trafalgar*. Two unrelated problems in the *Upholder* class generated considerable adverse publicity, and will be expensive to remedy: the interlock system for the hydraulic doors to the torpedo tubes is unsatisfactory, and the diesel exhaust hull valve can leak.

(c) Canada. The CPF project featured cost overrun disputes between Saint John Shipbuilding and Marine Industries Ltd. The twelve maritime coast defence vessels (MCDVs) ordered at a cost of $500m will effectively be patrol vessels manned by reserves, with limited MCM equipment; work will begin in 1993.

(d) USSR/Russia. The *Kuznetsov* will be the only new carrier completed; the *Varyag*, 80 per cent complete, was stricken and listed for disposal in February 1992 and is to be sold by an Oslo shipbroker. Work to scrap the 75,000t *Ulyanovsk* began and the last *Slava* may also be abandoned. Western cameramen obtained the first close-ups of the 'Beluga' class diesel research submarine, believed to be a prototype for an air-independent propulsion (AIP) system.

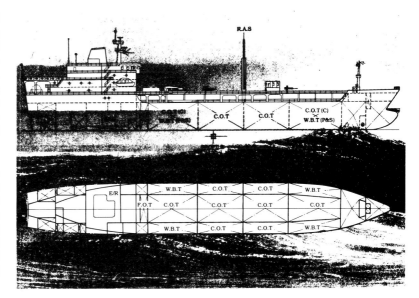

(e) Iraq. The four *Lupo* class frigates were taken over by Italy. Four of the six missile corvettes built for Iraq are offered for export by Fincantieri; the two boats transferred are laid up in Italy.

(f) Thailand. The helicopter support ship order placed with Bremer Vulkan was cancelled, because delays in the export licence would probably have delayed delivery and increased

The New Zealand fleet supply ship Endeavour *was built to a Hyundai HDA-12000 standard mercantile design, modified as a replenishment tanker.* (Hyundai)

The Indonesian corvette Kerapu *in May 1990.* (L & L van Ginderen)

USS John Barry *(DDG-52) after launch, May 1991. The first twenty-four units of the* Arleigh Burke *class, which have platforms but no hangars, may be equipped with unmanned aerial vehicles instead of helicopters.* (Litton Systems)

HMS Polar Circle, *the new Antarctic patrol ship, was leased in November 1991 to replace* Endurance. *Purchased outright in January 1992, she will take the older patrol ship's name later in the year.* (Crown Copyright 1992/MOD reproduced with the permission of the Controller of Her Majesty's Stationery Office)

cost; the contract was finally awarded to Bazan, to an enlarged design.

(g) China. New types seen during the year included the destroyer *Luhu*, the first 'Luda III' class destroyer and the first 'Jiangwei' class missile frigate. Full details of *Luhu* are not known – the ship was incomplete when photographed – but she may be fitted with Crotale Navale, and both destroyers are believed to have Ying Ji C-801 (Western CSS-N-4) SSM launchers; 'Jiangwei', a modified 'Jianghu', has a sextuple SAM launcher in 'B' position.

(h) Pakistan will take the French *Sagittaire* as its first tripartite minehunter; the second unit will be built in France and the third in Karachi.

D(ii). Ships entering service during the year

These are listed in Table 5 (the figures for USSR/Russia and China are approximate).

236

Table 5. *NEW SHIPS ENTERING SERVICE, 1 APRIL 1991 TO 31 MARCH 1992 (USSR, CHINA IN 1991)*

Type	USA	USSR/Russia	UK	France	China	India	Japan	Italy
CV (large)	–	–	–	–	–	–	–	–
CV (medium)	–	–	–	–	–	–	–	–
CV (small)	–	–	–	–	–	–	–	–
CAH	–	–	–	–	–	–	–	–
CG	CG-64 CG-66	–	–	–	–	–	–	–
DD	DDG-51	2 *Sovremenniy* 1 *Udaloy*	–	1	–	–	–	–
FF (fleet)	–	1 'Krivak III'	2 Type 23	–	–	–	–	–
(escort)	–	–	–	–	–	1	–	1
SSBN	SSBN-737	–	–	–	–	–	–	–
SSGN	SSN-757 SSN-758	1 'Oscar II'	–	–	–	–	–	–
SSN	SSN–759	2 'Akula' 1 'Victor III'	*Triumph*	1	1	–	–	–
SS (all)	–	3–4 'Kilo'	*Unseen*	–	1	1	1	–

Note: One or more of above 'Kilos' may be for export.

[Correction to Table 5 in *Warship 1991*: SSN-753, SSN-755 and SSN-756 were completed for the USN between 1 April 1990 and 31 March 1991]

D(iii). Reconstructions

(a) United Kingdom. In August, *Illustrious* began a 2.5-year, $170m refit at Devonport. *Renown*'s overhaul, due to finish in late 1992, is the last for a Polaris boat; it will enable her to run until the end of the decade, ensuring satisfactory overlap with the *Vanguard*s.

(b) Canada. The *Oberon* update will substitute passive towed sonar arrays for passive flank arrays. The chequered progress of the 'Tribal' TRUMP modernisation programme included leakage from the new water compensated fuel system into *Algonquin*'s interior during inclining tests, and the Defense Department taking over as prime contractor from Litton Systems Canada.

Other reconstructions may be summarised more briefly. AAW upgrade proposals for the Brazilian *Niteroi* class frigates are being examined, with contracts expected in 1992. The $200m+ contract for modernisation of two Venezuelan *Lupo* class frigates went to Ingalls.

D(iv). Fleet Depletions (decommissionings, transfers, etc)

Noteworthy items in this category are summarised below.

The physical disposal of nuclear submarines presents an increasing problem: already, over 100 American and ex-Soviet boats need proper storage and disposal. According to Greenpeace, old SSN hulks at Severomorsk appear to be contaminating areas of land, while Soviet practice until 1986 was to dump spent fuel encapsulated in metal containers in the cold but shallow Kara Sea. In the West, older suggestions of scuttling defuelled boats in deep water have been dropped; present proposals include beaching boats and leaving for a century until dismantling is safe, or cutting away bow and stern sections and storing reactor compartments only.

(a) United States. All submarines with Poseidon missiles were withdrawn from operational service; all *Permit* class SSN will go by the end of 1992, and many *Sturgeon* class are being withdrawn early. *Independ-*

ence succeeded *Midway* as US carrier homeported at Yokosuka, Japan, on 11 September, and *Forrestal* replaced *Lexington* on training duties; the last battleship, *Missouri*, re-entered reserve in 1992, and almost all *Coontz* and *Charles F Adams* DDG have paid off. The entire *Knox* class is scheduled for 180-day reserve, training duties or transfer by the end of 1993.

(b) United Kingdom. The disposal of warships outlined in 'Options for Change' included *Bristol* and almost all surviving *Leander*s; *Ariadne* was sold to Chile. *Revenge* ended her last Polaris patrol on 13 April 1992 and, with final refit cancelled, will pay off in late 1993. *Ocelot* and *Onyx* will be preserved at Chatham and Liverpool respectively. *Endurance*, unfit for further service in very cold conditions because of 1989 ice damage, was replaced by the Norwegian icebreaker *Polar Circle*.

(c) Germany. Two *Thetis* class corvettes were sold to Greece, to be followed by the other three. Almost all ex-DDR vessels in German service have been deleted; the USN is studying a 'Tarantul I' missile corvette, Poland acquired four incomplete *Sassnitz* class corvettes, and four

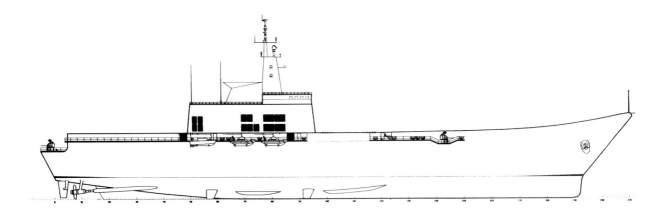

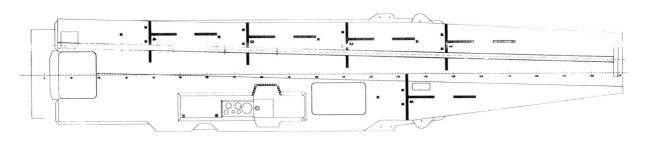

Outline drawings of the Thai offshore patrol helicopter carrier ordered from Bazan in March 1992. In general layout, the ship, by far the largest ever ordered for Thailand, resembles a reduced Principe de Asturias; *provision is made for a future fixed-wing air group.* (Bazan)

A waterline elevation of the Thai frigates Naresuan *and* Taksin, *building in China. The US and Western European systems shown will be fitted after delivery, in 1994.* (Official)

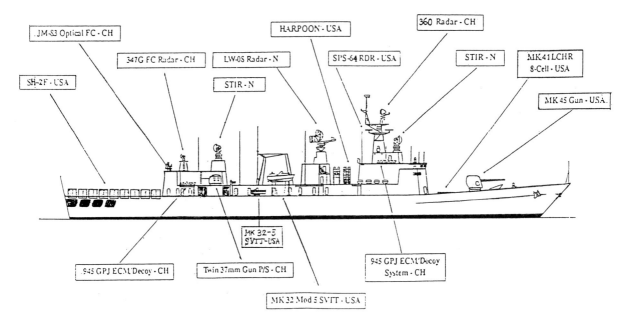

The Netherlands submarine Zeeleeuw, *first unit completed of the* Walrus *class. Use of HT steel permits a diving depth of 300m, 100m more than for the* Zwaardvis *class; the newer class has an* × *instead of a* + *stern. (*Directie Voorlichting*)*

The Spanish offshore patrol vessel Centinela, *second of four* Serviola *class. (*Bazan*)*

▲
The German submarine U 1, *as lengthened for fuel cell trials in 1989–1990. Decommissioned in November 1991, U 1 is currently being used by Thyssen Nordseewerke (TNSW) for trials of another AIP system, a closed-cycle diesel. (HDW)*

A cut-away model of the Swedish submarine Götland, *lead ship of the first class built with air-independent propulsion (AIP); a Stirling closed-circuit diesel motor will develop 820hp. (Kockums)*
▼

'Kondor II' MCMV went to Uruguay.

(d) USSR/Russia. All 'Echo', 'Hotel' and 'November' class SSGN/SSN have been or are about to be deleted, and the 'Victor I', 'Charlie I' and non-nuclear 'Juliet' classes are beginning to go. The scrapping overseas of old surface ships aroused considerable controversy; fleet commanders seemed to act independently of Moscow, and the Ukrainian Government objected to being kept in ignorance of Black Sea Fleet disposals.

(e) Chile. Four discarded warships, including the venerable cruiser *O'Higgins*, will be scrapped in Pakistan.

The Swedish Defence Material Administration's test vessel Smyge, a 140t catamaran powered by two KaMeWa waterjets, will be used to test stealth technology afloat: Smyge means 'stealth' in Swedish. (Karlskronavarvet)

E. NAVAL WEAPON SYSTEMS

Salient developments in naval weapon systems are listed below.

E(i). Missiles, including Ballistic Missiles

(a) United States. Suspension of production of the W-88 warhead for Trident II missiles will cause the fifth and later Trident II submarines to be fitted initially with the Trident I W-76 warhead. The first Block III Tomahawk SLCM was launched from a submerged submarine. A new stealthy air-launched stand-off 185km+ range cruise missile, designated TSSAM, was unveiled, but because of delays and changed requirements, the USN may instead buy more land-attack Harpoon missiles (SLAMs).

(b) United Kingdom. MOD claims that possible US safety problems with the Trident II missile did not apply to British missiles, which have a different warhead, were dismissed by the House of Commons Select Committee on Defence, as the point at issue is the safety of the system as a whole. Current purchases total around 23–26 missiles at about £15.5m each; warhead numbers will be kept to a minimum, perhaps even fewer than the Polaris total of 192 (64 Trident missiles can have up to 512 warheads).

(c) France. Germany rejoined France in developing the ANS supersonic anti-ship missile. Aerospatiale announced the new MM 15 anti-ship missile, a direct competitor to the ship-launched Sea Skua.

E(ii). Maritime Aircraft

Multinational. The development phase of the NH 90 helicopter will go ahead, and the maiden flight of the prototype is scheduled for 1995.

The Italian helicopter cruiser Vittorio Veneto, *as modernised betweeen 1982 and 1984; a replacement, tentatively named* Giuseppe Mazzini, *will be needed later in the 1990s.* (Official)

The Soviet carrier Minsk, *with seven Yak 38 'Forger' STOVL strike aircraft and four Ka-25 'Hormone' helicopters spotted on the flight deck. The future of this class is uncertain, as the 'Forger' is being withdrawn from 1992 and production of its replacement, the Yak-41 'Freestyle' has been cancelled;* Minsk *has been alongside at Vladivostok with machinery problems since early in 1989, but the necessary repair yard is in Nikolayev in independent Ukraine. (USN)*

(a) United States. A total of 575 of the future AX all-weather medium attack aircraft are proposed, at a total cost of $47.0b; the weapon load will be carried externally as well as internally. Satisfactory development of an improved, longer range F/A-18 Hornet, the E/F, needed in service from 1998 because of the A-12 fiasco and AX programme delays, is in doubt. The T-45 Goshawk trainer made its first carrier landing on 4 December. The EA-6B Prowler line may be re-opened. The tilt-rotor V-22 is kept alive against DoD opposition by Congress as the Marine Corps' possible next assault support aircraft. Other proposals in the pipeline include an AV-8B uprate, a STOVL strike fighter (SSF) as eventual Harrier replacement, an E-2C Hawkeye successor and a new-production P-3C Plus maritime patrol aircraft. Trials of the CL-227 Sentinel unmanned aerial vehicle (UAV) took place aboard *Doyle* (FFG-39).

(b) United Kingdom. A production order for forty-four EH 101 Merlin helicopters to cost £1.5b ($2.5b) was announced 2 September; the Westland/IBM consortium was the successful prime contractor, beating BAe/GEC.

(c) Canada's order for a maximum fifty EH 101 Merlins (thirty-five ASW, fifteen support) was approved in 1992.

(d) Italy. The latest naval aviation plans are for twenty-four, not sixteen, AV-8B Harrier II Plus STOVL aircraft, but the EH 101 order may be reduced from thirty-six to sixteen, with an option on a further eight.

(e) Greece will buy five S-70B-6 ASW Seahawks, with an option on three more, for the *Ydra* class frigates; the Norwegian Penguin anti-ship missile may be fitted.

(f) France. The prototype Rafaele M first flew on 12 December; land-based deck trials in America are expected in 1992, and the first carrier landing, on *Foch*, in 1993. No funds were allocated in 1992 for a carrier-capable lead-in jet trainer – the competitors are the USN's new T-45 and a proposed Dassault Alpha Jet Marine – and a cheaper option would be to train pilots with the USN.

(g) Spain intends to buy six more SH-60B ASW helicopters for new *Santa Maria* class frigates, augmenting the six ordered in 1984.

(h) USSR/Russia. Production aircraft types funded for the Navy are likely to include the Su-27K naval 'Flanker' interceptor, but not the Yak-41 'Freestyle' V/STOL or the MiG-29K 'Fulcrum' fighter. The slow progress of the supersonic Yak-41, believed due to technical difficulties, was attributed by Yakovlev to financial constraints. Yakovlev is designing an AEW aircraft for *Kuznetsov*, plans to use An-74 'Madcap' having apparently been dropped. Navy production contracts for the MPA and ASW versions of the A-40 Albatros, intended to replace the Be-12 'Mail' as SSBN 'Bastion' supports, are unlikely. Future naval aviation strike tactics appear to envisage using the 'Flanker' with anti-radiation missiles to suppress ships' air defences, and then attacking with surface- or submarine-launched missiles.

(i) Brazil will purchase five new Super Lynx helicopters, and upgrade seven Lynx Mk21/23 to Super Lynx standard for its frigate update programme.

E(iii). Anti-Aircraft and Anti-Missile Warfare (AAW)

Multinational. Development of the very expensive FAMS naval air warfare system continues, although some nations may quit the programme; the LAMS (area air defence) and SAMP/N (point defence) project definition studies may be merged into a single development programme, and the estimated in-service date is 2003/2004. A new US ship self-defence programme, the Evolved Sea Spar-

row missile (ESSM) and QRCC combat system, which will revive features of the terminated NAAWS, may draw support from FAMS. The worst perceived threat is multiple attack by highly agile, stealthy supersonic missiles with $0.01m^2$ radar cross-sections.

(a) United Kingdom. The lightweight 4-barrel Seawolf launcher (GWS 26 Mod 2) intended for the *Invincibles* and Batch 3 Type 42 destroyers was cancelled. Sea Dart may remain in service until 2011, while a mid-life upgrade for Seawolf is possible.

(b) France. The VT-1 missile for Crotale-NG began production in July; Crotale-NG has been ordered by France and a South-east Asian navy.

(c) Israel. First sea trials of the Barak PDMS were held in 1991; production of Barak, which will be fitted in the Israeli Navy and retrofitted in some Chilean ships, is due to start in 1993.

E(iv). Anti-Submarine Warfare (ASW)

(a) United States. To give a long-range stand-off capability, an ASW

version of the Tomahawk SLCM, with a range of several hundred miles, is being studied. The Fixed Distribution System (FDS), a major undersea sensor system under development, will not be purchased. The Anglo-American SSTD (Surface Ship Torpedo Defence) programme was slowed, and a 'soft kill' rather than 'hard kill' solution (*ie* decoy or countermeasure rather than homing torpedo) is likely.

(b) United Kingdom. The two largest sonar programes of the 1990s, the Type 2076 update for the *Swiftsure* and *Trafalgar* classes and the Type 2057 next generation passive towed array, may be merged. Type 2057 is now apparently only for frigates. Type 2075, the integrated sonar suite for the *Upholder* class, was cancelled.

E(v). Guns

The Royal Navy's medium calibre gun system contest for the Future Frigate programme began, while BAe/OTO Melara will start live demonstrations of its 76mm CCSS (Course-Corrected Shell System), designed to counter fast-moving targets such as agile anti-ship missiles, in 1993.

Yarrow's 1991 Super Type 23 frigate project, designed to meet the future RN air defence requirement. (Yarrow)

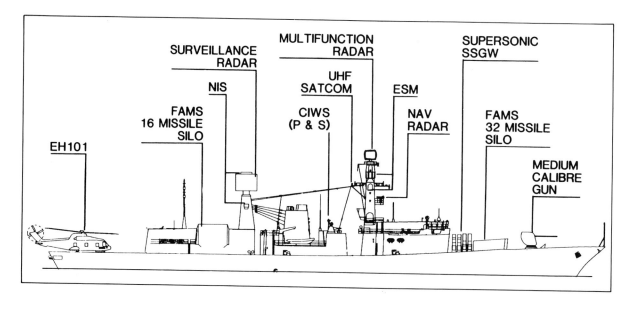

E(vi). Other Weapon Systems

A 'Krivak I' class frigate, modified with 'Steer Hide' VDS aft and SS-N-25 anti-ship missiles replacing RBU 6000; the missile tubes are not yet installed.

Kaman's 'Magic Lantern', an advanced airborne mine detector with a laser-based sensor, was used with reasonable success by USN helicopters to detect subsurface mines in the Gulf conflict, although affected by smoke from burning oil-wells, water depths below 15m and the helicopter's electronics.

The Swedish Defence Materiel Administration has awarded a contract to Bofors Underwater Systems for the series deliveries of a second batch of its new advanced torpedo. The contract was signed on 19 May. The new torpedo, known on the export market as Torpedo 43×2, is a lightweight, wire-guided ASW torpedo equipped with an advanced homing head that can track submarines not only in blue waters but also in the shallow and narrow straits of archipelagoes. Torpedo 43×2 is intended to be carried by the new Göteborg class corvettes as well as by helicopters and submarines. (Bofors)

F. NAVAL EVENTS

F(i) Areas of Conflict and Naval Actions

(a) The Gulf. In the aftermath of the Gulf conflict, Belgian and French MCMVs destroyed 460 mines between 3 March and 20 April 1991. Japanese MCMVs conducted sweeping operations from early June until the end of September, in the country's first overseas military operation since 1945. Sweeping to clear usual waterways was considered complete by July, but Kuwait ports were not repaired for normal operations. The naval blockade of Iraq in the Red Sea and Gulf continued.

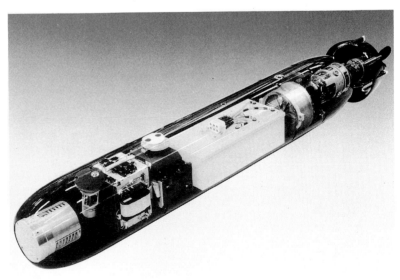

A test firing of the new Bofors 400mm wire-guided ASW Torpedo 43×2 from a Stockholm *class missile corvette. The armament fit is interchangeable and in the ASW role can include extra 400mm tubes and the VDS gear visible in this photo.* (Bofors)

Allied forces sent to Northern Iraq in April 1991 to provide a security net for the Kurds included US Marines of the 24th Expeditionary Unit, Sixth Fleet, and British Royal Marines of 3 Commando Brigade. In March 1992, naval forces returned in strength to press Iraq to obey Security Council instructions on elimination of weapons of mass destruction: the USS *America* carrier battle group (CVBG) re-entered the Gulf on 12 March.

The Gulf remained extremely tense, and several unconnected incidents took place. In May, the US command ship *La Salle* exchanged fire with two Iranian motor boats during Iranian naval exercises, and one Iranian was wounded; the Iranians later apologised. Bahrain and Qatar disputed ownership of the oil-rich Hawar Islands and nearby shoals at the International Court of Justice; several skirmishes involving naval units and survey boats, coastguard

craft or fishermen were reported. In March 1992, the North Korean ship *Dae Hung Ho*, suspected of carrying 'Scud C' missiles to Iran, reached Bandar Abbas without being intercepted by American forces.

(b) The Mediterranean.

Yugoslavia. Fighting began in Yugoslavia in June 1991. In contrast to Slovenia's brief and almost bloodless war of independence, the conflict between Croatia and Federal forces was prolonged and bitter. The Yugoslav navy was largely Croatian-manned, and most naval bases and construction and repair facilities were in Croatia. By August, the Federal Navy had begun moving ships and naval equipment south, to Montenegrin ports and to certain offshore islands. Full-scale operations on the coast began in mid-September when, to secure a complete Federal with-

drawal, Croatia surrounded army and navy bases within its territory. In retaliation, Federal warships blockaded the ports of Pula, Rijeka, Zadar, Sibenik, Split, Ploce and Dubrovnik. Joint attacks by Federal aircraft and gunboats on Ploce and Split were reported in the Western Press; a British ship was hit in Split on 20 September.

Greater attention was aroused by the plight of Dubrovnik, attacked by land, sea and air from the beginning of October; the blockade was enforced offshore by naval gunboats, and relief ships attempting to enter were searched. On 31 October, the car ferry *Slaviya* brought in a much-publicised 'love convoy' from Rijeka carrying relief supplies. On a return journey later in the month, the *Slaviya*, with 3000 refugees, had to dock at Pula because Split was under fire; shots were fired across the bows of a UNICEF-chartered hovercraft arriv-

▲
A recently released photo of the wrecked hull of an Iraqi T-43 minesweeper, hit during 'Desert Storm'. (Crown Copyright 1992/MOD reproduced with the permission of the Controller of Her Majesty's Stationery Office)

An ex-Kuwaiti FPB-57 FAC (missile) hit by Sea Skua missiles from RN helicopters during 'Desert Storm'; according to official figures, twelve patrol craft were sunk by the twenty-six Sea Skua missiles launched in the Gulf conflict. (Crown Copyright 1992/MOD reproduced with the permission of the Controller of Her Majesty's Stationery Office) ▼

The Saudi Arabian fast attack craft (missile) Oqbah, *photographed in September 1990 during 'Desert Shield'. Note hull numerals painted in Arabic script. (USN)*

ing to evacuate children. Because of these and other incidents, the WEU agreed to send ships to protect hospital ships ferrying wounded, and a multinational force led by Italy was proposed; the French support ship *Rance*, escorted by the Italian frigate *Euro*, was sent from Brindisi to Dubrovnik while the British *Minerva* and *Fearless* stood by in the area. The 3 January 1992 ceasefire gave the stricken city several months of respite.

By the end of the year, Federal forces had evacuated all Croatian mainland ports, and seemed ready to leave their remaining Croatian offshore islands; twenty-three Federal ships were sunk or damaged in this period, most notably the frigate *Split*, badly hit by shore batteries on 15 November.

Albania. In 1991, two waves of Albanian refugees caused considerable difficulties in the Italian south.

On 2 May, the crew of a 'Huchuan' class FAC hoisted the white flag and sought asylum at Otranto. At least two refugees were killed when another Albanian warship fired on a fishing boat crossing the Adriatic, 12 June. In August, three Italian warships, with orders to fire across the bows of suspect ships, and several aircraft, patrolled the Otranto Straits to reduce the influx of refugees, while attempts were made to escort some 15,000 existing refugees home. At the end of the month, the two countries agreed to deploy 300 Italian Marines at Valona and Durazzo to assist in controlling departing civilians.

Lebanon. General Aoun, the mutinous Christian army chief, was smuggled from the port of Dbayeh on 29 August in a speedboat under French naval protection; he was transferred in international waters to a French submarine.

(c) 'PACRIM' and Indian Ocean.
Sri Lanka. On 14 July, 2000 troops supported by 50 naval vessels landed to relieve a besieged army garrison; three weeks of fierce fighting in the biggest and bloodiest battle of the eight-year civil war resulted.

Malacca Straits. The rapid increase in piracy in the Malacca Straits and South China Sea led to claims that the highly organised night attacks were the work of Indonesian servicemen or customs officers; an international naval investigation, or even a naval patrol force, is possible.

Bay of Bengal. Tension on the Bangladesh–Burma border increased after a frontier clash on 21 December, and both countries moved warships to the area. In March, at least 100 Muslim refugees were feared dead when Burmese gunboats fired on two fishing trawlers ferrying refugees to Bangladesh, sinking one.

Indonesia mobilised nine warships to intercept and turn back the Portuguese ship *Lusitania Express*, carrying 150 peace activists to Dili, East Timor, to protest at the trial of thirteen men accused of provoking serious disturbances, March 1992.

South Pacific. French troops arrested Greenpeace protesters attempting to set up a 'peace camp' on Mururoa Atoll, France's nuclear testing site, 26 March 1992; the base ship *Greenpeace Warrior II*, trailed by a French warship and a tug, sailed within one mile of the atoll.

(d) Africa. The Ethiopian navy escaped from Asab as it fell to Eritrean insurgents; twelve ships with 3000 personnel and refugees fled to Mocha (Yemen), three ships with 2000 aboard to Djibouti, 26 May; return of the ships was delayed as Eritrea claimed independence from Ethiopia.

F(ii). Major Casualties at Sea, 1 April 1991 to 31 March 1992

(a) On 29 April, a cyclone wrecked much of Bangladesh's navy; a missile boat was reported capsized at Chittagong, and other sunken ships, including naval tugs, blocked the port, hindering relief efforts. American and British units in the Gulf area were diverted to the Bay of Bengal to assist in relief operations. The Chiefs of Naval and Air Force Staffs were later retired.
(b) The *Udaloy* class destroyer *Admiral Tributs* was severely damaged by fire while refitting at Vladivostok, 18 July.

(c) A seaman was charged following a hangar fire aboard the carrier *Clemenceau* at Toulon, 21 July.
(d) One crew member was killed aboard USS *Independence* (CV-62) in a fire near a liquid oxygen store, August.
(e) On 11 February, USS *Baton Rouge* (SSN-689) and a 'Sierra' class submarine collided in the Barents Sea at a depth of 20 metres; neither boat was seriously damaged. The collision took place in waters classed as international by the US, territorial by Russia. The US submarine commander was cautioned. An unidentified foreign SSN was chased from Russian territorial waters around Murmansk, 25 March.
(f) The *Udaloy* class destroyer *Admiral Zakharov* was damaged by fire off Vladivostok, killing one and injuring five, February.

F(iii). Footnotes.

(a) The 75th anniversary of the Battle of Jutland was marked by a joint services diving expedition to locate precisely the graves of the battle-cruisers *Queen Mary* and *Invincible*; the dead from these and other ships had yet to be properly memorialised.
(b) The 50th anniversary of Pearl Harbor revived suggestions that the attack was in part inspired by Hector Bywater's 1926 book, *The Great Pacific War*, which also described a US island-hopping amphibious response.
(c) The policy of *glasnost* permitted detailed revelations about peacetime disasters in the Soviet fleet; postwar submarine losses have been clarified and the relevant boats identified. In September 1955, the ex-Italian battleship *Novorossiysk* detonated an old German magnetic mine near Sevastopol. The ship remained afloat for nearly three hours after the explosion, but damage control was poor, no attempt was made at beaching and the order to abandon ship was given too late; at least five hundred men aboard survived the initial blast but perished when the stricken ship capsized. These factors led to the dismis-

The Admiral Tributs, *an* Udaloy *class destroyer, was severely damaged by fire at Vladivostok on 18 July.* (L & L van Ginderen)

The Soviet cruiser Admiral Ushakov *(ex-Kirov). All four units of this class were renamed after naval heroes in May 1992, symbolising the fall of Communism; the other new names are* Admiral Lazarev *(ex-Frunze),* Admiral Nakhimov *(ex-Kalinin) and* Petr Veliki *(ex-Yuri Andropov). (USN)*

The Danish submarine Tumleren *(ex-Norwegian* Utvaer*);* Saelen, *another ex-Norwegian boat of this class, sank while under tow and unmanned, 5 December 1990. Salvaged, she may be refitted by cannibalising ex-Kaura, purchased for spares. (RDN)*

sal of the Navy Commander-in-Chief, Admiral Kuznetsov, and the Black Sea Fleet Commander.

(d) Press reports suggest that the Italian DC-9 that crashed in the Tyrrhenian Sea on 28 June 1980 had been hit in error by a NATO Sea Sparrow missile from an unidentified warship; there have been accusations of a cover-up.

(e) The commander of the Soviet 'Whiskey' submarine that grounded off a Swedish naval base in 1981 admitted that his boat was nuclear armed, a fact already established by the Swedish Navy from external measurements.

(f) First details were published of a 1981 underwater collision between HMS *Sceptre* and a Soviet SSBN, near the northern ice edge. The Soviet boat scraped across the *Sceptre*'s bow, scoring and tearing the casing; the damage could not be examined for two days, as a Soviet SSN escort gave chase after the collision.

(g) In June, the Royal Navy admitted responsibility for the sinking of the trawler *Antares* by the submarine *Trenchant* on 22 November 1990. The 'perisher course' trainee commander, found guilty of negligence by court martial, was severely reprimanded. In future, submarine operations in the Clyde will be cut by 30 per cent, and there is to be a two-mile safety zone between fishing craft and submerged submarines. An inquest blamed the loss of the fishing boat *Inspire*, 5 September 1988, on an unknown submarine; inspection of log books showed that no British or other NATO vessel had been in the area at the time.

G. MISCELLANEOUS

(a) In June, the Soviet research ship *Akademik Boris Petrov*, invited by local councils to monitor radioactive waste levels round the Scottish coast but potentially also able to detect nuclear warheads at Rosyth Naval Base, was banned from British waters.

(b) The Soviet navy offered Western holidaymakers cruises in the northeast passage on demilitarised naval icebreakers, including *Sovetskiy Soyuz* and *Arktika*; a stateroom cost £11,950 for 20 days.

(c) Fuel oil leaking from the German cruiser *Blücher*, sunk in Oslo Fjord in April 1940, continued to threaten wildlife and beaches in the area; oil booms were brought to protect the resort town of Drobak.

(d) Six budgerigars used as part of the destroyer *Manchester*'s chemical protection system during the Gulf conflict were returned safely to the school that lent them.

The last active battleship, USS Missouri *(BB-63), decommissioned on 31 March 1992; here an Iraqi mine floats near* Missouri *prior to detonation by an ordnance disposal team, 12 January 1991. (USN)*

INDEX

Italicised page numbers refer to illustrations and diagrams. An illustrated page may also carry relevant text.